INTEGRAL AND DIFFERENTIAL CALCULUS:

an intuitive approach

HANS SAGAN

Professor of Mathematics and
Head of the Department of Mathematics
University of Idaho Moscow, Idaho

JOHN WILEY & SONS, INC. NEW YORK · LONDON

Library of Congress Catalog Card Number: 62-17469
Printed in the United States of America

PREFACE

This book is designed as a one-semester course for students of varying backgrounds. Those who wish to take this course with a reasonable chance to succeed should be familiar with elementary algebraic techniques as provided by a good high school preparation or a one-semester course customarily called *College Algebra*. Chapter I introduces as much analytic geometry as is needed in the sequel. Certain parts, e.g., the section on the quadratic equation (Sect. 9) can be omitted if this is warranted by the students' background. Appendix III is devoted to an introduction to trigonometry. This Appendix III should be taken up between Chapter II and Chapter III, if needed.

This book is intended for students who take the second semester of a one-year terminal course in mathematics as well as high school teachers of a specific category who attend refresher courses or summer institutes. This "specific category" embraces high school teachers who never had a formal course in calculus, or had a standard calculus course and either did not derive much profit from it or quickly forgot most of it, and are now called upon to teach the calculus in high school.

Lastly, this text is designed for a calculus course as offered by many high schools as part of an accelerated sequence for students of exceptional ability.

Once upon a time there was a young lady who enrolled in one of the universities in the Northwest. Because of her poor high school record in algebra, she was put into a refresher course in this subject. She was struggling along, just barely keeping from drowning, until suddenly, halfway through the course, her features lit up and her eyes sparkled with astonished enlightenment as she exclaimed: "Why didn't they tell me before that those letters stand for numbers?"

When writing this book, I was thinking of this young lady's plight and made an effort to stay in as close contact with numbers as possible. I frequently resorted to experimental methods at the expense of mathematical rigor to provide for a practical understanding of the limit processes that are basic for a good comprehension of the calculus.

The calculus is developed here in a fashion as it could have happened—and to some extent did happen—historically. Physical and geometric applications are interwoven with the text to provide sufficient motivation for the introduction of new mathematical concepts.

This treatment is not cluttered up with technical details and tricks. The reader will not learn to differentiate

$$y = \frac{\sqrt{\sin^5(\sqrt{x} + e^{\cos^2 x})^3 - \sqrt{27 + \log|\tan\sqrt{\pi/2 - x^2}|}}}{\log\left|\log\dfrac{x^2}{a^x}\right| + e^{\sqrt{\cot(x+\sqrt{1+x^2})^3 + e^{1000\sqrt{3x^x}}}}}$$

nor to integrate

$$\int (e^{x^2} + \sin\sqrt{x})^{15}\left(e^{2x^2} + \sin^2\sqrt{x} + 2e^{x^2}\sin\sqrt{x} + \frac{1}{\sqrt{3}}\right)^{36} \cdot \left(2xe^{x^2} + \frac{1}{2\sqrt{x}}\cos\sqrt{x}\right) dx.$$

Instead, it is the aim of this book to provide for a thorough understanding of the *limit of a sum process*, the *limit of the difference quotient*, and the *possible practical applications of the calculus.*

The sections on the *chain rule* (differentiation of a function of a function, Chap. III, Sect. 4) and the *inverted chain rule* (integration by substitution, Chap. III, Sect. 6), which deal with some more formal aspects of the calculus, are entirely independent of the main text and may or may not be included in the course. A bare minimum of formulas is developed, but great emphasis is placed on such items as the trapezoidal rule and Simpson's rule, which promote a very practical understanding of the limit process on which the definition of the definite integral is based.

Chapter II deals with integration. The concept of an area is developed in a semirigorous manner. The main purpose of the introductory sections, 1 and 2, is to make students aware of the fact that *area* is not something that "*is*" but, rather, an artificial concept which has to be defined in a manner that will meet our intuitive demands. A thorough discussion of the definite integral precedes the introduction of the derivative in this book because it was felt that it is easier to convince students of the necessity for measuring areas, rather than slopes. Another reason is a very practical one: if the derivative is discussed first and then the indefinite integral is introduced as the antiderivative and, subsequently, the definite integral is defined in terms of the indefinite integral, students will hardly pay much attention to what might be said later about the definite integral as a limit of a sum, being already in possession of a very simple routine for evaluating it. This would seem very unfortunate indeed, as the concept of the limit of a sum is really the key to most important applications of the definite integral.

At the end of Chapter II, the integrand is characterized as the rate of change of the definite integral with a variable upper limit. Thus a continuous transition from Chapter II to Chapter III is provided at the expense of the fundamental theorem of the calculus which loses its character as a theorem under such treatment.

Chapter III deals with the derivative and its geometric and physical interpretations. The basic theme concerning the discrepancy between physical reality and its mathematical description, which was already introduced in Chapter I, is now carried to a crescendo in the sections on *motion* and *freely falling bodies*. The ideas put forth here are those of logical positivism, presented in a simplified and personalized form.

Chapter IV finally deals with volumes as far as this is practical without having to introduce any more essentially new ideas beyond those that have been already developed in Chapters II and III.

There are certain sections and portions of sections that can be omitted without seriously jeopardizing the continuity of the development. These sections are clearly set apart from the main text by solid triangles which are set at the beginning and the end of each such portion. This does not mean, of course, that these sections should be omitted. On the contrary, they ought to be studied if this is feasible under the given circumstances, because most of these specially designated sections serve to round out the treatment or open up new avenues of thought that should stimulate the better students to deeper thinking and inspire them to further studies in mathematics.

Many problems are listed at the end of every section. The answers to most of the even-numbered problems are supplied in the back of the book. Some of these problems complement the text and serve to help the reader familiarize himself with the new notions and techniques that are introduced. Some problems supplement the text in exploring certain aspects of the material in greater depth than the main text. Still other problems lead the reader away from the text in a pursuit of sidelines which are only loosely connected with the material that is studied. There are many more supplementary problems supplied at the end of every chapter.

It is my belief that students have to be in possession of facts before they can make any attempt to fit them into a beautifully constructed deductive system. It was my aim to present in this book the facts, or some facts anyway, but I tried to give the reader occasionally a fleeting glimpse of the deductive system by leading him through some simple deductive arguments.

I hope that my book will promote interest in mathematics among noncommitted students as well as assist teachers in giving stimulating presentations of the calculus on the elementary level.

Moscow, Idaho
August 1962

HANS SAGAN

ACKNOWLEDGMENTS

I wish to express my gratitude to those who helped me in the preparation of this book. Specifically I thank my former colleague, Dr. Antony E. Labarre, Jr. (now at Fresno State College), for his attentive reading of my manuscript, and Mr. V. M. Sakhare, one of my graduate students, for working all the problems, supplying the answers, and calling my attention to many rough spots in the manuscript. Finally, I wish to thank my publishers for their help and cooperation in preparing this book.

H. S.

CONTENTS

CHAPTER I
FUNCTIONS

1. REPRESENTATION OF FUNCTIONS BY TABLES

The so-called exact sciences engage in a quantitative analysis of nature. There are basically two types of quantities that play a significant role in scientific systems: those that change their value, the so-called *variables*, and those that do not change their value, the so-called *constants*. Our attention in this treatment will be devoted primarily to a study of variables. In order to reach some understanding of this concept, let us discuss a few examples.

It is an experimentally established fact that the boiling point of water, i.e., the temperature at which water starts boiling, depends on the atmospheric pressure under which the water is brought to a boil. Every traveler knows that it takes 6 minutes to prepare a soft boiled egg in Bozeman, Montana, while it takes only $2\frac{1}{2}$ minutes to accomplish the same result in Redding, California. The realization of this phenomenon made men envision the pressure cooker which is in our days a gruesome reality that reduces the great variety of potato dishes to something which is hardly distinguishable from mashed potatoes. We are not about to introduce the American menu as our first example of a variable. So, let us return to the point at which we embarked on this culinary discussion: the boiling point of water. It can be experimentally established, as we mentioned above, that the boiling point of water changes with the atmospheric pressure. Specifically, the entries in the left column of Table I.1 indicate the different values of the atmospheric pressure under which the experiment was carried out and the entries in the right column give the corresponding temperatures at which boiling occurs.

We recognize in this example two physical quantities as variables, i.e., quantities that change their value: the atmospheric pressure and the boiling temperature of water. We observe at the same time that these two variables play a clearly distinct role because if we choose freely any pressure we please, the boiling point of the water is completely determined by the choice we make. In other words: even though the boiling temperature of water is

Table I.1

Under an atmospheric pressure in mm mercury	Water starts boiling at a temperature of degrees Celsius (centigrades)
9.209	10
17.53	20
31.824	30
55.32	40
92.51	50
149.38	60
233.7	70
355.1	80
525.8	90
760	100

a variable, its value is determined by the value of the variable that represents the pressure. We express this situation mathematically by stating that the boiling point of water is a *function* of the atmospheric pressure. The variable to which we can assign values freely (to some extent) we call the *independent variable* (here the atmospheric pressure). The other variable, the value of which is determined by the value of the independent variable, we call for obvious reasons the *dependent variable* (here the boiling temperature).

Table I.2

For an elevation above sealevel in m	The following atmospheric pressure in mm mercury at 0°C is found
0	760
2947	525.8
6087	355.1
9433	233.7
13012	149.38

Of course, the concept of dependent and independent variable is a rather relative one. Thus, the atmospheric pressure appears to be a dependent variable if we venture to measure it at different elevations. Specifically, we obtain the results in Table I.2. Here the elevation plays the role of an independent variable while the atmospheric pressure emerges as the dependent variable: the atmospheric pressure is a *function* of the elevation.

Combining Tables I.1 and I.2, we see that we may consider the boiling point of water as a function of the elevation, as given in Table I.3, and eliminate the pressure entirely.

Table I.3

Elevation in m	Boiling point of water in °C
0	100
2947	90
6087	80
9433	70
13012	60

Of course, we could go on now to consider the elevation as a function of the time, supposing we are sitting in a rocket that is shot straight upward. The application of such an analysis is quite obvious if we get the idea that we must have a boiled egg 6 minutes after launching time.

Table I.4

Pressure in mm mercury	Volume in cm^3
50	152
100	76
200	38
300	25.3
500	15.2
600	12.7
700	10.8
800	9.5
900	8.4
1000	7.6

Other examples of dependent and independent variables are easily found. Let us consider a cylinder that contains some gas and is closed tightly by a piston (see Fig. I.1). Clearly, if we increase the pressure on the piston, then the volume of the enclosed gas will become smaller, and vice versa.

Using crude experimental methods, we will find a relationship for some gas as revealed in Table I.4.

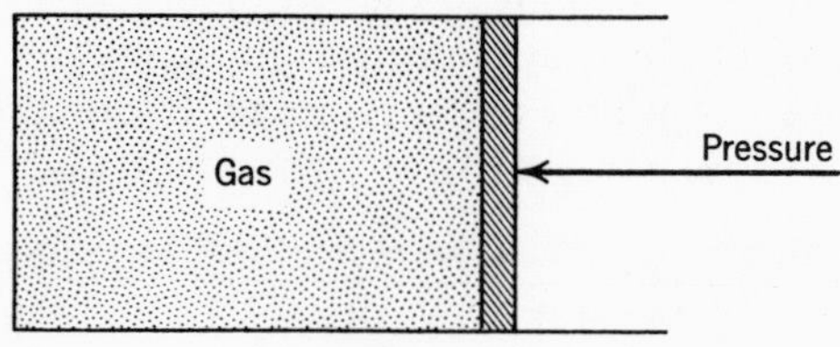

Fig. I.1

Here the volume of the enclosed gas appears as a function of the pressure which is applied to the piston. If we are interested in knowing how much pressure must be applied in order to compress the gas to a given volume, we have only to interchange the two columns in Table I.4 and consider the pressure as a function of the volume. Again, we can see that whether a variable is dependent or independent depends largely on the point of view.

2. REPRESENTATION OF FUNCTIONS BY GRAPHS

A common means of representing the relation between two variable quantities, if such a relation exists, is the graph. Let us return to Table I.1 for the purpose of an introductory discussion. This table contains ten pairs of values, one of which represents a certain atmospheric pressure, the other one the corresponding boiling temperature of water: (9.209, 10), (17.53, 20), (31.824, 30), (55.32, 40), (92.51, 50), (149.38, 60), (233.7, 70), (355.1, 80), (525.8, 90) and (760, 100). Our aim is to give a geometric representation of this relationship.

However, before we can endeavor to present pairs of numbers geometrically, we first have to settle a much simpler problem, namely: how do we represent a single numerical value geometrically? The answer is simply given by the ruler with an engraved scale or the thermometer. We consider a line (see Fig. I.2) and choose one point on this line quite arbitrarily. We call this point 0 and let it represent the number 0. Next we choose one more point which shall lie to the right of 0, but can otherwise be chosen quite arbitrarily, and call it 1. This point shall represent the number 1. The distance between the point 0 and the point 1 we call *unit distance*. Clearly, the number 2 will now be represented by a point one unit distance to the right of 1, etc. It is really quite clear how we have to proceed to locate the points which are supposed to represent all the positive integers.

Negative integers, as suggested by the scale of the thermometer, will be represented by points to the left of 0. (Historically, the concept of the *line of numbers* preceded the scale of the thermometer; however, although few students are acquainted with the line of numbers, it can be assumed that everybody has seen a thermometer at least once.) Specifically, the representative of the number -1 will be a point one unit to the left of 0, the representative of -2 one unit to the left of -1, etc.

Thus we have attained a geometric interpretation of all positive and negative integers. How do we now represent fractions? Clearly, the representative of $\frac{1}{2}$ will be a point halfway between 0 and 1, the representative

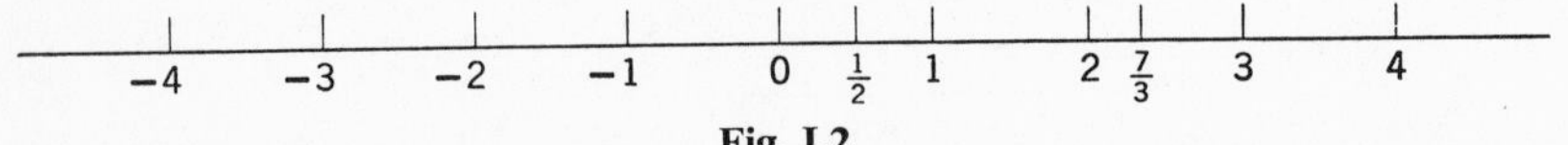

Fig. I.2

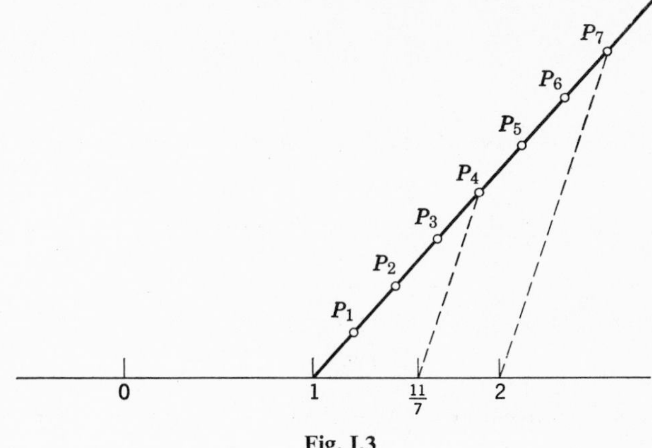

Fig. I.3

of $\frac{7}{3}$ will be a point between 2 and 3 such that its distance from 2 is one half of its distance from 3, and, finally, the point representing $\frac{11}{7}$ will be located between 1 and 2 so that its distance from 1 is $\frac{4}{7}$ of the unit distance. These few examples clearly indicate how we have to proceed in finding the representatives of *rational numbers** (fractions).

It is quite easy to construct those points which are supposed to represent fractions by the following device. Let us again consider the number $\frac{11}{7}$. In the following argument we refer to Fig. I.3. We draw a line through the point representing 1 at an acute angle with the line of numbers. Then we proceed to mark 7 points on this line at equal distances, starting with the point 1 (*equidistant* points). We call these points $P_1, P_2, P_3, \cdots, P_7$. We join the last point P_7 and the point representing the number 2 with a straight line and then draw a line parallel to the line through 2 and P_7 through the point P_4. This line will intersect the line of numbers in the point which represents the number $\frac{11}{7}$, i.e., the point $\frac{4}{7}$ of a unit to the right of 1. This can be seen quite easily by considering the two similar triangles $(1, 2, P_7)$ and $(1, \frac{11}{7}, P_4)$.

The problem of locating points that represent *irrational numbers*† (numbers which are not fractions) is not so simple. While it is quite easy to construct the representative of $\sqrt{2}$ (see Fig. I.4), it is not so clear how and if one can construct the representative of $\sqrt[3]{7}$ or, to make matters

* a is a rational number if, and only if, it can be represented in the form $a = \frac{m}{n}$, where m and n are positive or negative integers. ($n \neq 0$).

† A number b is irrational if, and only if, it is *not* possible to write it in the form $b = \frac{m}{n}$ where m, n are positive or negative integers. ($n \neq 0$).

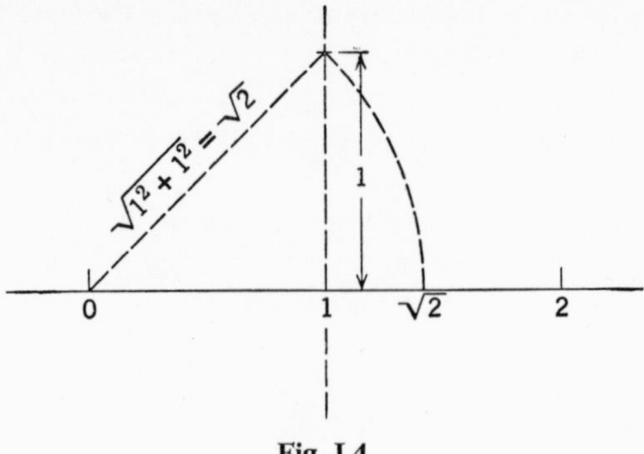

Fig. I.4

worse, the representative of π. We wish to state here only that while all such numbers have a uniquely determined place on the line of numbers, it is generally impossible to locate them by a construction process using ruler, compass, and even more sophisticated instruments.

We will base the following discussion on the assumption that every number has a point representing it on the line of numbers, and for every point on the line of numbers there is a number which is represented by this point, without entering a discussion of the justification of this assumption. (This question is quite delicate and complicated. There have been professors who embarked on such a discussion at the beginning of their calculus course and have still been talking about it at the end of the school year.) This correspondence between points and numbers is a *one-to-one correspondence*—as we express it mathematically—inasmuch as it is unique both ways.

Now that we have settled the problem of representing numbers geometrically, we can proceed to the more complicated problem of representing pairs of numbers geometrically. The first thought that comes to mind, of course, is to draw two lines of numbers parallel to each other whereby the correspondence of pairs is expressed by lines joining the two points that

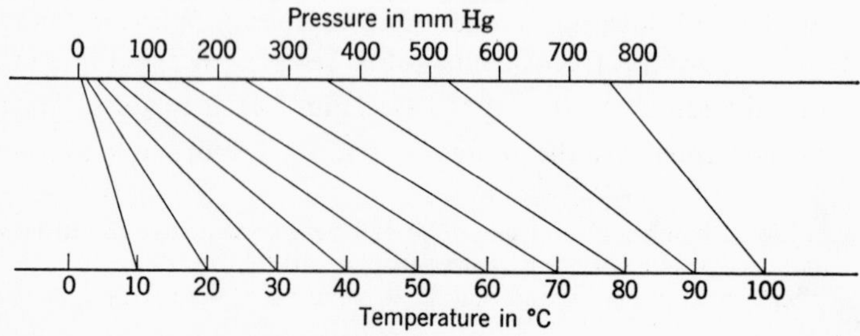

Fig. I.5

correspond to each other according to our table. Figure I.5 illustrates this method for the case of Table I.1.

This representation, however, is quite awkward. A much better—not to say, ideal—representation can be obtained by drawing the two lines of numbers so that they intersect at a right angle, preferably such that the two points representing 0 on the two lines coincide (see Fig. I.6). Now all we have to do is to agree that the first number in the pair (a, b) is to be represented by a point on the horizontal line and that the second number in the pair (a, b) is to be represented by a point on the vertical line and the pair (a, b) itself is represented by this point in the plane which, if projected vertically onto the horizontal line, has the representative of *a* as an image; and if projected horizontally onto the vertical line, has the representative of *b* as an image. Clearly, by this method we obtain a one-to-one correspondence between all possible *ordered pairs* of numbers and all possible points in the plane. To every ordered pair of numbers there corresponds one, and only one, point in the plane; and to every point in the plane there corresponds one, and only one, ordered pair of numbers.

Applying this method to a graphic representation of Tables I.1, I.2, I.3, and I.4, we obtain by appropriate choice of the units and the intersection point of the two lines of numbers, the graphs which are given in Figs. I.7, I.8, I.9 and I.10.

The system which consists of two lines of numbers that intersect each other at a right angle is called a *coordinate system* or more accurately, a *right* coordinate system. (This is to distinguish it from coordinate systems where the lines do not intersect at a right angle and which are of significance in some areas of mathematics.)

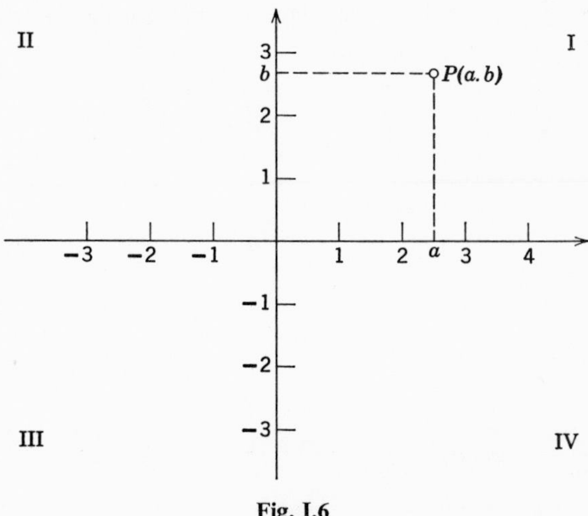

Fig. I.6

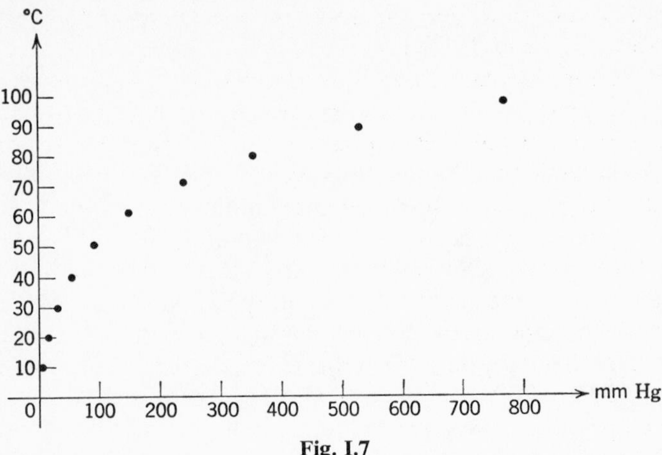

Fig. I.7

The two lines themselves, we call the *coordinate axes*. Specifically, in Fig. I.7, we talk about the pressure axis and the temperature axis; in Fig. I.8, about the elevation axis and the pressure axis; in Fig. I.9, about the elevation axis and the temperature axis; and finally, in Fig. I.10, about the pressure axis and the volume axis.

In a mathematical analysis in which no specific physical significance is attributed to the coordinate axes, we generally call the horizontal axis the *x-axis* and the vertical axis the *y-axis*. The two numbers in the pair (a, b) are called the *coordinates* of the point which represents this pair. Specifically, we talk about pressure coordinate, temperature coordinate, volume

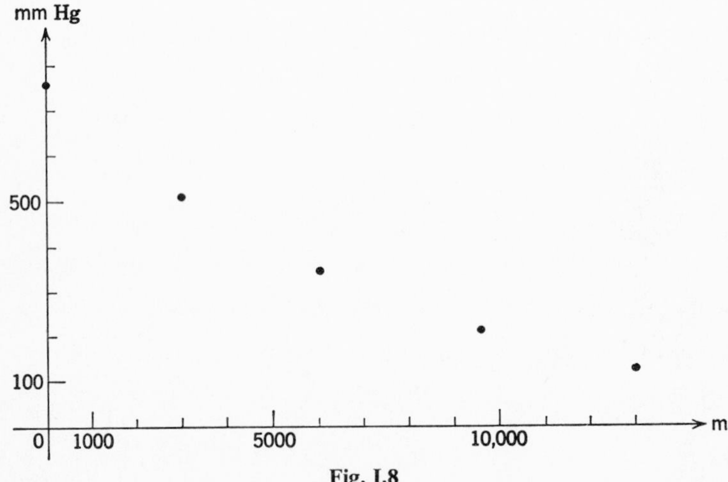

Fig. I.8

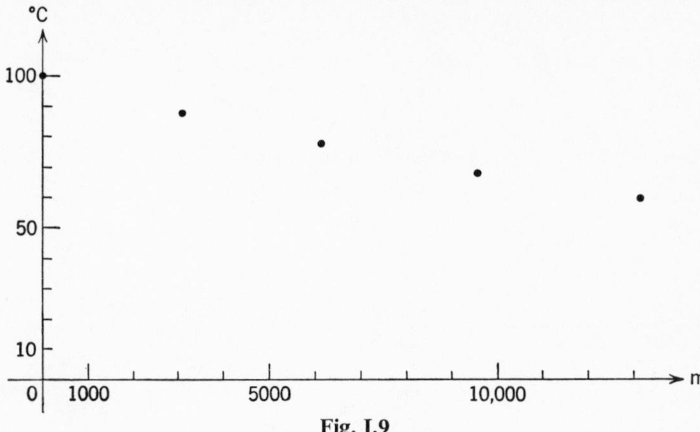

Fig. I.9

coordinate, etc., and in general: *x-coordinate* and *y-coordinate*. The x-coordinate is also frequently called the *abscissa* and the y-coordinate the *ordinate*.

This section of the plane, located between the *positive* x-axis and the *positive* y-axis, we call the first quadrant of the coordinate system and we proceed to enumerate the remaining quadrants in the counterclockwise direction as indicated by roman numerals in Fig. I.6. Thus the section between negative x-axis and positive y-axis is the second quadrant, etc. . . .

Thus far we have not gained any advantage from representing the functions as given in Tables I.1 to I.4 by points in coordinate systems as represented in Figs. I.7 to I.10. On the contrary, finding for a given value of the

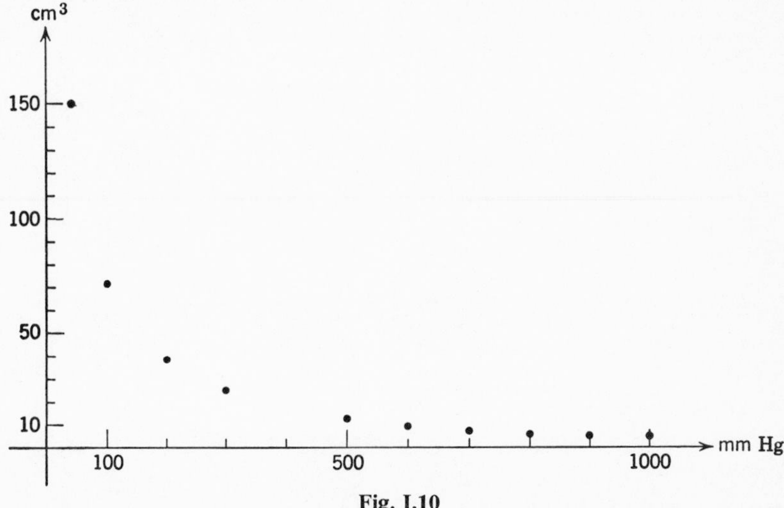

Fig. I.10

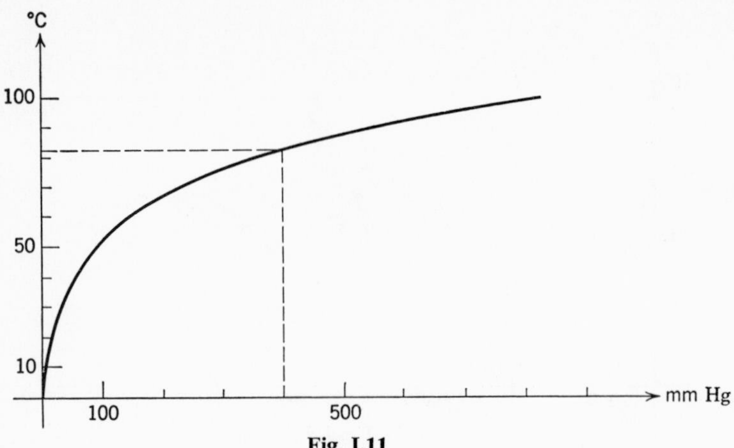

Fig. I.11

independent variable the corresponding value of the dependent variable seems to be more complicated if we utilize the graphs rather than the tables. However, suppose we want to know the value of the dependent variable for a value of the independent variable which is not listed in the tables. Then the tables do not provide for an immediate enlightenment. Neither do the graphs in Figs. I.7 to I.10 in their present form, for that matter. But if we join the points in these graphs by a curve, as we have done in Figs. I.11 to I.14, then all we have to do in order to find the value of the dependent variable for some value of the independent variable is to erect a vertical line at the point which represents the given value of the independent variable, intersect this line with the curve, and draw a line through this intersection

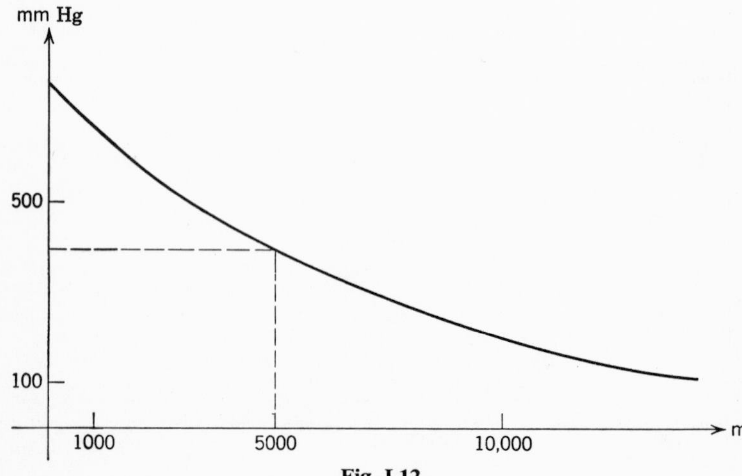

Fig. I.12

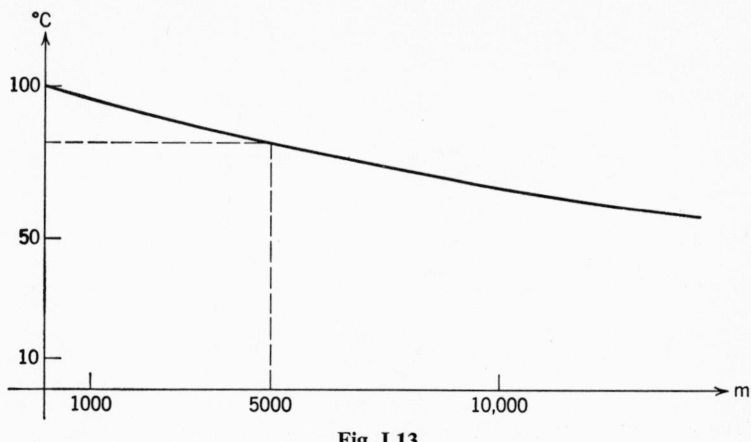

Fig. I.13

point parallel to the horizontal axis. The intersection point of this line with the vertical axis is then the representative of the value of the corresponding dependent variable. (See dotted lines in Figs. I.11 to I.14.)

Now this procedure seems to be very simple and tempting, indeed—too compelling, really, to be acceptable. Of course, there is a great logical difficulty involved in this process which we camouflaged with our persuasive argument. What does it really mean to join the points in the graphs of Figs. I.11 to I.14 by curves? Are we justified in doing this? The answer is: *no* and *yes*. From a logical standpoint, it is *no*. From a practical standpoint it is *yes*. So let us enlarge on this somewhat mystifying answer.

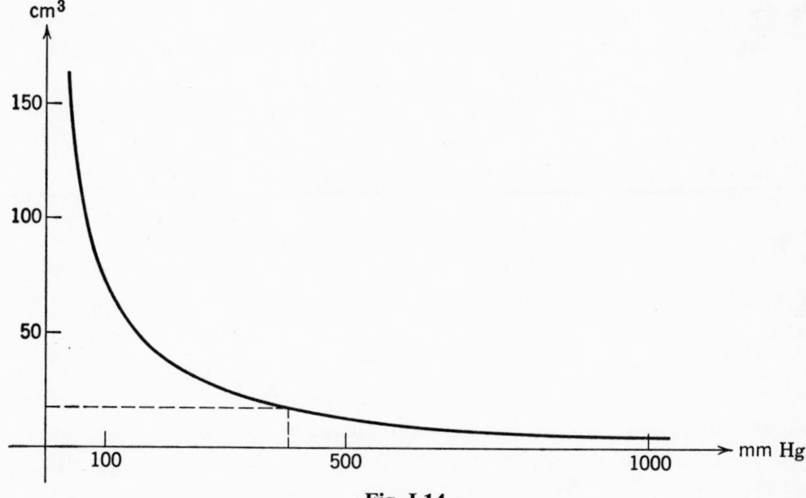

Fig. I.14

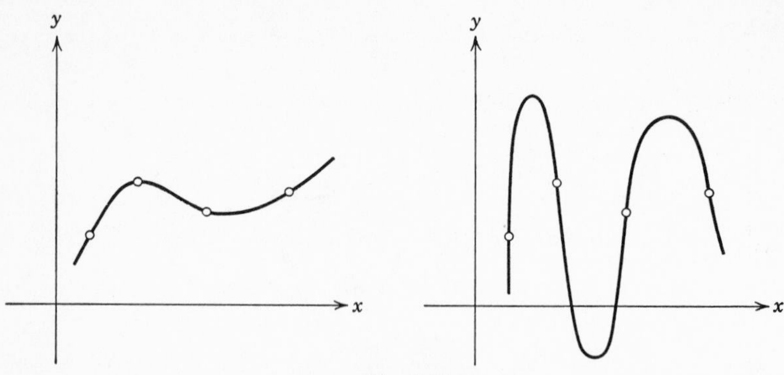

Fig. I.15

Clearly, an atmospheric pressure, which appears in Table I.1 as an independent variable, may assume any value (within reasonable limits, if we want to remain in contact with reality). It is also clear that water will boil under any given pressure at some temperature. So, for any given value of the independent variable, the dependent variable has to have some value. Now the only logically satisfactory way of finding this value is, of course, to carry out an experiment. But, no matter how many experiments we may carry out, all we will ever obtain is a table with finitely many entries or a graph such as the one in Fig. I.9 with finitely many points.

We now have to make the assumption that, if we should carry out further experiments, the results would be such that they fit the pairs of values which are obtained simply by joining the points of the graph by a curve. There is, of course, some ambiguity in this statement, because we did not specify the character of the curve. For example, we demonstrated in Fig. I.15 that the same points can be joined by a curve in a number of different ways and the results we obtain from determining the values of the function between measured points are consequently quite different. Since only one value can be right, the others have to be wrong. But how do we know that a certain curve will yield the right results while others do not? Well, we *don't*. (See also remarks on this subject in Chapter III, Sections 10 and 14.)

As the reader can already see, the whole problem boils down to whether we wish to be practical or not. If we do obtain—by chance—a curve which proves to be reliable in predicting results of experiments, then we have won a great deal. If the curve does not permit any reliable predictions—which we have to assume after it has "misfired" a number of times— then we have not lost anything (except for possible material losses), because we still have the table into which the results from all our measurements are entered.

Problems I.1–I.8

I.1. Represent the following pairs of numbers by points in a right coordinate system:

$$P(3, 5),\ P(-1, 4),\ P\left(-7, \frac{1}{2}\right),\ P\left(\frac{1}{2}, -\frac{1}{4}\right),\ P(12, 8),\ P(-3, -2),\ P(4, -18).$$

I.2. Construct the points on the line of numbers which represent the following rational numbers:

$$\frac{1}{5}, \frac{4}{9}, \frac{19}{5}, \frac{17}{7}, \frac{3}{11}, \frac{5}{12}, \frac{9}{23}, \frac{16}{31}.$$

I.3. Construct the points on the line of numbers which represent the following irrational numbers:

$$\sqrt{5},\ \sqrt{13},\ \sqrt{45},\ \sqrt{145}.$$

I.4. Represent the following table by a graph and join the points by a curve.

x	y
−5	2
−4	1
−3	1
−2	0
−1	−1
0	−1
1	−2
2	−3
3	−3
4	−4
5	−6

I.5. Interchange x and y in the table in Problem I.4 and represent the function which is thus obtained by a graph, again joining the points by a curve.

I.6. Let (a, b) be some point on the x-axis. What can you say about a and about b?

I.7. Let (a, b) be some point on the y-axis. What can you say about a and about b?

I.8. Let (a, b) be some point on the line which bisects the right angle between x-axis and y-axis. What is the relation between a and b?

3. MATHEMATICAL REPRESENTATION OF FUNCTIONS

Once we have transferred the data from a table to a coordinate system, joined the points in the coordinate system by a curve, and made peace with our conscience over the latter step, we pose the question: Isn't there a more compact, easily accessible form which would enable us to store our data, the ones which we obtained honestly by toiling with apparatus and measuring instruments, as well the points we boldly obtained by an arbitrary stroke of our pencil in joining the data points by a curve? There is indeed—or we wouldn't have posed this question in the first place.

For the following argument, let us consider an independent variable x and a dependent variable y. The relation between these two variables, namely, the fact that y is a *function* of x, we indicate by writing

$$y = f(x)$$

(*Read:* "y is a function of x" or "y is ef of x".)

Now, suppose that the functional relationship between x and y is such that the value of y, which corresponds to any given x, is obtained by doubling the value of x, or, as we may write,

$$y = 2x.$$

This is a (very) special example of a functional relationship between two variables, expressed mathematically. So let us express this same functional relationship by a graph.

Table I.5

x	y
−3	−6
−2	−4
−1	−2
0	0
1	2
2	4
3	6

First of all, even if this appears as a step backward, let us set up an arrangement of corresponding values as presented in Table I.5. Next we transfer these pairs of values into a right coordinate system (see Fig. I.16) and obtain seven points. Let us now join these points by a curve. If the construction of the points in the coordinate system was reasonably accurate, and if we do not engage in any escapades upon joining these points by a curve, the result will look very much like a straight line as indicated by the solid line in Fig. I.16. Of course, we could also produce something that may look like the broken line in Fig. I.16, but we will have to reject this nightmare on the basis of the subsequent argument:

Let (x_1, y_1) be a point on the straight line joining the points (1, 2) and (2, 4)—see Fig. I.16. Then we have, because of a well known theorem on similar triangles,

$$\frac{y_1 - 2}{x_1 - 1} = \frac{4 - 2}{2 - 1}$$

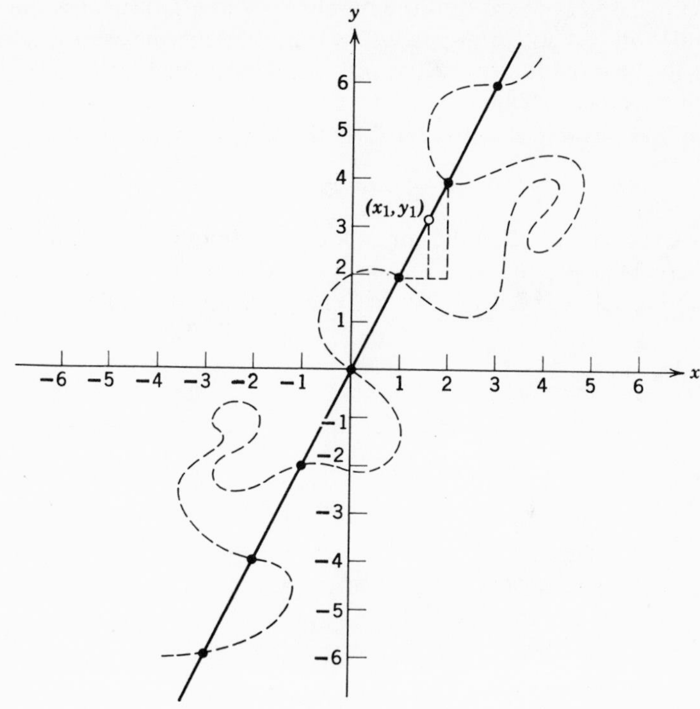

Fig. I.16

and from this

$$y_1 - 2 = 2x_1 - 2.$$

Hence,

$$y_1 = 2x_1,$$

i.e., the point with the coordinates (x_1, y_1) which by hypothesis lies on the straight line joining the points (1, 2) and (2, 4) is such that its coordinates satisfy the functional relation $y = 2x$.

The same argument applies, of course, to any point lying on a straight line that joins any two points in Fig. I.16.

However, we have not yet settled the question as to whether these are all the points that are represented by $y = 2x$. In other words: are there points whose coordinates satisfy $y = 2x$ but which do not lie on the straight line in Fig. I.16? Suppose that there is such a point with coordinates $(\bar{x}, \bar{y})$. Then this point lies either above the line or below the line (see Fig. I.17). Since all points on the line are such that their distance from the x-axis is twice their distance from the y-axis (the ratio of vertical side over horizontal side in any triangle that is formed by the line, the x-axis and a vertical line through any point is 2) it follows that either $\bar{y}$ is greater than $2\bar{x}$ or $\bar{y}$

is less than $2\bar{x}$ as opposed to our assumption that $(\bar{x}, \bar{y})$ satisfies the functional relation $\bar{y} = 2\bar{x}$. Thus we see that the straight line as drawn in Fig. I.16 is the geometric representation of the mathematically formulated functional relation $y = 2x$.

As an other example, let us consider the functional relation

$$y = x^2.$$

Again we can easily obtain the corresponding values given in Table I.6. If we represent these pairs of values in a coordinate system, we obtain the points indicated in Fig. I.18. We are greatly tempted to join these points

Table I.6

x	y
-2	4
$-\frac{3}{2}$	$\frac{9}{4}$
-1	1
0	0
$\frac{1}{2}$	$\frac{1}{4}$
1	1
$\frac{3}{2}$	$\frac{9}{4}$
2	4
3	9

by a curve, as indicated by a solid line in Fig. I.18, even though it is not as easy to justify this action as it was in the preceding example. As a matter of fact, it will be some time until we will see a justification of this process.

In order to return to our original problem of representing a finite number of discrete measure data by a curve from which we can (rightly or wrongly) predict results of experiments which have not yet (and probably never will be) carried out on the basis of the results of experiments that have been carried out, let us restate our position: We have finitely many points in a coordinate system. We wish to join these points by a curve which in turn we wish to express in a mathematically compact formula. It seems indicated—in order to achieve some progress toward this goal—that we have first to study mathematical relationships (mathematical functions) and their geometric representations and then, once we are familiar with the types of curves that are obtained from mathematical formulas, try to fit the appropriate mathematical relationship with its known geometric representation to a given situation.

This seems to be quite a straightforward program. We wish to mention that the more we will penetrate into this matter, the more it will reveal its

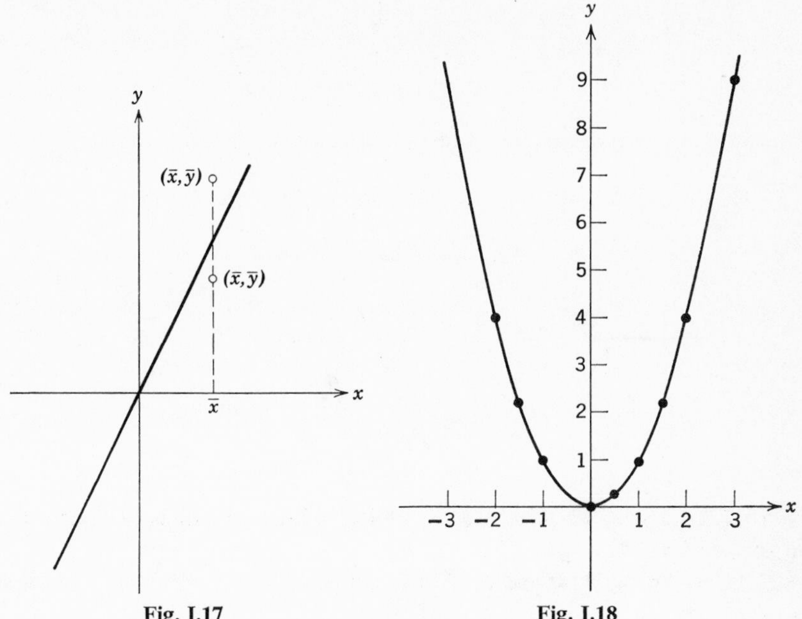

Fig. I.17

Fig. I.18

complexity, and at the end we will be happy to have solved only a very few of the problems that are involved in this process.

Before we close this section, we wish to present two more examples of mathematical functions to destroy the incorrect mental image of a mathematical function as something that has to be expressed by a formula that can be written as an equality between two expressions in x and y, before this image has a chance to implant itself in the students' unspoiled minds.

The following is a mathematical function:

$$y = \begin{cases} 1 \text{ for all rational values of } x \\ 0 \text{ for all irrational values of } x. \end{cases}$$

Given any value x, this relation enables us to find the corresponding value y. For $x = 27$, the corresponding y-value is 1. For $x = \frac{1}{4}$, the corresponding y-value is also 1. For $x = \sqrt{2}$, we have $y = 0$, because $\sqrt{2}$ is irrational. For $x = \dfrac{1}{\sqrt{7}}$ we have $y = 0$ for the same reason, etc. · · · All we have to know is whether a given x is rational or irrational.* Then the corresponding y-value can easily be found. Since every number is either

* Unfortunately, we do not know this of all numbers.

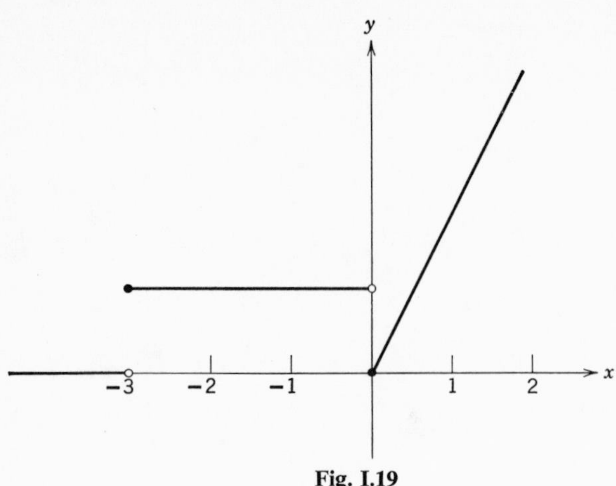

Fig. I.19

rational or irrational, this function is defined for all values of x, i.e., it has a y-value for every value of x.

Here is another example of a function:

$$y = \begin{cases} 0 \text{ for all } x \text{ which are less than } -3 \\ 1 \text{ for } x = -3 \\ 1 \text{ for all } x \text{ that are greater than } -3 \text{ but less than } 0 \\ 0 \text{ for } x = 0 \\ 2x \text{ for all } x \text{ which are positive.} \end{cases}$$

In this case, we can even supply a geometric representation of this function (graph) as indicated in Fig. I.19. (The student may investigate the possibility of representing by a graph the function which we mentioned before this one. If it is not possible, then why?)

Problems I.9–I.18

I.9. Represent $y = 2x + 1$ by a graph.

I.10. Represent $y = x^2 - 1$ by a graph.

I.11. Given a straight line through the points $P_1(1, 4)$ and $P_2(2, 8)$. Try to find a mathematical representation of this straight line.

I.12. Sketch the function:

$$y = \begin{cases} -1 \text{ for all negative values of } x \\ 0 \text{ for } x = 0 \\ x \text{ for all values of } x \text{ between 0 and 5} \\ 5 \text{ for } x = 5 \text{ and all values of } x \text{ greater than 5.} \end{cases}$$

I.13. Sketch the following functions:

(*a*) $$y = \frac{1}{x} \text{ for all } x \neq 0.$$

(*b*) $$y = \frac{1}{1 - x} \text{ for all } x \neq 1.$$

(*c*) $$y = x^2 + 2x + 1 \text{ for all } x.$$

I.14. Sketch the function $y = \sqrt{x}$. (*Hint:* Tabulate the values for $x = 0$, 1, 4, 9, 16, 25, and join the data points by a curve.)

I.15. Let $f(x) = x^2 + 4$. What is $f(1), f(2), f(-3), f(a)$?

I.16. Given $f(x) = \dfrac{1}{x + 1}$, $x \neq -1$. What is $f(0)$, $f(1)$, $f(t)$, $f(t^2)$, $f\left(\dfrac{1}{t}\right)$, $f(\sqrt{t})$?

I.17. Given $f(x) = x^2$. Find $f(x + 1), f(x + h), f(x - h)$.

I.18. Given $f(x) = \sqrt{x}$. Find $f(x + h)$ and $\dfrac{f(x + h) - f(x)}{h}$. Simplify the latter.

4. STRAIGHT LINE

We have seen in the preceding section that the function

$$y = 2x$$

represents a straight line in a right coordinate system. In this section we will establish the mathematical representation of a straight line in general.

First, however, let us consider an example. We know from plane geometry that a straight line is uniquely determined by two points. Let us consider the two points $P_1(1, 1)$ and $P_2(3, 5)$ (see Fig. I.20) and let $P(x, y)$ be a third point on the line L which is determined by P_1 and P_2. It is our aim to find a mathematical condition for the coordinates x and y of P which will guarantee that P lies on L. This condition is then the mathematical representation of L, since it will yield for any x a corresponding y-value such that (x, y) are the coordinates of a point P on L.

We consider in Fig. I.20 the two similar triangles $\triangle(P_1Q_2P_2)$ and $\triangle(P_1, Q, P)$. Since the ratio $\dfrac{P_2Q_2}{Q_2P_1}$ is the same as $\dfrac{PQ}{QP_1}$ we obtain in view of

$$\begin{aligned} P_2Q_2 &= 4 \\ Q_2P_1 &= 2 \\ PQ &= y - 1 \\ QP_1 &= x - 1 \end{aligned}$$

the relation

$$\frac{y - 1}{x - 1} = \frac{4}{2} = 2. \tag{I.1}$$

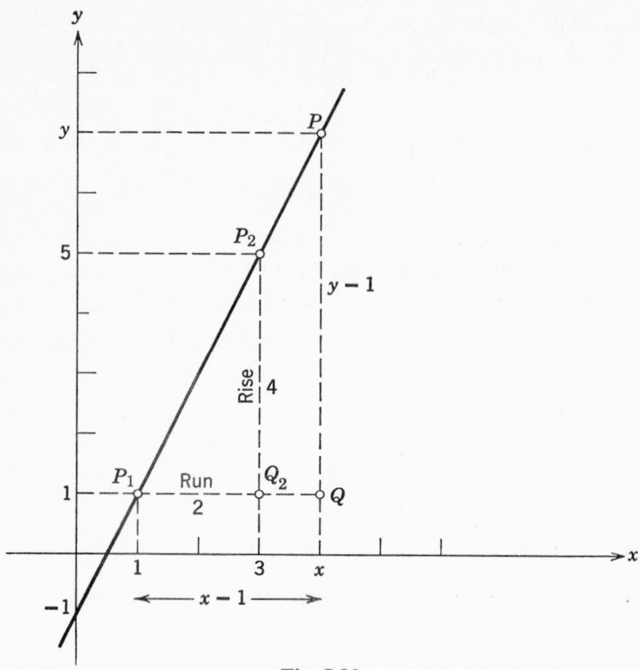

Fig. I.20

So we see that whenever $P(x, y)$ lies on the line L, its coordinates (x, y) also satisfy the relation (I.1). We see at the same time that, whenever (x, y) satisfy the relation (I.1), they are also coordinates of a point P on the line L.

From (I.1) follows immediately

$$y - 1 = 2(x - 1)$$

or

(I.1a)
$$y = 2x - 1.$$

We can easily interpret the coefficients on the right side of (I.1a). Clearly, -1 is the y-value that is obtained if we let $x = 0$, i.e., the line L intersects the y-axis at $y = -1$. We call this point the *y-intercept*. The coefficient 2 of x is also of great importance. We remember that 2 was obtained as the ratio $\frac{P_2Q_2}{Q_2P_1}$, i.e., "rise over run" which is the same for all right triangles that have two sides parallel to the two coordinate axes and the third side lying on L (see Fig. I.20). This ratio is called the *slope* of the line L because it is a measure of the rise relative to the run, or, in other words, it tells by how much y increases as x increases by one unit. (If the point P_2 in Fig. I.20 would be higher up, e.g., have the y-coordinate 6, then the slope would amount to $\frac{5}{2}$ which is greater than 2, i.e., the rise is higher for the same run and, consequently, the slope is greater. However, if the point P_2 in Fig. I.20 would be farther down, say, have the y-coordinate 4, then the slope would be $\frac{3}{2}$ which is smaller than 2, i.e., the rise is smaller for the same run.)

We are now ready to discuss the general case. Let us consider two points $P_1(x_1, y_1)$ and $P_2(x_2, y_2)$ where we assume that $x_1 \neq x_2$. This assumption simply means that P_1 and P_2 do not lie on a vertical line, a case which we have to exclude from our considerations for the time being.

Let $P(x, y)$ be a third point on the line L which is determined by P_1 and P_2 (see Fig. I.21). Again we consider the two similar triangles $\triangle(P_1Q_2P_2)$ and $\triangle(P_1QP)$, and we see that if P is a point on L, then

$$\frac{P_2Q_2}{Q_2P_1} = \frac{PQ}{QP_1}.$$

Since

$$P_2Q_2 = y_2 - y_1$$
$$Q_2P_1 = x_2 - x_1$$
$$PQ = y - y_1$$
$$QP_1 = x - x_1$$

we obtain

(I.2) $$\frac{y - y_1}{x - x_1} = \frac{y_2 - y_1}{x_2 - x_1}$$

or

(I.3) $$y - y_1 = \frac{y_2 - y_1}{x_2 - x_1}(x - x_1).$$

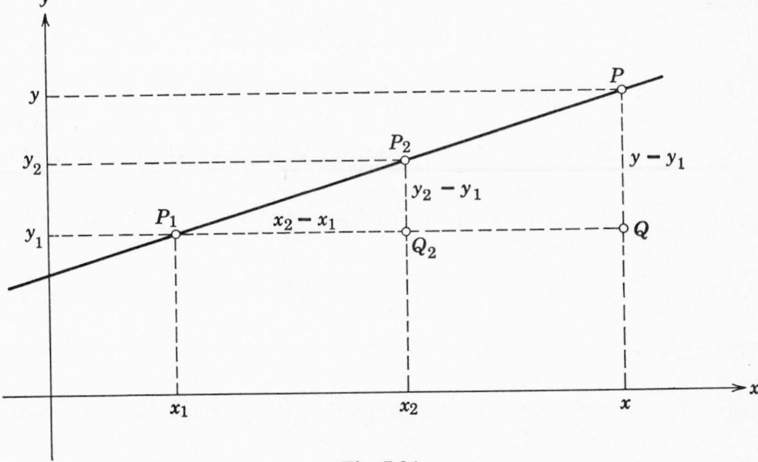

Fig. I.21

This relation is the mathematical representation of a straight line, which is not vertical, through the points $P_1(x_1, y_1)$ and $P_2(x_2, y_2)$. It is customarily referred to as the *point-point formula* because it is obtained by making use of the coordinates of two points.

Let us take, for example, the points $P_1(1, 7)$ and $P_2(3, 5)$; Then the equation of the line through these two points is given according to (I.3) by

$$y - 7 = \frac{5 - 7}{3 - 1}(x - 1)$$

from which we obtain, after a few manipulations,

$$y = -x + 8.$$

We see that the y-intercept is 8, i.e., the line intersects the y-axis at $y = 8$; and the slope is -1, i.e., the rise is -1 per run 1. That means: if x increases by one unit, then y increases by minus one unit—which is just a complicated way of saying that y *decreases* by one unit.

Now suppose we know one point of the line, $P_1(x_1, y_1)$, and its slope m. Of course, we could immediately find another point P_2, since we know that y increases by m units as x increases by one unit. Hence, the coordinates of such another point on the line would be $x_2 = x_1 + 1$ and $y_2 = y_1 + m$. Once we have these coordinates, we can use (I.3) to set up the line equation. However, this is really quite unnecessary because we know anyway that

$$m = \frac{y_2 - y_1}{x_2 - x_1}$$

and can thus write the line equation in terms of the coordinates of one point and the slope m.

(I.4) $$y - y_1 = m(x - x_1),$$

which we call the *point-slope formula*.

Let us now consider the point $P_1(3, 4)$ and find the equation of a line through this point with the slope $\frac{5}{3}$. With $m = \frac{5}{3}$ we obtain from (I.4)

$$y - 4 = \tfrac{5}{3}(x - 3)$$

and then, after simplifications,

$$y = \tfrac{5}{3}x - 1.$$

Problems I.19–I.32

I.19. Find the equation of the line through the two given points.

(*a*) $(1, 4), (3, -1)$ (*b*) $(5, 8), (2, 1)$
(*c*) $(5, 9), (-1, 5)$ (*d*) $(1, 0), (0, 8)$

I.20. Graph the lines in Problem I.19 all in the same coordinate system in different colors.

I.21. Find the equation of the line through the given point with the given slope.

(*a*) (4, 1), $m = -7$ (*b*) (−1, −5), $m = 12$

(*c*) $\left(5, -\frac{1}{4}\right), m = -\frac{1}{2}$ (*d*) $\left(\frac{1}{5}, -\frac{7}{3}\right), m = -3$

I.22. Graph the lines in Problem I.21 all in the same coordinate system in different colors.

I.23. Sketch the lines given by:

(*a*) $y = \frac{1}{2}x - 3$ (*b*) $y = -\frac{1}{4}x + 1$

(*c*) $y = 12x$ (*d*) $y = -6x + 3$

I.24. Prove: a horizontal line has the slope 0.

I.25. Prove: the equation $y = c$ (c is a constant) represents a horizontal line.

I.26. Find the equation of all nonvertical lines through the point (1, 4).

I.27. Pick out the one line from the lines in Problem I.26 which passes through the point (−1, 12).

I.28. Find the equation of all lines with the slope 2.

I.29. Pick out the one line from the lines in Problem I.28 which passes through the point (3, 4).

I.30. Pick out the one line from the lines in Problem I.26 which has the slope $-\frac{3}{4}$.

I.31. Do the three given points lie on one line?

(*a*) (1, 2), (2, 3), (3, 5) (*b*) (3, 4), (4, 6), (5, 8)

(*c*) (6, 4), (8, 3), (10, 2) (*d*) (1, −1), (2, −4), (3, −7)

I.32. Show that a line with slope m_1 is perpendicular to a line with slope m_2 if, and only if, $m_1 m_2 = -1$.

5. THE GENERAL LINE EQUATION

If we take the point-point formula (I.3) from the preceding section and shift all terms except y to the right side, we obtain

$$y = \frac{y_2 - y_1}{x_2 - x_1}\,x - \frac{y_2 - y_1}{x_2 - x_1}\,x_1 + y_1$$

where

$$\frac{y_2 - y_1}{x_2 - x_1} = m \quad \text{and} \quad -\frac{y_2 - y_1}{x_2 - x_1}\,x_1 + y_1 = c$$

are constant numbers that are determined by the coordinates of the points P_1 and P_2.

Thus we see that a function of the type

$$y = mx + c, \tag{I.5}$$

where m, c are constants, represents a straight line. However, we cannot say that every straight line is representable in the form (I.5) because we remember that we assumed in our derivation of the point-point formula and the subsequent derivation of the point-slope-formula that the two points P_1 and P_2 do not lie on a vertical line (i.e., a line parallel to the y-axis): $x_1 \neq x_2$. We can see now quite easily why we were compelled to make such an assumption. If a line is vertical, then $x_2 - x_1 = 0$ and the denominator in

$$m = \frac{y_2 - y_1}{x_2 - x_1}$$

becomes zero. Since it is the content of the first mathematical commandment that division by zero is prohibited, we had better not do this. There is, however, a way to get around this difficulty and we will now show how an all-embracing line equation can be obtained—i.e., an equation which is such that *every* line can be represented in its form.

Again we start with (I.3), multiply through by the denominator $x_2 - x_1$, assuming, of course, that it is not 0, and obtain

$$(x_2 - x_1)(y - y_1) = (y_2 - y_1)(x - x_1).$$

If we shift all terms that contain neither x nor y to the right side and change the sign, then we obtain

$$(y_2 - y_1)x - (x_2 - x_1)y = (y_2 - y_1)x_1 - (x_2 - x_1)y_1. \tag{I.6}$$

If we simply consider this equation, forgetting conveniently how we obtained it, then we see now that it does not matter whether $x_2 - x_1$ is 0 or not. That (I.6) is indeed the representation of a straight vertical line for $x_2 = x_1$ can be seen directly:

Let $x_2 = x_1$ in (I.6). Then (I.6) reduces to

$$(y_2 - y_1)x = (y_2 - y_1)x_1$$

and after cancellation by $y_2 - y_1$ we obtain

$$x = x_1$$

which means: take all points which have x_1 as abscissa (x-coordinate). These points form, indeed, a vertical line at distance x_1 from the y-axis.

Since

$$y_2 - y_1 = A, \ -(x_2 - x_1) = B, \ (y_2 - y_1)x_1 - (x_2 - x_1)y_1 = C$$

in (I.6) are constants which are determined by the coordinates of the two points which determine the line, we can see that

$$(\text{I.7}) \qquad Ax + By = C$$

where A, B, C are constants, is the general representation of a straight line.

If $B \neq 0$, we can write this equation in the form (I.5) with $m = -\frac{A}{B}$ and $c = \frac{C}{B}$; and if $B = 0$, then we obtain a vertical line $x = \frac{C}{A}$ at the distance $\frac{C}{A}$ from the y-axis.

Let us now demonstrate how we can determine the constants A, B, C in (I.7) such that (I.7) represents a straight line through two given points P_1 and P_2. For this purpose we will discuss three examples which are characteristic of what can possibly happen in this process.

(1) Let $P_1(1, 3)$, $P_2(2, 4)$. We have to find A, B, C such that $x = 1$, $y = 3$ as well as $x = 2$, $y = 4$ satisfy equation (I.7), i.e.,

$$A + 3B = C,$$
$$2A + 4B = C.$$

These are two linear equations in three unknowns, A, B, and C. So it would appear that we have either too many unknowns or too few equations, depending on how we look at it. However, we can see quite easily that (I.7) will not change if we multiply both sides of this equation by a nonzero constant, i.e., if A, B, C are a set of solutions of our two equations, so are nA, nB, nC where n is any number that is different from zero. In other words, the solutions A, B, C of our two equations are determined but for a common multiple. Now, if we subtract the second equation from the first equation, we obtain

$$-A - B = 0$$

or $A = -B$. If we now substitute $-B$ for A in the first equation, we obtain

$$-B + 3B = C$$

or $C = 2B$. We see that we could determine A and C in terms of B. Thus the equation of the line through the two given points becomes

$$-Bx + By = 2B.$$

We multiply both sides of this equation by $\frac{1}{B}$ and obtain

$$-x + y = 2 \qquad \text{or} \qquad y = x + 2.$$

(2) Let $P_1(4, 3)$, $P_2(4, 7)$. Then we obtain the equations

$$4A + 3B = C,$$

$$4A + 7B = C.$$

Again, if we subtract the second equation from the first equation, we obtain

$$-4B = 0$$

i.e., $B = 0$. Now, if we let $B = 0$ in the first equation, we obtain

$$4A = C$$

i.e., $A = \frac{C}{4}$. Thus our line equation appears in the form

$$\frac{C}{4}x = C.$$

If we multiply both sides by $\frac{4}{C}$, we obtain

$$x = 4$$

which is a vertical line at a distance 4 from the y-axis.

(3) Let us now consider the case where P_1 coincides with P_2 and see whether our algebraic apparatus breaks down. Let $P_1(1, 4)$, $P_2(1, 4)$. Then we obtain

$$A + 4B = C$$

$$A + 4B = C$$

and we see that we really have only one equation from which we obtain the solution $C = A + 4B$. Thus the equation of our line becomes

$$Ax + By = A + 4B.$$

Division by B and renaming of the ratio $\frac{A}{B} = m$ yields

$$mx + y = m + 4$$

where m is any number. Thus we see that we have obtained infinitely many lines, namely, all lines through the point $P(1, 4)$ except for the vertical line. In order to obtain the vertical line through $P(1,4)$, we cannot divide through by B in the above equation, but rather divide through by A. Since $B = 0$, we see that we obtain the vertical line $x = 1$.

Problems I.33–I.38

I.33. Two nonvertical lines are parallel if, and only if, they have the same slope. Prove that the two lines given by

$$Ax + By = C$$
$$Dx + Ey = F$$

are parallel if, and only if, $A = nD$, $B = nE$ for some number n.

I.34. What can you say about two lines which are given by the two equations in problem I.33 with $A = nD$, $B = nE$, $C = nF$?

I.35. Find the equation of the line through the two points

(*a*) (4, 1), (7, 1) (*b*) (6, −3), (6, 15)

(*c*) (3, 3), (6, −9) (*d*) (12, 1), (−4, −7)

I.36. A triangle is given by the three points $A(4, 1)$, $B(6, -3)$, $C(1, 8)$. Find the equations of the sides.

I.37. A parallelogram is determined by the three vertices (1, 4), (5, 1) and (6, −4) with the understanding that the fourth vertex is opposite the point (1, 4). Find the equations of the four sides.

I.38. Graph the lines

(*a*) $3x + 4y = 12$ (*b*) $-x + 6y = 3$

(*c*) $5x + 5y = 1$ (*d*) $x + y = 1$.

▶6. INTERSECTION OF TWO LINES*

If two lines in the plane are given by the two equations

$$A_1x + B_1y = C_1$$
$$A_2x + B_2y = C_2$$

we can see by geometric inspection that there are three possibilities:

(1) The two lines intersect,
(2) The two lines are parallel and distinct,
(3) The two lines coincide, i.e., both equations represent the same line.

To see how these possibilities find their algebraic expression, let us consider three examples.

(1) Given the two lines

$$x + 3y = 2$$
$$2x - y = 1.$$

* All sections starting with ▶ and ending with ◀ can be omitted without jeopardizing the continuity of the course.

If these two lines have an intersection point, then there exists a pair of values (x, y), the coordinates of the intersection point, such that these values satisfy *both* line equations. In order to find these values, provided they exist, we proceed as follows. We multiply the first equation by -2 and add it to the second equation

$$-2x + 2x - 6y - y = -4 + 1$$

i.e.,

$$7y = 3 \qquad \text{or} \qquad y = \frac{3}{7}.$$

Now, if we substitute this value into one of the two equations, say, the second one, we obtain

$$2x - \frac{3}{7} = 1 \quad \text{or} \quad x = \frac{10}{14} = \frac{5}{7}.$$

We see that the values $x = \frac{5}{7}$ and $y = \frac{3}{7}$ indeed satisfy both equations, and we conclude that $P(\frac{5}{7}, \frac{3}{7})$ lies on both lines, i.e., it is the intersection point of the two lines.

(2) Consider

$$x + 2y = 1$$
$$2x + 4y = 5.$$

If we proceed as before, i.e., multiply the first equation by -2 and add it to the second equation, we obtain

$$-2x + 2x - 4y + 4y = -2 + 5$$

or

$$0 = 3$$

which is clearly nonsense. This can only mean one thing: there is no point with coordinates (x, y) such that these values x,y satisfy both equations, i.e., the two lines do not have an intersection point; the two lines are parallel.

(3) Take

$$x + y = 1$$
$$3x + 3y = 3$$

and proceed as before: multiply the first equation by -3 and add it to the second equation. Thus we obtain

$$-3x + 3x - 3y + 3y = -3 + 3$$

i.e.,

$$0 = 0$$

which is clearly satisfied for all values of y. Of course, we could expect such a thing because, if we look at the two equations, we can see that they both represent the same line. (The one equation is obtained from the other one by multiplication by 3, and if we multiply both sides of an equation by the same nonzero constant, we do not change the equation.)

Now that we have discussed examples of all the possibilities, let us proceed to discuss the situation in general terms.

We have the two line equations

$$\begin{aligned} A_1x + B_1y &= C_1 \\ A_2x + B_2y &= C_2. \end{aligned} \tag{I.8}$$

Again, if we wish to solve the two equations by elimination of one unknown, we have to multiply, e.g., the first equation by $-A_2$ and the second equation by A_1, after which we obtain

$$\begin{aligned} -A_1A_2x - A_2B_1y &= -A_2C_1 \\ A_1A_2x + A_1B_2y &= A_1C_2. \end{aligned}$$

Now, if we add the two equations, we obtain

$$(A_1B_2 - A_2B_1)y = A_1C_2 - A_2C_1 \tag{I.9}$$

and from this

$$y = \frac{A_1C_2 - A_2C_1}{A_1B_2 - A_2B_1}. \tag{I.10}$$

In order to find x, we could substitute this value for y into one of the two equations (I.8) and then solve for x. However, we prefer to do it independently of the result which we have already obtained and proceed similarly as before: we multiply the first equation by B_2 and the second equation by $-B_1$:

$$\begin{aligned} A_1B_2x + B_1B_2y &= B_2C_1 \\ -A_2B_1x - B_1B_2y &= -B_1C_2. \end{aligned}$$

Adding these two equations yields

$$(A_1B_2 - A_2B_1)x = B_2C_1 - B_1C_2 \tag{I.11}$$

and from this we obtain

$$x = \frac{B_2C_1 - B_1C_2}{A_1B_2 - A_2B_1}. \tag{I.12}$$

We see that in (I.10), as well as in (I.12), we have the denominator

$$D = A_1B_2 - A_2B_1.$$

The results in (I.10) and (I.12) are senseful only if

(I.13) $$D = A_1B_2 - A_2B_1 \neq 0.$$

Thus we can state: The system of two linear equations in two unknowns (I.8) has a solution if (I.13) is satisfied. In this case, the solution is unique.

Now let us discuss the case where

(I.14) $$D = A_1B_2 - A_2B_1 = 0.$$

It follows from (I.14) that

$$\frac{A_1}{A_2} = \frac{B_1}{B_2}.$$

If we denote this ratio by n, we have

$$\frac{A_1}{A_2} = n, \qquad \frac{B_1}{B_2} = n$$

and, consequently,

$$A_1 = nA_2, \; B_1 = nB_2,$$

i.e., the coefficients A_1,B_1 of the first equation are a multiple of the coefficients A_2,B_2 of the second equation. In this case, (I.9) and (I.11) read

$$0 = A_1C_2 - A_2C_1,$$
$$0 = B_2C_1 - B_1C_2.$$

These equations are senseless, unless the right sides vanish by themselves. Now, if the right sides vanish by themselves, we have

$$A_1C_2 = A_2C_1,$$
$$B_2C_1 = B_1C_2$$

and it follows that

$$\frac{A_1}{A_2} = \frac{C_1}{C_2} \quad \text{and} \quad \frac{B_1}{B_2} = \frac{C_1}{C_2}.$$

Since $\dfrac{A_1}{A_2} = n$ and $\dfrac{B_1}{B_2} = n$, it follows that also $\dfrac{C_1}{C_2} = n$, or $C_1 = nC_2$.

Thus we can state: The system (I.8) has no solution (the two lines are parallel) if A_1,B_1 are a multiple of A_2,B_2 ($A_1 = nA_2$, $B_1 = nB_2$), but $C_1 \neq nC_2$. However, if $A_1 = nA_2$, $B_1 = nB_2$ and $C_1 = nC_2$, then the two equations have infinitely many solutions (the two lines are identical).

Problems I.39–I.47

I.39. Find the intersection point of the lines given below. If there is none, state whether the lines are parallel or coincide.

(*a*) $x + 4y = 1, \quad 2x - 5y = 1$, sketch.

(*b*) $x + 9y = 3, \quad -2x - 18y = 5.$

(*c*) $2x + 4y = 8, \quad x + 2y = 4$, sketch.
(*d*) $3x - 2y = 1, \quad y = 5$.
(*e*) $4x + 7y = 8, \quad x = 10$, sketch.
(*f*) $x = 5, \quad x = 18$.
(*g*) $x = 12, \quad y = -1$, sketch.

I.40. What quantities of silver 76 per cent pure and 82 per cent pure must be mixed together to obtain 20 pounds of silver (*a*) 80 per cent pure? (*b*) 70 per cent pure? (*c*) 82 per cent pure?

I.41. Two cars left towns 400 miles apart and traveled toward each other. The average speed of the larger car is 25 mph slower than the average speed of the smaller. If they meet after 5 hours, what was the average speed of the smaller car?

I.42. We denote the expression $A_1B_2 - A_2B_1$ by $\begin{vmatrix} A_1 & A_2 \\ B_1 & B_2 \end{vmatrix}$ and call it a *determinant*. Evaluate the following determinants:

(*a*) $\begin{vmatrix} 1 & 0 \\ 2 & 3 \end{vmatrix}$ (*b*) $\begin{vmatrix} 3 & 5 \\ 7 & 9 \end{vmatrix}$ (*c*) $\begin{vmatrix} 2 & 4 \\ -1 & -2 \end{vmatrix}$ (*d*) $\begin{vmatrix} a & b \\ na & nb \end{vmatrix}$ (*e*) $\begin{vmatrix} 1 & 0 \\ 27 & 0 \end{vmatrix}$.

I.43. Evaluate the determinants

$$\begin{vmatrix} 3 & 5 \\ 2 & 1 \end{vmatrix}, \quad \begin{vmatrix} 3 + 5x & 5 \\ 2 + x & 1 \end{vmatrix}, \quad \begin{vmatrix} 3 & 5 + 3x \\ 2 & 1 + 2x \end{vmatrix},$$

where x is any number. The result will puzzle you. Try to explain.

I.44. Show that

$$\begin{vmatrix} A_1 + nA_2 & A_2 \\ B_1 + nB_2 & B_2 \end{vmatrix} = \begin{vmatrix} A_1 & A_2 \\ B_1 & B_2 \end{vmatrix}$$

by expanding both determinants according to their definition in Problem I.42.

I.45. Evaluate the determinants

$$\begin{vmatrix} 100000 & 99999 \\ -73581 & -73579 \end{vmatrix}, \quad \begin{vmatrix} 80000 & 79999 \\ 52 & 26 \end{vmatrix}$$

by making use of the result in Problem I.44.

I.46. Find the equation of a line which passes through the intersection point of the two lines $x + y = 1$ and $2x - 3y = -1$ and through the point $P(1, 7)$.

I.47. Find the equation of all lines which pass through the intersection point of the two lines $x - 2y = 1$, $2x - 3y = 4$. (*Hint:* If you multiply the one line equation by some constant number k and add it to the other line equation, you obtain a linear equation in x and y. Clearly, this is a line equation. Of what line?) ◀

7. DISTANCE BETWEEN TWO POINTS

We consider two points P_1 and P_2 with the coordinates $P_1(x_1, y_1)$ and $P_2(x_2, y_2)$. In order to find the distance $d_{P_1P_2}$ between these two points, we

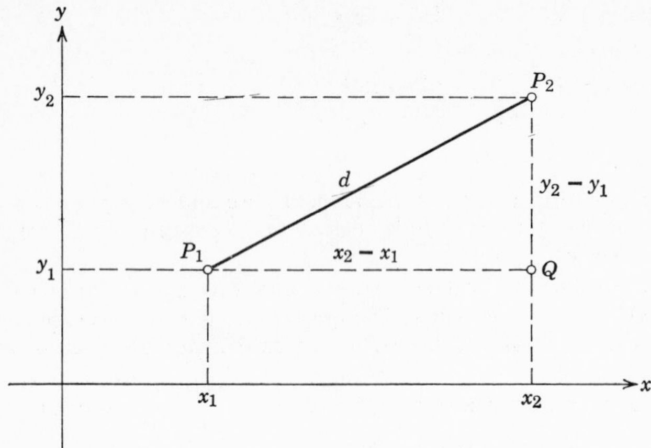

Fig. I.22

consider the triangle $\triangle(P_1QP_2)$ in Fig. I.22. We obtain directly from the theorem of Pythagoras that

$$(x_2 - x_1)^2 + (y_2 - y_1)^2 = d^2$$

and hence

$$d = \sqrt{(x_2 - x_1)^2 + (y_2 - y_1)^2} \qquad \text{(I.15)*}$$

where the square root is to be understood as positive. (It is quite senseless to talk about negative distances.)

Let us discuss three applications of the *distance formula* (I.15). First, we want to find all points (x, y) which are equidistant (have the same distance) from two given points, namely, $P_1(1, 1)$ and $P_2(3, 4)$. According to (I.15), the distance from the unknown point $P(x, y)$ to $P_1(1, 1)$ is

$$d_{PP_1} = \sqrt{(x - 1)^2 + (y - 1)^2}$$

and from $P(x, y)$ to $P_2(3, 4)$

$$d_{PP_2} = \sqrt{(x - 3)^2 + (y - 4)^2}.$$

These two distances have to be equal: $d_{PP_1} = d_{PP_2}$; hence, it follows that on squaring both expressions we have

$$(x - 1)^2 + (y - 1)^2 = (x - 3)^2 + (y - 4)^2$$

which simplifies after a few manipulations to

$$4x + 6y = 23.$$

* This formula may be considered as the definition of the distance of two points in a plane and it can be subsequently shown that it fits the intuitive notion of a distance which we developed in the past.

Since this is the equation of a straight line, we can say that all points which are equidistant from the two given points lie on a straight line, or we could formulate it as follows: the *locus* of all points that are equidistant from the two given points is a straight line. (It is easy to see that this is not only true for this special case but for the locus of all points equidistant from any two given points.)

As a next illustration of the distance formula, let us find the locus of all points that are equidistant from one given point, namely the point with the coordinates (p, q) assuming the fixed distance to be r. We know from geometry that this locus is a circle with center at (p, q) and radius r.

It follows from (I.15) that

$$\sqrt{(x-p)^2 + (y-q)^2} = r$$

or, after squaring both sides,

$$(x-p)^2 + (y-q)^2 = r^2, \tag{I.16}$$

which is the customary form in which we ordinarily state the equation of a circle with center at (p, q) and radius r. In the case the origin is the center of the circle, we put $p = 0$ and $q = 0$ to get

$$x^2 + y^2 = r^2.$$

Finally, let us find the locus of all points which have the same distance from a given point P_1 and a given line L.

Let the point P_1 have the coordinates $P_1(0, p)$ and let $y = -p$ be the equation of the line L (see Fig. I.23).

The concept of distance of a point from a line is quite ambiguous. In order to make our problem meaningful, we have to state what we mean by

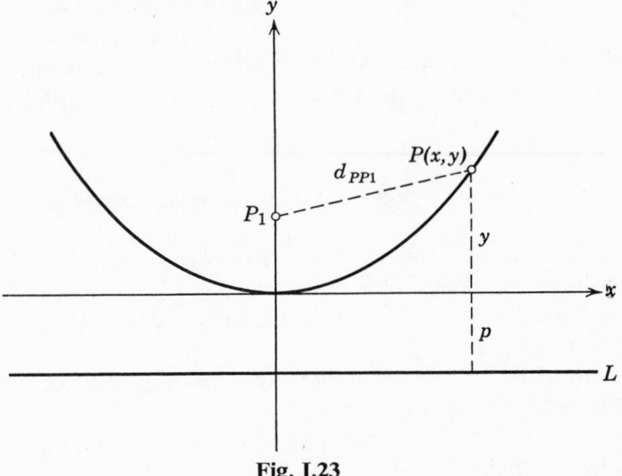

Fig. I.23

that. The mathematician understands under distance of a point from a line the shortest possible distance from the point to the line, and the reader can easily convince himself that the shortest distance from a point to a line is the one which is measured along a straight line through the given point perpendicular to the line. In the light of this definition, it is obvious from Fig. I.23 that the distance from a point $P(x, y)$ to L is given by

$$d_{PL} = y + p.$$

From (I.15) we obtain for the distance from P to P_1

$$d_{PP_1} = \sqrt{(x - 0)^2 + (y - p)^2}.$$

We wish to find the locus of all points for which

$$d_{PL} = d_{PP_1},$$

which is clearly equivalent to $d_{PL}^2 = d_{PP_1}^2$.
Thus, we set

$$(y + p)^2 = x^2 + (y - p)^2$$

and from this, if we solve for y, we have

$$y = \frac{1}{4p} x^2. \tag{I.17}$$

The graph of this function, as indicated in Fig. I.23 by a solid line, is called a *parabola* or, more precisely, a *quadratic parabola*.

Problems I.48–I.58

I.48. Find the distance between the following two points:
(*a*) $(-3, 1), (1, -1)$ (*b*) $(3, 7), (3, 9)$
(*c*) $(12, 5), (97, 5)$ (*d*) $(-1, -5), (-7, -4)$

I.49. State the equation of a circle with center at $(-1, 3)$ and radius 2.

I.50. Find the equation of the circle which passes through the three points $A(2, 1)$, $B(1, 2)$, $C\left(\frac{1}{2}, \frac{\sqrt{3}}{2} + 1\right)$.

I.51. Find the locus of all points equidistant from the two points $P(1, 3)$ and $Q(4, 9)$.

I.52. Find the locus of all points which have the same distance from the point $P_1(0, \frac{1}{4})$ and the line L: $y = -\frac{1}{4}$.

I.53. Find the locus of all points which have the same distance from the point $(p, 0)$ and the line L: $x = -p$.

I.54. Find the locus of all points which have the same distance from the point $(1, 1)$ and the line $x + y = 12$.

I.55. The three points $A(1, 0)$, $B(3, 6)$ and $C(2, 9)$ determine a triangle. What are the lengths of the three sides?

I.56. Let the three points in Problem I.55 determine a parallelogram with the understanding that the fourth point is opposite A. What is the length of the longer diagonal?

I.57. What is the distance of a point $P(9, 9)$ from a point (x, y) on the periphery of the circle $x^2 + y^2 = 1$?

I.58. In equation (I.16) express y as a function of x. What do you obtain if the square root is taken (*a*) positive? (*b*) negative? (*c*) positive and negative?

8. THE PARABOLA

We consider the parabola

$$y = x^2 \tag{I.18}$$

(see Fig. I.24).

Let us now investigate what happens to (I.18) if we leave the parabola where it is but consider a new $\bar{x}, \bar{y}$-coordinate system as indicated in Fig. I.24 by broken lines. Let the x- and $\bar{x}$-axis be parallel to each other b units apart and let the y- and $\bar{y}$-axis be parallel to each other a units apart. Clearly, we can see from Fig. I.24 that, if $P(x, y)$ is any point in the plane with the x, y-coordinates x and y and the $\bar{x}, \bar{y}$-coordinates $\bar{x}$ and $\bar{y}$, the following relations hold between x, y and $\bar{x}, \bar{y}$:

$$\begin{aligned} x &= \bar{x} + a \\ y &= \bar{y} + b. \end{aligned} \tag{I.19}$$

These relations hold for any point in the plane and, in particular, for all the points on the parabola (I.18). In order to obtain the equation of this parabola in the new $\bar{x}, \bar{y}$-coordinate system, we have to substitute for x

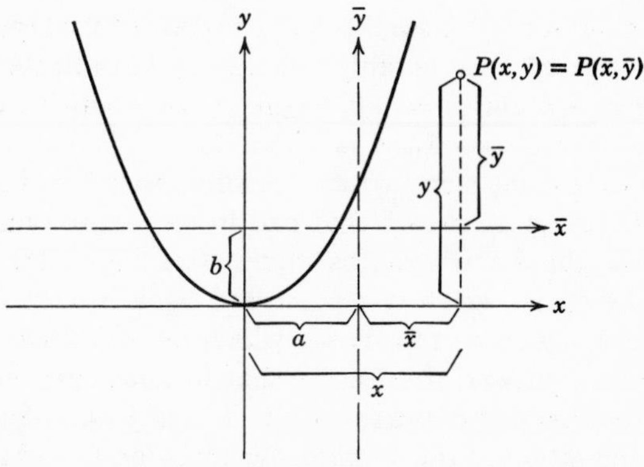

Fig. I.24

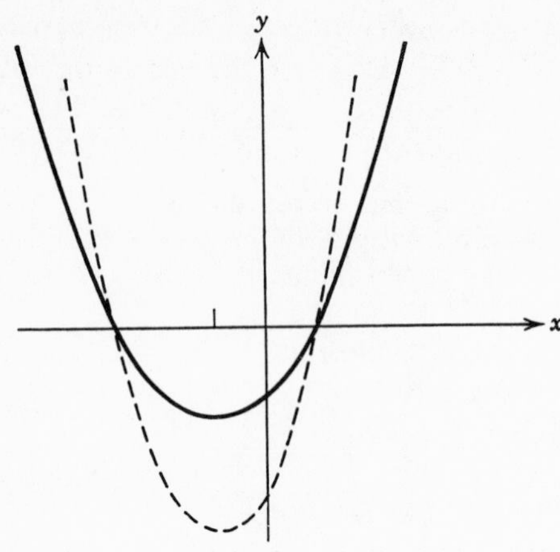

Fig. I.25

and y in (I.18) the corresponding expressions in $\bar{x}$, $\bar{y}$ according to (I.19). The result is

$$\bar{y} + b = (\bar{x} + a)^2$$

or

$$\bar{y} = \bar{x}^2 + 2a\bar{x} + a^2 - b.$$

Let us introduce new constants A and B for a and b as follows:

(I.20) $$2a = A, a^2 - b = B.$$

Then, we can write the equation of the parabola in the new $\bar{x}$, $\bar{y}$-coordinate system as follows:

(I.21) $$\bar{y} = \bar{x}^2 + A\bar{x} + B.$$

Retracing our steps, we see that any equation of the type (I.21) represents a parabola $y = x^2$ in a suitably chosen x, y-coordinate system with the origin at $\bar{x} = -a$ and $\bar{y} = -b$, where a and b can be determined from (I.20) in terms of the coefficients A and B.

Let us now go one step further. Assume that Fig. I.24 is drawn on a rubber pad and let us stretch that pad in the y-direction with the understanding that the $\bar{x}$-axis remains at rest (see Fig. I.25). The result is a parabola-like curve which is represented by a broken line in Fig. I.25. What is the equation of this curve, which we will again call a parabola? To arrive at an answer, we observe that in stretching the plane in the y-direction, we change the measure units on the $\bar{y}$-axis. Suppose we stretch the pad in the ratio 1:2 (i.e., a point that previously had a distance d from the $\bar{x}$-axis has a distance $2d$ from the $\bar{x}$-axis after the completion of the stretching process). Consequently, what was one unit before—on the $\bar{y}$-axis—is now 2 units, and if we stretch the pad in the ratio $1:s^2$ (we write s^2 to emphasize that this quantity is to be positive) then what was one unit before now becomes s^2 units. (We observe that, if s^2 is larger than 1, we have a genuine stretching process. On the other hand, if s^2 is less than 1, we actually have a shrinking process.) If we call the new $\bar{y}$-axis $\bar{\bar{y}}$ (incidentally, it coincides with the old $\bar{y}$-axis), then we have the following relation between the measure units on $\bar{y}$ and $\bar{\bar{y}}$

(I.22) $$\bar{\bar{y}} = s^2\bar{y}$$

(see also Fig. I.26).

If we substitute (I.22) into (I.21), we obtain

$$\frac{1}{s^2}\,\bar{\bar{y}} = \bar{x}^2 + A\bar{x} + B$$

and if we let

$s^2 = \alpha$, $s^2A = \beta$, $s^2B = \gamma$, we have

(I.23) $$\bar{\bar{y}} = \alpha\bar{x}^2 + \beta\bar{x} + \gamma.$$

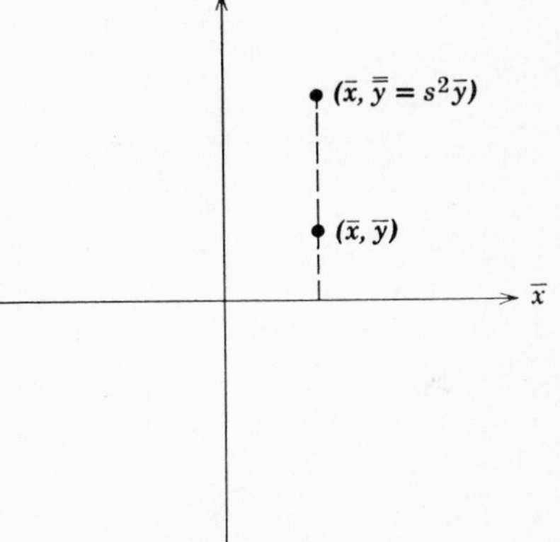

Fig. I.26

Again we see that, if we retrace our steps, every equation of the form (I.23) represents a (stretched) parabola.

Let us consider the example

$$\bar{\bar{y}} = 4\bar{x}^2 + 16\bar{x} + 4.$$

We have, in view of $s^2 = 4$, $4A = 16$ and $4B = 4$:

$$s^2 = 4,\ A = 4,\ B = 1$$

and in view of (I.20)

$$a = 2,\ b = a^2 - B = 4 - 1 = 3.$$

Thus, this parabola is obtained from $y = x^2$ by carrying out the transformation

$$x = \bar{x} + 2$$
$$y = \bar{y} + 3$$

and successively stretching in the ratio 1:4, i.e., the transformation $\bar{\bar{y}} = 4\bar{y}$ (see Fig. I.27).

Let us now consider such a stretched parabola

(I.24) $$y = \alpha x^2 + \beta x + \gamma$$

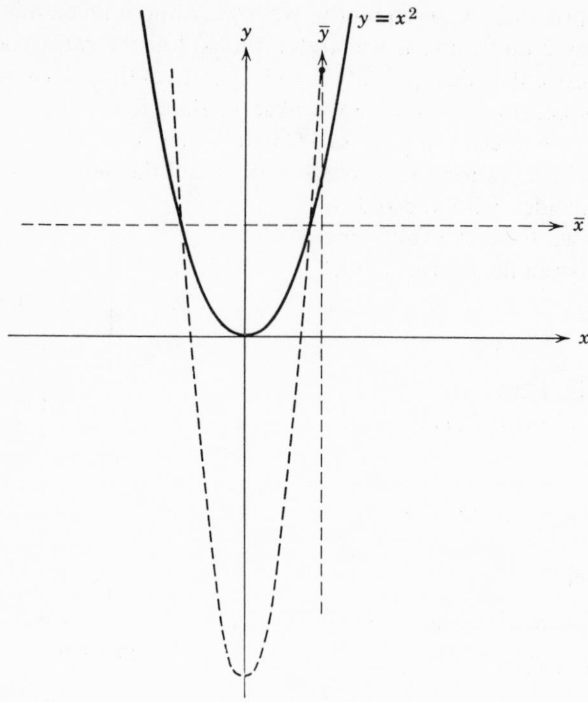

Fig. I.27

and a straight line

(I.25) $$y = ax + b.$$

We observe that the line in (I.25) is certainly not perpendicular to the x-axis (see Section 5 of this chapter), i.e., not parallel to the symmetry axis of the parabola.

We will now investigate all the possible intersections of the parabola (I.24) with the straight line (I.25). For this purpose, we have to let the equations (I.24) and (I.25) coexist, i.e., find all values of x and y for which both equations are satisfied. Since the y-values have to be equal, we obtain

$$ax + b = \alpha x^2 + \beta x + \gamma$$

or

$$\alpha x^2 + (\beta - a)x + \gamma - b = 0.$$

This is a quadratic equation of the type

$$ax^2 + bx + c = 0$$

(where a, b, c are new constants and have no relation to the ones used before), the solution of which will be discussed in the following section.

Problems I.59–I.67

I.59. Given $y = x^2$. Introduce new coordinates x,y according to

$$x = \bar{x} + 3$$
$$y = \bar{y} - 4$$

and write the parabola equation in terms of $\bar{x}$ and $\bar{y}$.

I.60. Given $y = x^2 + 6x - 4$. Introduce a new coordinate system $\bar{x},\bar{y}$ such that the equation of this parabola in the new coordinate system becomes $\bar{y} = \bar{x}^2$.

I.61. Same as in Problem I.60 for $y = -x^2 + 4x + 1$ ($\bar{y} = -\bar{x}^2$).

I.62. Given $y = x^2 + 2x - 2$. Stretch the y-axis in the ratio 1:4 and write the equation of the stretched parabola. Sketch the parabola before and after the stretching process.

I.63. Reduce $y = 9x^2 - 36x + 4$ to type form, i.e., to the form $\bar{\bar{y}} = \bar{\bar{x}}^2$ in some $\bar{\bar{x}},\bar{\bar{y}}$-coordinate system.

I.64. Given $y = x^2 - 4x - 1$. (*a*) Carry out the translation $x = \bar{x} + 1$, $y = \bar{y} - 2$ and then stretch the $\bar{y}$-axis in the ratio 1:2. (*b*) Carry out the operations in (*a*) in the opposite order and compare your results.

I.65. Given $y = x^2$. Consider the transformation $x = \bar{x} + a$, $y = \bar{y} + b$. Draw the translated parabolas for $a = 0$, $b = 1, 2, 3, 4$ in red and for $b = 0$, $a = 1, 2, 3, 4$ in blue.

I.66. Given the parabola $y = x^2 - 2x + 1$ and the straight line $x + y = 2$. Find the quadratic equation, the solution of which will yield the x-coordinates of the intersection points.

I.67. Same as in Problem I.66 for the y-coordinates of the intersection points.

9. THE QUADRATIC EQUATION*

It is our aim to find all values of x for which the quadratic equation

$$ax^2 + bx + c = 0 \tag{I.26}$$

is satisfied. We can assume, of course, that $a \neq 0$, because if it were equal to zero, we would not have a quadratic equation in the first place.

If the term bx is not present, i.e., if $b = 0$, the solution of equation (I.26) will not cause any difficulties at all. For example, if we have

$$4x^2 - 9 = 0,$$

we obtain after some simple manipulations

$$x^2 = \frac{9}{4}$$

and, consequently,

$$x = \pm\sqrt{\frac{9}{4}} = \pm\frac{3}{2}.$$

* The reader who is already familiar with the solution of the quadratic equation may omit this section.

Thus the two solutions of our equation are

$$x_1 = +\sqrt{\frac{9}{4}} = \frac{3}{2}, \quad x_2 = -\sqrt{\frac{9}{4}} = -\frac{3}{2}.$$

If we have the equation

$$x^2 + 1 = 0,$$

after shifting the absolute term to the right we obtain

$$x^2 = -1.$$

There is no real number which is such that its square is a negative number (if we multiply a positive number by itself, we obtain a positive number as a result and if we multiply a negative number by itself, we obtain again a positive number as a result), i.e., the equation $x^2 + 1 = 0$ has no solution in the domain of real numbers.

This, however, should not disturb us at all. After all, at the time when we worked only with the natural numbers $1, 2, 3, \cdots$, adding and subtracting them, we eventually came across a subtraction of the type

$$4 - 7$$

which, as we know now, does not yield a natural number (positive integer). Well, when we were confronted with this problem we did not hesitate a moment to introduce the negative numbers, boldly writing

$$4 - 7 = -3,$$

whatever that might mean. Now we are doing essentially the same thing in the present case. We invent new numbers which have the property that their square is negative. Specifically, we call

$$\sqrt{-1} = i \tag{I.27}$$

the *imaginary unit* and denote it by i for obvious reasons.* (The electrical engineers denote it by j for reasons of their own.) Thus, according to well established rules and in view of (I.27), $\sqrt{-17}$ becomes

$$\sqrt{-17} = \sqrt{-1}\,\sqrt{17} = i\sqrt{17}$$

and

$$\sqrt{-4} = \sqrt{-1}\,\sqrt{4} = i2.$$

* If you want a "simple" interpretation of this abstract concept, here it is: A line with the slope i is perpendicular to itself, because, as we have seen in Problem I.32, two lines are perpendicular to each other if, and only if, the product of their slopes is -1. Now, if the line has the slope i, then $i \cdot i = -1$ and here you are.

All the numbers of the type ib, where b is real, are called *imaginary* numbers. If we add a real number a to an imaginary number ib, we obtain a *complex number*

$$a + ib$$

(No further simplification is possible for the same reason as in adding up 3 tomatoes and 4 potatoes. This yields 3 tomatoes and 4 potatoes and not 7 pomatoes or something like that.)

Now let us return to our quadratic equation (I.26)

$$ax^2 + bx + c = 0$$

where we now assume that $a \neq 0$, $b \neq 0$. In this case, a simple extraction of a square root will not lead us anywhere unless we tamper with the left side a little. This is accomplished by a process which is called *completing the square*. For example, if we have

$$4x^2 + 6x - 4 = 0 \tag{I.28}$$

we can first write it in the form

$$4(x^2 + \tfrac{3}{2}x - 1) = 0.$$

Now $x^2 + \frac{3}{2}x$ are the first two terms in the expansion of

$$\left(x + \frac{3}{4}\right)^2 = x^2 + \tfrac{3}{2}x + \frac{9}{16}.$$

We see that this expression differs from the one in (I.28), after the factor 4 is taken out, only in the absolute terms. Instead of -1 we obtained $\frac{9}{16}$, i.e., an excess of $\frac{25}{16}$. Hence

$$\left(x + \frac{3}{4}\right)^2 - \frac{25}{16}$$

will yield the desired result. Indeed, if we evaluate this expression, we obtain

$$\left(x + \frac{3}{4}\right)^2 - \frac{25}{16} = x^2 + \tfrac{3}{2}x + \frac{9}{16} - \frac{25}{16} = x^2 + \tfrac{3}{2}x - 1.$$

Thus we can write the left side of (I.28) as

$$4\left[\left(x + \frac{3}{4}\right)^2 - \frac{25}{16}\right].$$

This is the process which we call completing the square. Now, as we can easily see, this process enables us to solve the quadratic equation (I.28) in the following manner. First, we can write it after division by 4 in the form

$$x^2 + \tfrac{3}{2}x - 1 = 0.$$

We next complete the square on the left side

$$\left(x + \frac{3}{4}\right)^2 - \frac{25}{16} = 0,$$

shift the absolute term to the right side, and obtain

$$\left(x + \frac{3}{4}\right)^2 = \frac{25}{16}.$$

Once we have the equation in this form, we can extract the square root on both sides and obtain

$$x + \tfrac{3}{4} = \pm\sqrt{\frac{25}{16}}.$$

Thus,

$$x_1 = -\frac{3}{4} + \frac{5}{4} = -\frac{1}{2}, \qquad x_2 = -\frac{3}{4} - \frac{5}{4} = -2$$

are the two solutions of the quadratic equation (I.28).

Let us now carry out the same process with the general quadratic equation (I.26). First, we factor out the coefficient of x^2:

$$a\left(x^2 + \frac{b}{a}x + \frac{c}{a}\right) = 0.$$

Next, we divide by a and complete the square as follows

$$\left(x + \frac{b}{2a}\right)^2 = x^2 + \frac{b}{a}x + \frac{b^2}{4a^2}.$$

Thus we see that

$$x^2 + \frac{b}{a}x + \frac{c}{a} = \left(x + \frac{b}{2a}\right)^2 - \frac{b^2}{4a^2} + \frac{c}{a}.$$

Hence, we can write equation (I.26) in the form

$$\left(x + \frac{b}{2a}\right)^2 = \frac{b^2}{4a^2} - \frac{c}{a}.$$

It is easy to extract the square root on both sides:

$$x + \frac{b}{2a} = \pm\sqrt{\frac{b^2}{4a^2} - \frac{c}{a}}$$

i.e.,

$$x = -\frac{b}{2a} \pm\sqrt{\frac{b^2}{4a^2} - \frac{c}{a}}.$$

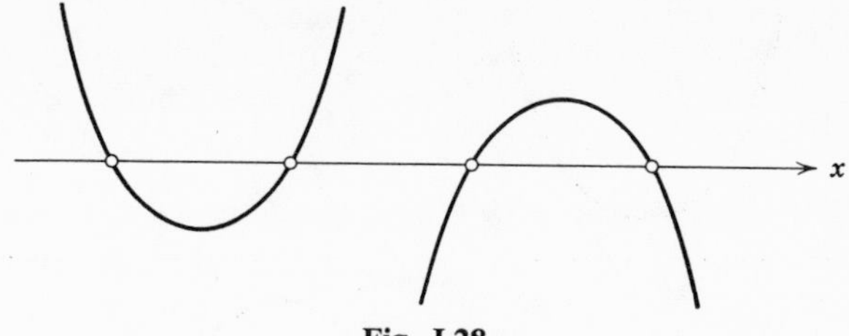

Fig. I.28

For this we obtain, after a few simple algebraic manipulations,

$$x = \frac{-b \pm \sqrt{b^2 - 4ac}}{2a}.$$

Thus we have the following two solutions of the quadratic equation (I.26):

$$\text{(I.29)} \qquad x_1 = \frac{-b + \sqrt{b^2 - 4ac}}{2a}, \qquad x_2 = \frac{-b - \sqrt{b^2 - 4ac}}{2a}.$$

(I.29) is called the *quadratic formula.*

We can see immediately from the quadratic formula:

(1) If $b^2 - 4ac$ is positive, then the quadratic equation (I.26) has two real and distinct roots (solutions), i.e., the parabola $y = ax^2 + bx + c$ intersects the x-axis in two distinct points (see Fig. I.28). If the quadratic equation arises out of a problem concerning the intersection of a parabola and a line, as we discussed it at the end of the preceding section, then there are two distinct intersection points of parabola and line in this case (see Fig. I.29).

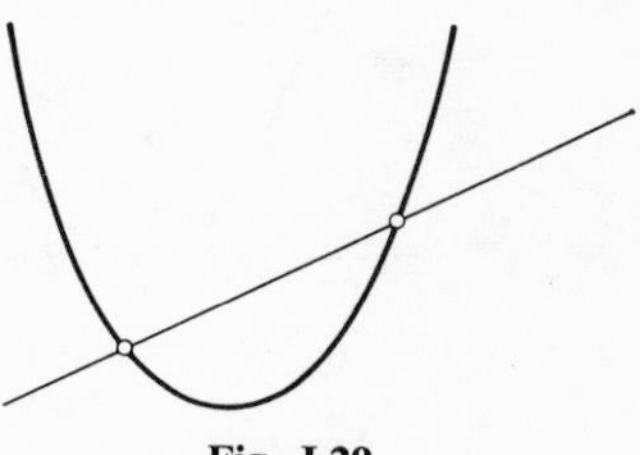

Fig. I.29

(2) If $b^2 - 4ac$ is negative, then $\sqrt{b^2 - 4ac}$ is imaginary and the two solutions of equation (I.26) are complex numbers. (Since they differ only in the sign of the imaginary part, we call them *conjugate complex numbers.*) In this case, the parabola $y = ax^2 + bx + c$ does not have any real intersection points with the x-axis (see Fig. I.30), or the parabola and the line of section 8 do not intersect at all (see Fig. I.31).

(3) Finally, if $b^2 - 4ac = 0$, then equation (I.26) has one real solution only, namely, $x = -\dfrac{b}{2a}$. In this case, the parabola $y = ax^2 + bx + c$ has only one intersection point with the x-axis and that is only possible if

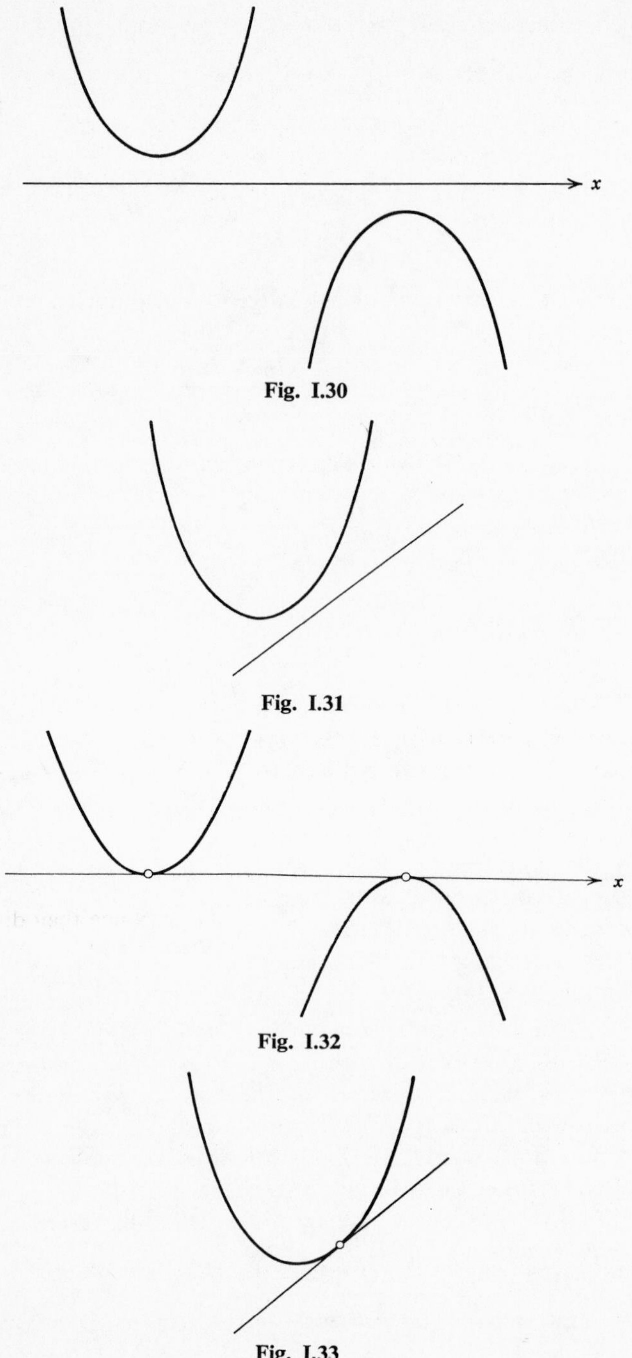

Fig. I.30

Fig. I.31

Fig. I.32

Fig. I.33

the parabola is located entirely on one side of the x-axis, touching the axis at this particular point $x = -\frac{b}{2a}$ (see Fig. I.32). In this case we call the x-axis *tangent line* to the parabola, or, if the quadratic equation arises from an intersection of a parabola with a line, the line will be *tangent* to the parabola (see Fig. I.33). We will discuss this case in some detail in the next section.

Problems I.68–I.74

I.68. Complete the square:

(*a*) $x^2 - 8x + 12$ (*b*) $x^2 + 9x - 1$

(*c*) $16x^2 + 4x + 18$ (*d*) $3x^2 - 5x + 13$

I.69. $a + ib$ is a complex number, if a and b are real. a is called the *real part* and b is called the *imaginary part*. A sum (difference) of two complex numbers is a complex number with the sum (difference) of the real parts as real part and the sum (difference) of the imaginary parts as the imaginary part. Find:

(*a*) $(3 + i2) + (4 - i6)$ (*b*) $(-2 + i9) - (4 - i7)$

(*c*) $(0 - i\frac{1}{2}) - (\frac{1}{4} + i7)$ (*d*) $(4 + i) + (4 - i)$

I.70. Solve the quadratic equations which you obtained in Problems I.66 and I.67 and discuss the geometric significance of the solutions.

I.71. Solve the following quadratic equations by the quadratic formula:

(*a*) $x^2 - 5x + 7 = 0$ (*b*) $5x^2 + 6x + 7 = 0$

(*c*) $x^2 - 17x + 1 = 0$ (*d*) $4x^2 - 16x + 1 = 0$

I.72. Given a circle with center in (1, 2) and radius 3. Find the intersection points of this circle with the line $y = 3x - 1$.

I.73. Find the intersection points of the circle with center in (3, −1) and radius 3 with the unit circle (circle of radius 1) with the center at the origin.

I.74. Given the quadratic equation

$$x^2 + bx + 1 = 0.$$

(*a*) For what values of b are the solutions real? (*b*) For what values of b does the equation only have one solution? (*c*) For what values of b are the solutions complex?

10. TANGENT TO A PARABOLA

We consider a (stretched) quadratic parabola

$$y = ax^2 + bx + c \tag{I.30}$$

and a straight line

$$y = Ax + B. \tag{I.31}$$

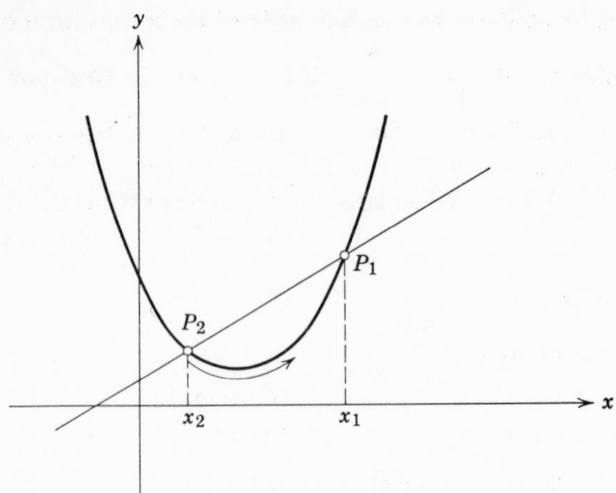

Fig. I.34

In general, the line (I.31) will intersect the parabola (I.30) in two points, if it intersects at all. The x-coordinates of the intersection points are found if we let (I.30) and (I.31) co-exist as follows:

$$ax^2 + bx + c = Ax + B.$$

This is a quadratic equation which, after rearrangement of terms, can be written in the form

$$ax^2 + (b - A)x + c - B = 0 \tag{I.32}$$

and has, according to (I.29), the solutions

$$x_{1,2} = \frac{-(b - A) \pm \sqrt{(b - A)^2 - 4a(c - B)}}{2a}. \tag{I.33}$$

Figure I.34 illustrates the situation for the case where the solutions (I.33) are real and different.

Now let us keep the intersection point P_1 of the parabola with the line which has the x-coordinate $x = x_1$ fixed and move the other intersection point P_2 along the parabolic arc towards P_1, i.e., let the x-coordinate of the second intersection point x_2 approach x_1, the x-coordinate of the intersection point P_1. During this process, the line through P_1 and P_2 will turn as indicated in Fig. I.35 where we have depicted the situation for several positions of P_2.

We see that the closer x_2 is to x_1, the closer the line through P_1 and P_2 will resemble what we consider to be the tangent line to the parabola at the point P_1. The tangent line is drawn in Fig. I.35 as a bold line.

Let us now investigate what happens algebraically in formula (I.33), if we turn the line through P_1 and P_2 in this manner through suitable changes of A and B. Because the two solutions x_1 and x_2 of the quadratic equation (I.32) move closer together, their difference becomes smaller. Since we have from (I.33)

$$x_1 = \frac{-(b - A) + \sqrt{(b - A)^2 - 4a(c - B)}}{2a},$$

$$x_2 = \frac{-(b - A) - \sqrt{(b - A)^2 - 4a(c - B)}}{2a},$$

we obtain for the difference

$$x_1 - x_2 = \frac{\sqrt{(b - A)^2 - 4a(c - B)}}{a}. \tag{I.34}$$

This difference can only become smaller if the expression under the square root becomes smaller, or the denominator a becomes larger, or a combination thereof. That a becomes larger can be excluded on the grounds that the parabola remains the same during the entire process and, therefore, a is a fixed number.

Hence, we can say the smaller

$$(b - A)^2 - 4a(c - B),$$

the closer the line through P_1 and P_2 will resemble the tangent line to the parabola at the point P_1 and, consequently, it appears that we will obtain

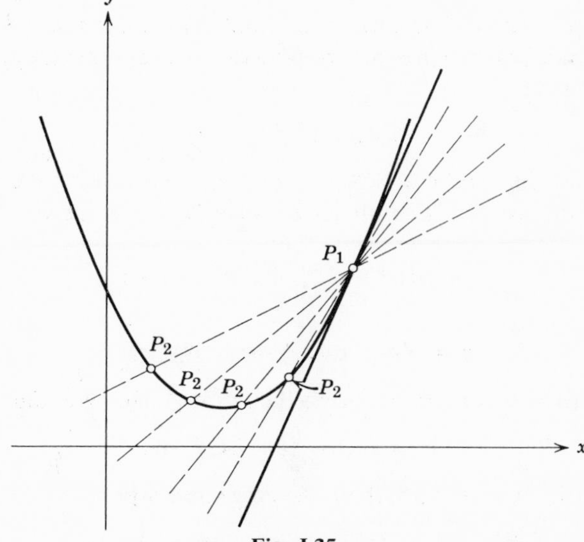

Fig. I.35

the tangent line itself, if P_1 and P_2 coincide, i.e., if

$$(b - A)^2 - 4a(c - B) = 0.$$

This leads to the condition: The line $y = Ax + B$ is tangent line to the parabola $y = ax^2 + bx + c$ if

$$(b - A)^2 = 4a(c - B). \tag{I.35}$$

Let us consider an example: Given the parabola

$$y = x^2 \qquad (a = 1, b = 0, c = 0)$$

and the line

$$y = Ax - 1 \qquad (B = -1).$$

Let us determine the slope A of the line such that the line becomes tangent to the parabola. From (I.35)

$$(0 - A)^2 = 4(0 + 1)$$

or

$$A = \pm 2.$$

Thus it would appear that

$$y = 2x - 1$$

as well as

$$y = -2x - 1$$

are tangent to the parabola $y = x^2$. This is indeed the case, as illustrated in Fig. I.36.

Utilizing condition (I.35), we are now able to find the slope of the tangent line to the parabola (I.30) at any point with the x-coordinate x_0. It follows from (I.30) that

$$P_0(x_0, ax_0^2 + bx_0 + c) \tag{I.36}$$

is a point on the parabola (I.30) for any x_0. Now, using the point-slope formula (I.4), we consider all lines through this point and obtain the equation

$$y - ax_0^2 - bx_0 - c = A(x - x_0)$$

or

$$y = Ax + ax_0^2 + (b - A)x_0 + c \tag{I.37}$$

as the equation of all lines through the point (I.36). We note that

$$B = ax_0^2 + (b - A)x_0 + c$$

and obtain in view of (I.35) the following condition on A:

$$(b - A)^2 = 4a[c - ax_0^2 - (b - A)x_0 - c]$$

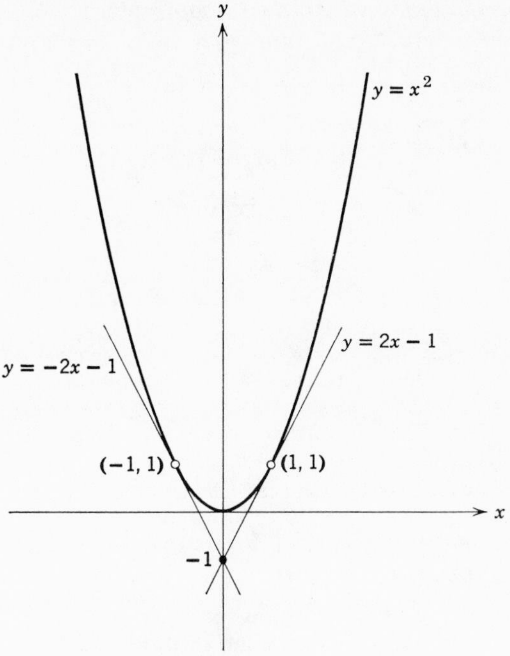

Fig. I.36

or, after some algebraic manipulations,

$$A^2 - (2b + 4ax_0)A + b^2 + 4a^2x_0^2 + 4abx_0 = 0.$$

The solution of this quadratic equation is obtained from

$$A_{1,2} = \frac{2b + 4ax_0 \pm \sqrt{4b^2 + 16abx_0 + 16a^2x_0^2 - 4b^2 - 16a^2x_0^2 - 16abx_0}}{2}.$$

Since the expression under the square root vanishes, we have

(I.38) $$A = 2ax_0 + b.$$

Thus we can say: The tangent line to the parabola $y = ax^2 + bx + c$ at the point with the x-coordinate x_0 has the slope $2ax_0 + b$. (In Chapter III, Section 2, we will obtain a more general result which will contain this one as a special case.)

As an example, let us consider

$$y = 2x^2 - 4x + 3$$

and the point on the parabola with the x-coordinate $x_0 = 2$. Then for the slope of the tangent line at this point we have, according to (I.38),

$$A = 8 - 4 = 4.$$

The y-value corresponding to $x_0 = 2$ is found to be $y_0 = 3$. Hence we find the equation of the tangent line from the point-slope formula to be

$$y - 3 = 4(x - 2),$$

and from this

$$y = 4x - 5.$$

Problems I.75–I.84

I.75. Is it possible that a line $y = Ax + B$ crosses a parabola $y = ax^2 + bx + c$ in one point only? (*Hint:* Assume that the line crosses the parabola in the point with the x-coordinate x_0, but is not the tangent line to the parabola at this point, i.e., has a slope which is different from $2ax_0 + b$. Is it then possible that no other intersection takes place?

I.76. Find the equation of the tangent line to the parabola at the indicated point.

(*a*) $y = 4x^2 - 6x + 3, \quad (1, 1)$ (*b*) $y = -2x^2 + 7, \quad (2, -1)$

(c) $y = x^2 + 12x + 3, \quad (-1, ?)$ (*d*) $y = -3x^2 + 3x - 3, \quad (2, ?)$

I.77. Find the tangent line(s) to the parabola $y = ax^2 + bx + c$ which pass(es) through a point P_0 that does not lie on the parabola:

(*a*) $a = 1, \quad b = 3, \quad c = -1, \quad P_0(1, -2)$

(*b*) $a = -2, \quad b = 1, \quad c = -1, \quad P_0(3, 12)$

(c) $a = 1, \quad b = 2, \quad c = 1, \quad P_0(-4, -10)$

(*d*) $a = -4, \quad b = -1, \quad c = 1, \quad P_0(2, 7)$

I.78. Find the equation of the tangent line to the parabola $y = x^2 + 4x - 3$ which is parallel to the line $y = 5x + 12$.

I.79. Same as in Problem I.78 for $y = 2x^2 - 3x + 2$ and $y = 13x - 4$.

I.80. Determine a such that the quadratic equation

$$ax^2 + ax - 4 = 0$$

has one solution only.

I.81. Determine b such that the quadratic equation

$$x^2 + bx + b = 0$$

has one solution only.

I.82. At what point does the parabola

$$y = 2x^2 + 3x - 4$$

have a horizontal tangent line? (A horizontal line has the slope 0.)

I.83. Show that the x-axis is tangent line to the parabola

$$y = x^2 - 4x + 4.$$

I.84. Show that a parabola always has one, and only one, horizontal tangent line.

11. INTERVAL NOTATION

In many cases we will not study a function which is given by a mathematical formula for the entire domain of x-values. Sometimes, as in the example $y = \frac{1}{x}$, it will be necessary to exclude certain values from the x-domain. At other times, how a function behaves on only a certain part of the x-range will be of interest to us and what the function does elsewhere will be immaterial. In order to state in a simple and precise manner for what values of x a function is to be studied, we will introduce in this section a special notation.

First, let us introduce two new symbols. $a < b$ is read "a is less than b" and means that the point representing a on the line of numbers is to the left of the point representing b on the line of numbers. $a \leq b$ is read "a is less than or equal to b" and means that the point representing a on the line of numbers is either to the left of the point representing b on the line of numbers or coincides with the latter.

For example,

$$x < 3$$

indicates that all values of x which are less than 3 are considered, while

$$x \leq 2$$

signifies that all values of x which are either less than 2, or at most equal to 2, are to be considered.

Similarly, we use the symbols $a > b$ and $a \geq b$, which stand for "a greater than b" and "a greater than or equal to b" respectively.

Thus, for example, to characterize all the values of x which are between -1 and 4, but neither equal to -1 nor to 4, we write

$$-1 < x < 4.$$

If we wish to include the numbers -1 and 4 in our consideration, we write

$$-1 \leq x \leq 4.$$

We call such a section of the x-axis, which is terminated by two points, an *interval*.

Specifically, we call $a < x < b$ an *open* interval. Here x may range over all values that are between a and b, but must not assume the values a and b themselves. $a \leq x \leq b$ is called a *closed* interval. Here x is allowed to assume the values a and b in addition to all values between these. Finally, $a \leq x < b$ and $a < x \leq b$ are called *semiclosed or semiopen* intervals for obvious reasons.

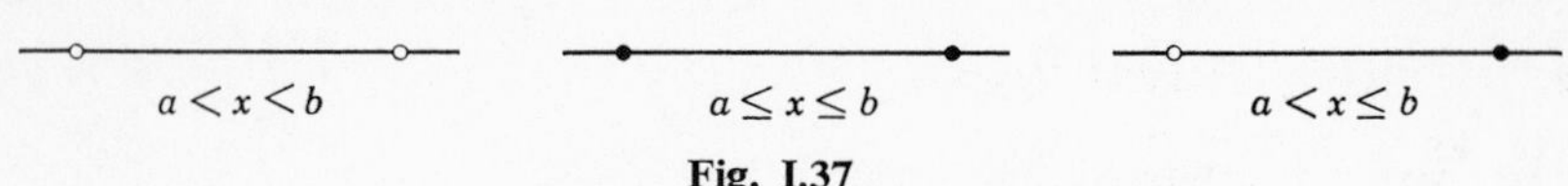

Fig. I.37

Graphically, we represent intervals as demonstrated in Fig. I.37. Intervals are not necessarily bounded on one of their ends. We then speak of *half-lines*. For example, $x \geq 1$ denotes that part of the x-axis that begins at $x = 1$ and proceeds to the right.

As an example, let us find the interval within which the function

$$y = x^2 - x - 2 = (x + 1)(x - 2)$$

is negative, i.e., $y < 0$. We can see immediately that y vanishes at $x = -1$ and at $x = 2$. At $x = 0$, we have $y = -1$. So it appears obvious that

$$y < 0 \text{ for all } x \text{ in } -1 < x < 2 \; (y \leq 0 \text{ for all } x \text{ in } -1 \leq x \leq 2).$$

As a second example, let us find the intervals in which the function

$$y = \frac{1}{(x - 3)x}$$

is defined (meaningful). Clearly, at $x = 0$ and at $x = 3$ the denominator vanishes and the function is, therefore, not defined at these points. However, for all values of x which are located in any one of the intervals

$$x < 0, \; 0 < x < 3, \; x > 3$$

the function is defined.

Problems I.85–I.92

I.85. Represent the following intervals graphically:

(*a*) $-2 \leq x \leq 7$ (*b*) $5 < x < 7$

(*c*) $-4 < x \leq -1$ (*d*) $4 \leq x < 18$

(*e*) $-3 < x$ (*f*) $x < -5$

I.86. Find the interval(s) in which the function

$$y = x^2 - x - 2$$

is positive.

I.87. For which intervals does the function

$$y = \sqrt{(x - 1)(x - 2)(x - 3)}$$

have real values?

I.88. For which intervals is the function $y = \dfrac{1}{x^2 - x - 2}$ defined?

I.89. Shade the region in the x,y-plane for which $1 \leq x \leq 4$ and $-1 \leq y \leq 3$.

I.90. For what values of x is $x^2 \leq x$ true?

I.91. Given the function

$$y = x^3.$$

For which values of x does the inequality

$$1 < y < 8$$

hold?

I.92. Find the interval which is common to the intervals

$$-1 < x < 3 \quad \text{and} \quad 1 < x < 29.$$

12. MORE EXAMPLES OF FUNCTIONS—CONTINUITY

Let us discuss in this section some functions which are somewhat out of the ordinary.

First, we discuss the function

$$y = |x| . \tag{I.39}$$

(*Read:* "Absolute value of x".) Let us shortly explain the meaning of the "*absolute value symbol.*" Any number can be represented as a point on the line of numbers, as we explained in Section 2. This point has a certain unique distance from the origin and this distance—which as a distance is a positive number—is what we call the *absolute value* of a number.

For example,

$$|4| = 4, \qquad |9.031| = 9.031,$$

however,

$$|-3| = 3, \qquad |-0.561| = 0.561, \text{ etc.} \cdots$$

As a rule, we may remember that, if a number is positive, it is equal to its absolute value. On the other hand, if a number is negative, its absolute value is obtained by changing the sign from $-$ to $+$ or, as we can state it, by multiplying the number by -1.

Thus, if $x \geq 0$, then $|x| = x$; but, if $x < 0$, then $|x| = -x$. To illustrate the latter case, let $x = -2 < 0$. Then $|-2| = -(-2) = 2$.

Now we are ready to discuss the function in (I.39). We have

$$y = |x| = \begin{cases} x \text{ if } x \geq 0 \\ -x \text{ if } x < 0. \end{cases}$$

Thus, for all $x \geq 0$, the function is given by

$$y = x, x \geq 0$$

which is represented by the half-line which bisects the first quadrant of the right coordinate system (see Fig. I.38).

For all $x < 0$ we have

$$y = -x, x < 0$$

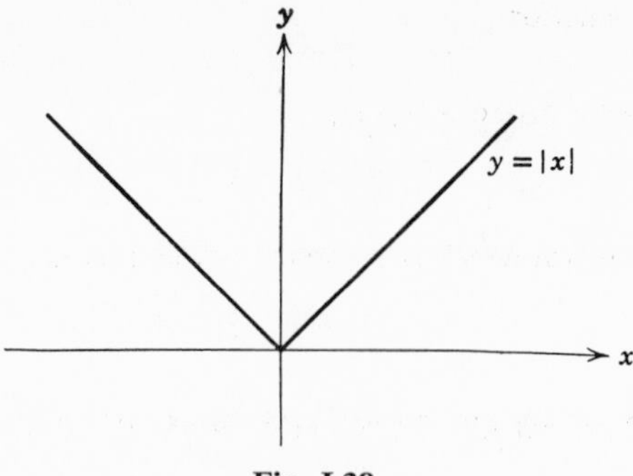

Fig. I.38

which is represented by the half-line which bisects the second quadrant of the right coordinate system (see Fig. I.38). Thus we see that the function $y = |x|$ is represented by a bent line with a sharp corner at the origin.

Next, let us consider the function

$$y = \frac{1}{x}. \tag{I.40}$$

We were strictly brought up in the belief that division by 0 is prohibited. So we have to exclude the value $x = 0$ from our discussion, since $\frac{1}{0}$ would be quite meaningless. However, we can still discuss this function for all values $x \neq 0$ which includes values that are very close to 0, and as a matter of fact, as close to 0 as we please to choose them. For example, if $x = \frac{1}{100}$ then, $y = 100$. If we take $x = \frac{1}{10000000000000000}$, then, $y = 10000000000000000$ etc. $\cdots$ We see that the closer the value of x comes to 0, the larger the corresponding value of y will be. We express this simply by stating that as x *approaches* 0 ($x \to 0$), the corresponding value of y *approaches infinity* ($y \to \infty$). Note that the symbol ∞ means neither more nor less than what it means on the lens of a photographic camera. It just expresses numbers (distances) which are larger than any number (distance) which we would care to state (measure).

Remember

∞ is **not** a number.

It is just a symbol that helps us abbreviate the awkward statement "larger than any number one cares to state."

The graph of the function (I.40) is found in Fig. I.39. We can see that the curve representing this function comes closer and closer to the y-axis. It will never reach the y-axis, however, because reaching the y-axis would mean that the function $y = \dfrac{1}{x}$ has a value for $x = 0$ which is not the case.

We call a line that is approached in such a manner an *asymptote*: the y-axis is an asymptote of $y = \frac{1}{x}$. By the same token, we can state that the x-axis is an asymptote, since it is approached by the curve in a similar manner, i.e., as $x \to \infty$, then $y \to 0$ (and as $x \to -\infty$, then $y \to 0$).

Next, let us consider the function

(I.41) $$y = [x],\ x \geq 0.$$

(*Read:* "Largest integer less than or equal to x.") As the note in parentheses indicates, the bracket symbol signifies that we have to take the largest integer which is smaller than or equal to x. Thus,

$$[0.3] = 0, \qquad [4.2] = 4, \qquad [5] = 5, \qquad [9.9865] = 9, \text{ etc.} \cdots$$

If we wish to draw the graph of this function for all $x \geq 0$, we have to discuss the function for every interval which is terminated by two consecutive integers. If $0 \leq x < 1$, then we have clearly

$$y = 0,\ 0 \leq x < 1.$$

In the interval $1 \leq x < 2$, we obtain

$$y = 1,\ 1 \leq x < 2$$

and for $2 \leq x < 3$ we have

$$y = 2,\ 2 \leq x < 3, \text{ etc.} \cdots$$

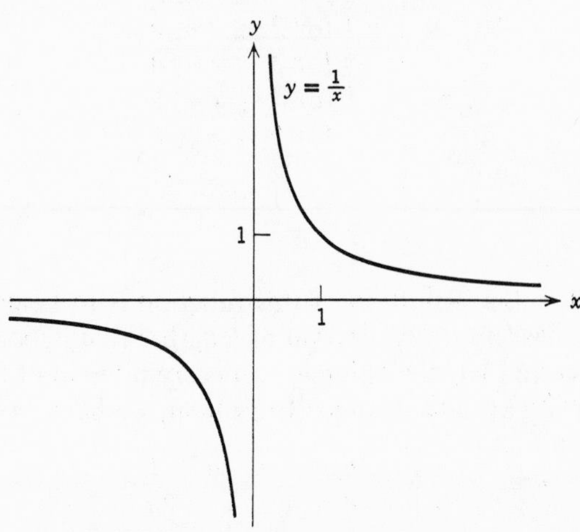

Fig. I.39

The reader can see that we obtain for $y = [x]$ the following definition if we wish to avoid the brackets symbol:

$$y = \begin{cases} 0 \text{ for } 0 \leq x < 1 \\ 1 \text{ for } 1 \leq x < 2 \\ 2 \text{ for } 2 \leq x < 3 \\ 3 \text{ for } 3 \leq x < 4 \\ 4 \text{ for } 4 \leq x < 5 \\ 5 \text{ for } 5 \leq x < 6 \\ 6 \text{ for } 6 \leq x < 7 \\ 7 \text{ for } 7 \leq x < 8 \\ \cdot \\ \cdot \\ \cdot \\ n \text{ for } n \leq x < n + 1 \\ \cdot \\ \cdot \\ \cdot \end{cases}$$

which is to be continued ad infinitum. Now we can see clearly that the function defined in (I.41) is represented by the graph in Fig. I.40. Since this graph resembles the steps in a staircase, we call the function $y = [x]$ the *step function*.

▶ Next, we discuss the function

$$\text{(I.42)} \qquad y = \begin{cases} 1 \text{ for } 0 \leq x < 1 \\ -1 \text{ for } 1 \leq x < 2 \\ 1 \text{ for } 2 \leq x < 3 \\ -1 \text{ for } 3 \leq x < 4 \\ 1 \text{ for } 4 \leq x < 5 \\ -1 \text{ for } 5 \leq x < 6 \\ \cdot \\ \cdot \\ \cdot \end{cases}$$

It is obvious how the definition of this function is to be continued. It always has the value 1 in every interval of length 1 that is bounded below by an even integer and has the value -1 in every interval of length 1 that is bounded below by an odd integer. In general, we have

$$y = \begin{cases} 1 \text{ for } 2n \leq x < 2n + 1 \\ -1 \text{ for } 2n + 1 \leq x < 2n + 2 \end{cases}$$

where n assumes all nonnegative integral values.

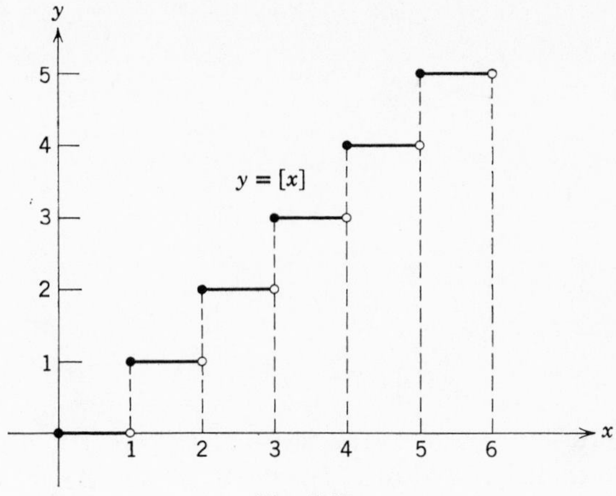

Fig. I.40

The graph of this function is given in Fig. I.41. We can see that this function exhibits a peculiar behavior inasmuch as it repeats itself every 2 units. We call such a function a *periodic function.* The function in (I.42), in particular, is a function of *period* 2.

We can describe such a function very economically by making use of the symbol $f(x)$ as follows:

(I.42a) $$y = f(x) = \begin{cases} 1 \text{ for } 0 \leq x < 1 \\ -1 \text{ for } 1 \leq x < 2 \end{cases}$$

with the additional information that

(I.43) $$f(x + 2) = f(x) \text{ for all } x \geq 0,$$

i.e., if we know the value of $f(x)$ for some x, then we know that it has the same value at $x + 2$. Since we know the values of the function for all

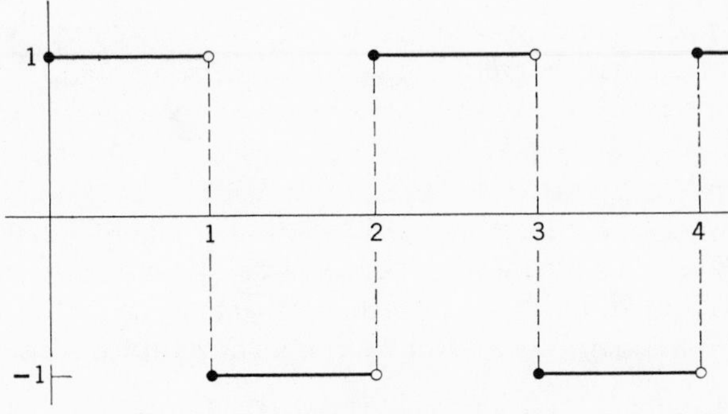

Fig. I.41

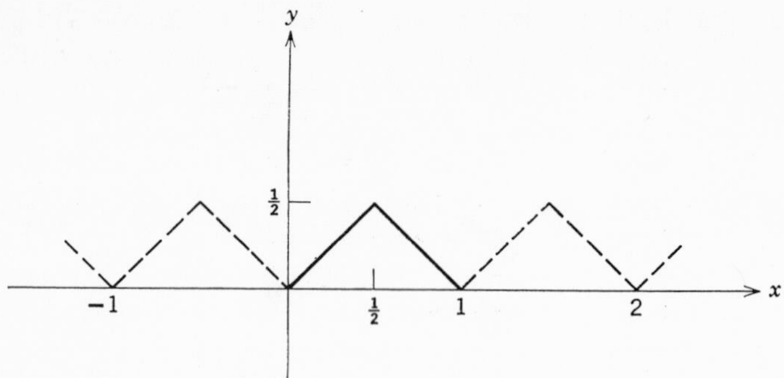

Fig. I.42

values of x in $0 \leq x < 2$ from (I.42a), we also know it for all values of x which are greater than 2 because of (I.43). It is left to the reader to extend the definition of this function for negative values of x such that the periodicity is preserved.

Finally, let us consider one more periodic function, namely,

(I.44) $$y = f(x) = \begin{cases} x & \text{for } 0 \leq x < \frac{1}{2} \\ -x + 1 & \text{for } \frac{1}{2} \leq x < 1 \end{cases}$$

where

(I.45) $$f(x + 1) = f(x).$$

This is a function with period 1. In order to graph this function, we first focus our attention on the interval $0 \leq x < 1$ where we easily obtain the graph as indicated by a solid line in Fig. I.42. Then we simply repeat the graph to the left and the right as demanded by the periodicity 1 of our function. This is indicated by a broken line in Fig. I.42. ◀

The functions represented in Figs. I.39, I.40, and I.41 exhibit a property (or properties) which we have not encountered before in dealing with straight lines and parabolas. It is easier to discuss the phenomenon we have in mind from a negative standpoint by pointing out what properties these functions do not have rather than explaining directly what they do have.

Consider a river between the point of origin and the termination point. A river cannot suddenly cease to exist and continue at some other distant point. (It can go underground for a while but that does not mean that it ceases to exist.) And this "river property" is what those functions in Figs. I.39, I.40, and I.41 do not have. The branch of the function in Fig. I.39 to the left of the y-axis as well as the branch to the right of the y-axis could conceivably represent rivers. However, the entirety of this function could not because the water cannot cross the y-axis along the graph of $y = \dfrac{1}{x}$.

The point $x = 0$ is called a *point of discontinuity* of our function. Likewise, the points represented by integral values of x are points of discontinuity of the functions represented in Figs. I.40 and I.41. If a function does not have discontinuities, then we call it *continuous*.

Let us suppose that we are in possession of a microscope of infinite magnifying power and we focus this microscope on a point of the graph of a function. Then, if the image in the viewer turns out to be an uninterrupted line through this point, the function is continuous at the point. Otherwise, the point is one of discontinuity. Of course, there are no microscopes of infinite magnifying power and, even if there were, there are no means of drawing a "continuous" curve that would stand up to such a microscopic investigation.

So the question of whether a function is continuous or not cannot be settled by an examination of its graph. What we have to do is examine the mathematical function itself after having translated the intuitive concept of the "river property" into rigorous mathematical language. We will not indulge in such a discussion in our treatment. The functions which we will deal with in future are continuous or, if they have points of discontinuity, these can be easily noticed.

We will, however, introduce in the next section the stronger concept of uniform continuity (which is equivalent to continuity in every point of a closed interval) of which we will make use in Chapter II, Section 8, in a limited way.

Problems I.93–I.103

I.93. Sketch the function $y = |x - 1|$.

I.94. Sketch the function $y = |x|^3$.

I.95. Show that $|x + y| = |x| + |y|$, if $x \geq 0$ and $y \geq 0$ or $x \leq 0$ and $y \leq 0$; and that $|x + y| < |x| + |y|$ if either $x > 0$, $y < 0$ or $x < 0$, $y > 0$.

I.96. Sketch the function $y = [|x|]$ for all x (within reason).

I.97. Show that $[x - \frac{1}{2}] \leq x$. For what values of x does the equal sign hold?

I.98. Sketch the function

$$y = f(x) = \begin{cases} 1 \text{ for } 0 \leq x < \frac{1}{2} \\ 0 \text{ for } \frac{1}{2} \leq x < 1 \end{cases}$$

where $f(x + 1) = f(x)$.

I.99. Graph the function

$$y = f(x) = x \quad \text{for} \quad -1 \leq x < 1$$

where $f(x + 2) = f(x)$.

I.100. Graph the function

$$y = \frac{1}{x - 1}.$$

I.101. Graph the function

$$y = \frac{1}{1 - x^2}$$

I.102. Graph the function

$$y = [x] - |x|.$$

I.103. Graph the functions $y = \dfrac{1}{\sqrt{x}}$, $y = \dfrac{1}{x}$, and $y = \dfrac{1}{x^2}$ in the same coordinate system in different colors. Discuss the behavior of these functions relative to each other.

▶13. UNIFORM CONTINUITY*

The functions defined in (I.40), (I.41), and (I.42) in the preceding section show some characteristic features that set them apart from the functions which we discussed on previous occasions, i.e., linear functions and parabolas. What makes these functions so special is that once we start drawing the curves which represent them, it is not possible to do so without having to interrupt the process at certain points [e.g., the points where the functions in (I.41) and (I.42) jumped from one level to another, or where the function in (I.40) "jumped" from $-\infty$ to $+\infty$]. In other words, these functions are not representable by "continuous" graphs, if we accept for the moment the unsophisticated everyday meaning of the term "continuous."

If we attempt to make a study embracing all functions from an elementary standpoint, using simple and elementary techniques, we encounter almost insurmountable difficulties. It turns out that a great simplification can be obtained if we exclude all these functions that jump, either through a finite distance or through an infinite distance, or show some other erratic behavior of which we will exhibit examples later. In order to eliminate such functions, we have to establish a criterion which will enable us to distinguish in a formal mathematical fashion between "well-behaved" and "not-so-well-behaved" functions. The criterion which would seem obvious, namely, that we should be able to draw the graph of the function with an uninterrupted stroke of the pencil, is, unfortunately, inadequate because it would eliminate functions which exhibit neither of the frowned upon phenomena but still defy graph drawing as is shown in Appendix II.

In order to arrive at some workable criterion, let us consider three functions, each one in a closed interval of finite length $a \leq x \leq b$, as represented in (*a*), (*b*), and (*c*) of Fig. I.43. A function of the type as represented in Fig. I.43(*a*) we consider acceptable. Functions as depicted in (*b*) and (*c*) we will reject in the future. Now, what is it that distinguishes the function in Fig.

* The reader may omit this section for the time being and take it up at a later time when he has reached greater mathematical maturity.

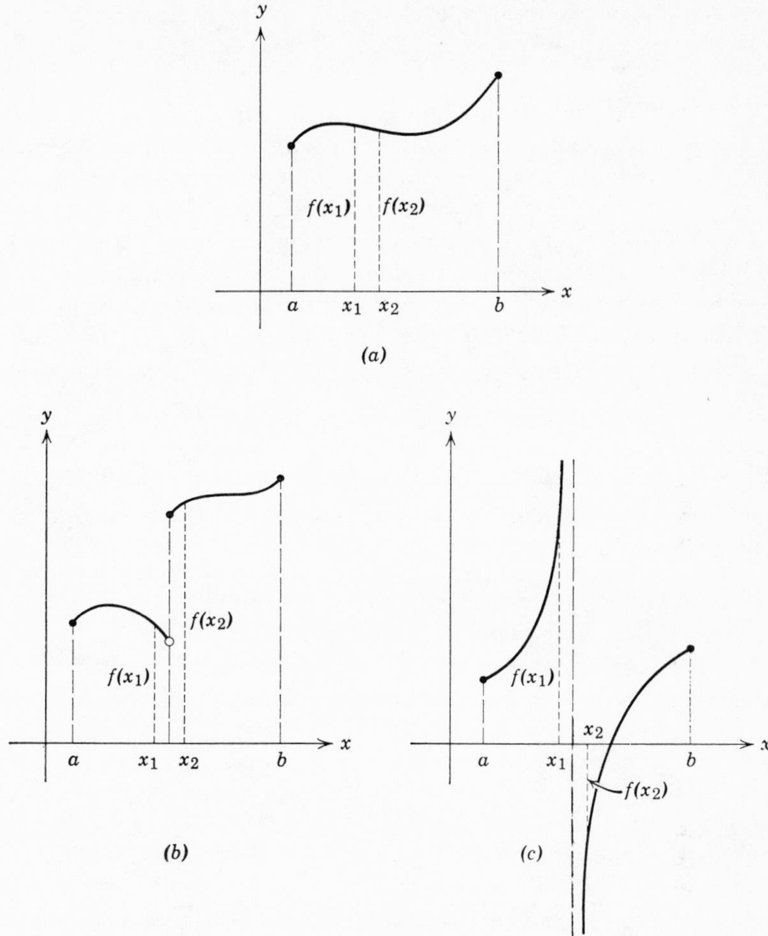

Fig. I.43

I.43(a) from those in (b) and (c)? Clearly, if we choose any two x values x_1, x_2 in $a \leq x \leq b$ which are very close together, then we can see that the corresponding y-values $f(x_1)$, $f(x_2)$ are also quite close together in case of Fig. I.43(a). However, if we look at (b) and (c) of Fig. I.43 we can see that it is possible to choose two x-values such that the corresponding y-values are far apart, no matter how close the two x-values are.

This is really the whole situation in a nutshell. All we have to do now is to formulate this idea mathematically so that it is accessible to formal manipulations. Let us consider for this purpose an enlargement of Fig. I.43(a) as presented in Fig. I.44.

Let us choose a positive number ε (*read:* epsilon) quite arbitrarily. Now draw a net of horizontal parallel lines which are $\frac{\varepsilon}{2}$ units apart, as indicated in Fig. I.44. We embark on a journey on our curve, starting at the point $a, f(a)$ and proceeding to the right. On this journey, we will have to cross some of the parallel lines one at a time. Whenever we do, we mark the intersection point. If we project these intersection points vertically onto the x-axis, we obtain the points that are designated by $\alpha_1, \alpha_2, \alpha_3, \cdots \alpha_{11}$ in Fig. I.44. We can see now that whenever we pick out two x-values, x_1 and x_2, which are both located in an interval terminated by two consecutive points α_k, α_{k+1} ($k = 0, 1, 2, \cdots, 11$ if we agree to let $a = \alpha_0$ and $b = \alpha_{12}$), then the corresponding y-values, $f(x_1)$ and $f(x_2)$, differ from each other by than less $\frac{\varepsilon}{2}$, because the portion of the curve between α_k and α_{k+1} remains entirely between two adjacent horizontal lines which are a distance $\frac{\varepsilon}{2}$ apart.

Let us denote the lengths of the subintervals which are terminated by the points α_k by δ_k (*read:* delta k):

$$\delta_1 = \alpha_1 - \alpha_0, \delta_2 = \alpha_2 - \alpha_1, \cdots, \delta_{12} = \alpha_{12} - \alpha_{11}$$

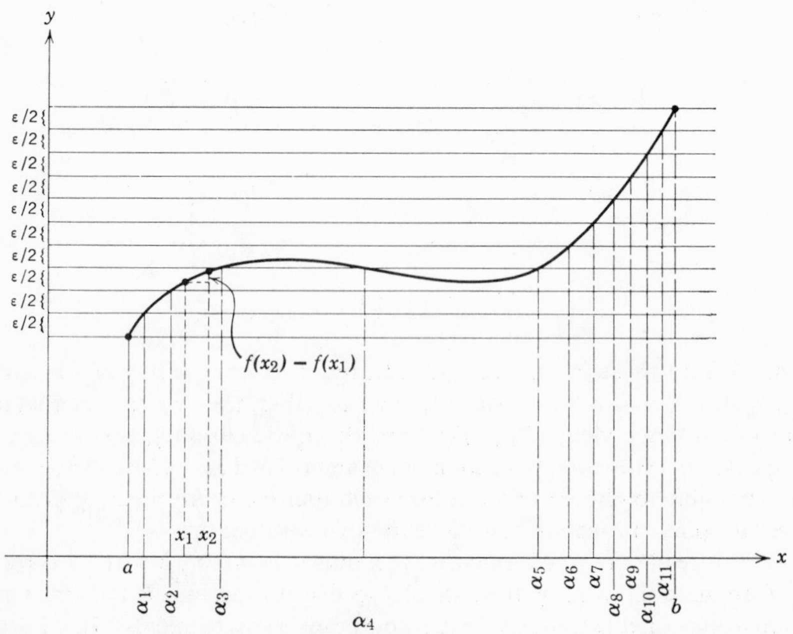

Fig. I.44

and let us pick from these δ_k's the smallest one and denote it by δ_ε

$$\delta_\varepsilon = \text{minimum } (\delta_1, \delta_2, \cdots, \delta_{12}).$$

We can see now that the following is true.

If x_1, x_2 are two points on the x-axis which are less than δ_ε apart:

$$-\delta_\varepsilon < x_1 - x_2 < \delta_\varepsilon,$$

then the corresponding values of the function $f(x_1)$ and $f(x_2)$ cannot be farther apart than ε:

$$-\varepsilon < f(x_1) - f(x_2) < \varepsilon,$$

for the following reason.

Either x_1 and x_2 both lie in the same interval $\alpha_k < x < \alpha_{k+1}$ ($k = 0, 1, 2, 3, \cdots$, or 11) or they don't. If they do, then both the corresponding values of the function lie in the same horizontal strip formed by two adjacent parallel lines, $\frac{\varepsilon}{2}$ apart.

On the other hand, if x_1 and x_2 do not lie in the same interval $\alpha_k < x < \alpha_{k+1}$, then suppose x_1 lies in $\alpha_k < x < \alpha_{k+1}$. It follows that x_2 will either lie in $\alpha_{k-1} < x < \alpha_k$ or in $\alpha_{k+1} < x < \alpha_{k+2}$. It cannot lie in any other interval because it is less than δ_ε apart from x_1 and the length of either adjacent interval is at least δ_ε.

But then the value of the function corresponding to x_1 will lie in one strip of width $\varepsilon/2$ and the value of the function corresponding to x_2 will lie either in the strip above or below—if not in the same strip. Now, the maximum vertical distance between any two points in adjacent horizontal strips is certainly less than ε, and our assertion is proved.

Before we go any further, let us consider an example. Let

$$y = f(x) = x^2$$

in the interval $0 \leq x \leq 1$ (see Fig. I.45). Let $\varepsilon = \frac{1}{4}$. We can see that our function shows the steepest increase at the end of the interval. At $x = 1$, the function has the value 1. Now, where does it have a value that is $\frac{1}{8}\left(= \frac{\varepsilon}{2}\right)$ smaller than 1, i.e., where does the function have the value $\frac{7}{8}$? Clearly, the positive solution of $\frac{7}{8} = x^2$, which is $x = \sqrt{\frac{7}{8}}$ is the answer. Thus it follows that the values of our function for any two x-values between $\sqrt{\frac{7}{8}}$ and 1 differ by less than $\frac{1}{8}$. But we see at the same time that the difference between any two values of our function is less than $\frac{1}{4}$ whenever the two x-values are less than $1 - \sqrt{\frac{7}{8}}$ apart. This is the smallest δ_k which we called δ_ε (in our case $\delta_{1/4}$).

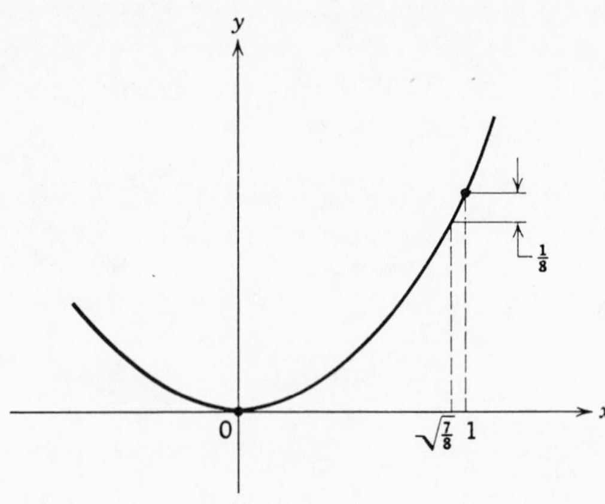

Fig. I.45

What we have done up to now will not get us very far. For example, consider the function

$$y = \frac{1}{2000}[x] \qquad \text{in} \qquad 0 \leq x \leq 10$$

which is drawn in Fig. I.46 with a considerably enlarged y-scale and take $\varepsilon = \frac{1}{1000}$. Obviously, two values of this function are certainly not farther apart than $\frac{1}{1000}$ as long as the x-values for which these values are taken are not farther apart than 1 and yet, this function is one of those which we wish to reject. But now we arrive at the crux of the matter: While it is still possible to find a δ_ε that will work with $\varepsilon = \frac{1}{1000}$ in the entire interval, it

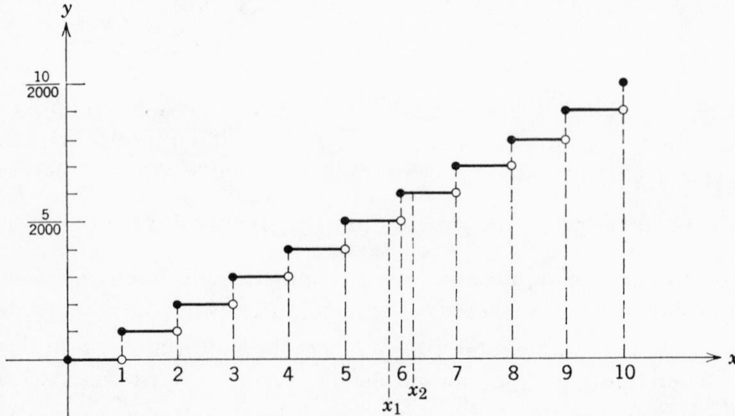

Fig. I.46

will be impossible to find one if we choose $\varepsilon = \frac{1}{10000}$. For then, no matter how small we would choose δ_ε, there are always pairs of x-values less than δ_ε apart such that the corresponding y-values of the function differ by more than $\varepsilon = \frac{1}{10000}$.

So in order finally to get rid of stepfunctions and similar manifestations of sophisticated mathematical minds, we will have to require that no matter how small we choose our ε, it shall always be possible to find a δ_ε which is such that

$$-\varepsilon < f(x_1) - f(x_2) < \varepsilon$$

whenever

$$-\delta_\varepsilon < x_1 - x_2 < \delta_\varepsilon.$$

Hence, we put forth the following definition, using absolute value symbols instead of the awkward two-sided inequalities:

We call a function $y = f(x)$ *uniformly continuous* in the interval $a \leq x \leq b$ if it is possible to find for any $\varepsilon > 0$, no matter how small, a number δ_ε which is such that

$$|f(x_1) - f(x_2)| < \varepsilon$$

whenever

$$|x_1 - x_2| < \delta_\varepsilon.$$

(The prefix "uniformly" in front of "continuous" is used to distinguish this property from the *ordinary continuity* which is a point property rather than an interval property and was mentioned at the conclusion of the preceding section.)

In the light of this definition, we can see right away that the function $y = x^2$ is uniformly continuous in $0 \leq x \leq 1$ (or, as a matter of fact, in any closed interval). To demonstrate this, we will show that it is possible to find for any $\varepsilon > 0$, no matter how small, a δ_ε such that

$$|f(x_1) - f(x_2)| = |x_1^2 - x_2^2| < \varepsilon$$

as long as $|x_1 - x_2| < \delta_\varepsilon$.

Now,

$$|x_1^2 - x_2^2| = |(x_1 - x_2)(x_1 + x_2)| < 2\,|x_1 - x_2|\,,$$

since $x_1 \leq 1$, $x_2 \leq 1$.

Thus we can see that whenever

$$|x_1 - x_2| < \frac{\varepsilon}{2} = \delta_\varepsilon.$$

then $|x_1^2 - x_2^2| < \varepsilon$, no matter how small we have chosen our ε.

On the other hand, if we consider the function

$$y = [x]$$

(see Fig. I.40), we see that if we choose, for example, $\varepsilon = \frac{1}{2}$, then no matter how small we choose δ_ε, we will always find two points x_1 and x_2 closer than δ_ε such that the corresponding values of the function are more than $\frac{1}{2}$ apart. Clearly, all we have to do is choose x_1 on one side of a jump and x_2 on the other side of the jump, and we have it.

Finally, it is almost needless to say that the function

$$y = \frac{1}{1 - x}$$

in $0 \leq x \leq 2$, which is the type depicted in Fig. I.43(*c*), is certainly not uniformly continuous in $0 \leq x \leq 2$. How could it be? Choose x_1 on the left of $x = 1$ and x_2 to the right of $x = 1$ as close together as you please, and you will find that the corresponding values of the function will be farther apart than you would care to measure, instead of being less than a small distance ε apart.

Before we close this section let us mention a few other types of functions we rid ourselves of through restricting our considerations to uniformly continuous functions in accordance with the definition which we presented in this section.

Take, for example, the function

$$y = f(x) = \begin{cases} 1 \text{ for } x = 0 \\ 0 \text{ for } x \neq 0 \end{cases}$$

in $-1 \leq x \leq 1$ (see Fig. I.47). Let $\varepsilon = \frac{1}{2}$ and take $x_1 = 0$. No matter how close to 0 the value x_2 is chosen, the difference of the two corresponding values of the function will be 1 and not less than $\frac{1}{2}$. (A discontinuity of the type as exhibited by this function at $x = 0$ is called a *removable discontinuity* because this function can be made uniformly continuous in the interval $-1 \leq x \leq 1$—or in any interval including the origin, for that matter—by redefining its value at $x = 0$ as $f(0) = 0$.)

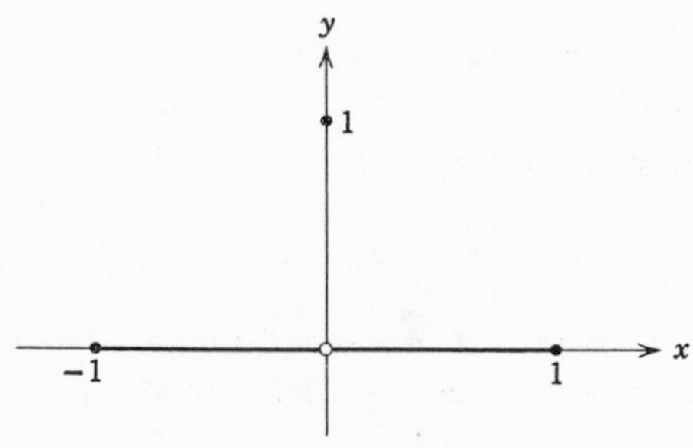

Fig. I.47

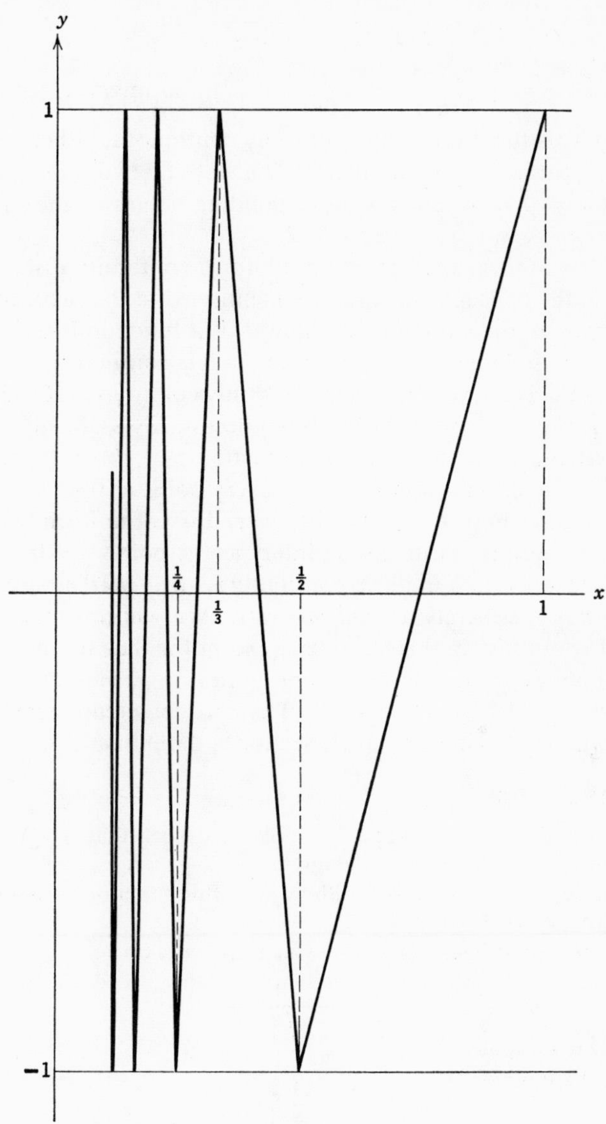

Fig. I.48

Finally, we consider a function that is graphically represented by a polygon that oscillates between $y = -1$ and $y = 1$, assuming the value $y = 1$ at the points $x = 1, \frac{1}{3}, \frac{1}{5}, \frac{1}{7}, \frac{1}{9}, \frac{1}{11}, \ldots, \frac{1}{2n+1}, \ldots$, and the value $y = -1$ at the points $x = \frac{1}{2}, \frac{1}{4}, \frac{1}{6}, \frac{1}{8}, \ldots, \frac{1}{2n}, \ldots$, in the interval $0 \leq x \leq 1$ (see Fig. I.48). This function is not uniformly continuous, either. Take any ε and a δ_ε no matter how small, there will always be two points x_1, x_2 in the vicinity of $x = 0$ such that the corresponding values of the function will differ by more than ε, provided $\varepsilon < 2$.

In order to connect the concept of uniform continuity discussed in this section with the concept of continuity mentioned in the preceding section, let us summarize the situation as follows: if a function is uniformly continuous in a closed interval $a \leq x \leq b$, then it is continuous at every point of the interval. However, if a function is only continuous at every point of an open interval $a < x < b$, then it is not necessarily uniformly continuous in the closed interval $a \leq x \leq b$. The function $y = 1/x$ illustrated this very clearly. This function is continuous at every point of $0 < x \leq 1$, i.e., has no discontinuities in $0 < x \leq 1$. However, it is not uniformly continuous in $0 \leq x \leq 1$ because of its discontinuity at the point $x = 0$.

We wish to stress that uniform continuity is an *interval property*, whereas plain continuity is merely a *point property*. We will not make use of the concept of continuity in this treatment, except for the fact that we will not consider functions which have discontinuities or, if they do have discontinuities, they will be easy to spot. The concept of uniform continuity, however, will be used in Chapter II, Section 8, though only in a limited way.

Problems I.104–I.108

I.104. Given $y = x^2 + 7$. Let $\varepsilon = \frac{1}{4}$. Find a δ_ε such that $|f(x_1) - f(x_2)| < \varepsilon$ for all $|x_1 - x_2| < \delta_\varepsilon$ for all x in the interval $1 \leq x \leq 2$.

I.105. Given $y = x^2 + 2x + 5$. Show that this function is uniformly continuous in the interval $-1 \leq x \leq 1$.

I.106. State closed intervals within which the function

$$y = \frac{1}{(x-1)(x+2)}$$

is uniformly continuous.

I.107. Is the function

$$y = \begin{cases} \dfrac{x^2 - 1}{x - 1} & \text{for } x \neq 1 \\ 4 & \text{for } x = 1 \end{cases}$$

continuous at the point $x = 1$?

I.108. If the function in problem I.107 is not continuous at $x = 1$, then redefine the function at $x = 1$ so that it becomes continuous. ◀

Supplementary Problems I

3.1. Sketch the function

$$y = \begin{cases} x \text{ for } -\infty < x < 0 \\ 1 \text{ for } x = 0 \\ x^2 + 2 \text{ for } 0 < x \leq 1 \\ 3 \text{ for } 1 < x < 2 \\ \dfrac{x}{2} + 2 \text{ for } 2 \leq x < \infty \end{cases}$$

3.2. Given $f(x) = \dfrac{1}{\sqrt{x}}$. Find $\dfrac{f(x+h) - f(x)}{h}$ and simplify.

3.3. Given $f(x) = x^4$. Find $f(x + h)$ and expand.

3.4. Given $y^2 = x$. Sketch the function. How many y-values correspond to each x-value?

4.1. Find the equations of all lines through the point $P(1, -2)$.

4.2. Find the equations of all lines with the slope $m = \frac{7}{2}$.

4.3. Which line meets the specifications of problems 4.1 and 4.2 simultaneously?

4.4. Given the line L: $y = 3x + 1$. Find the equation of the line perpendicular to L which passes through the point $P(1, 3)$. (See Problem I.32.)

4.5. Find the equations of all lines which are perpendicular to the line $y = -\frac{1}{3}x + 3$.

4.6. From the lines in Problem 4.5, pick out the one which passes through the origin.

5.1. Find the equation of the line which is perpendicular to the line $y = 3$ and passes through the point $P(1, 4)$.

5.2. Given $3x + 4y = 1$ and $6x + 8y = F$. Assign such a value to F that (*a*) the two lines are parallel and intersect the y-axis at points 3 units apart, (*b*) the two lines coincide.

5.3. Sketch the lines (*a*) $x + y = 1$, (*b*) $x + y = 2$, (*c*) $x + y = 3$. What feature is common to all these lines?

5.4. Find the equation of the line through the two points (*a*) $P_1(1, 3)$, $P_2(1, 5)$ and (*b*) $P_1(4, 7)$, $P_2(13, 7)$.

5.5. Given two vertices $A(0, 0)$ and $B(4, 0)$ of an isosceles triangle, the two equal sides of which terminate in the third vertex C. Find the equation of the line through B and C. Note that C is not uniquely determined.

6.1. Find the equation of the line which passes through the intersection point of the two lines $x + y = 2$ and $3x + 2y = 5$ and the intersection point of the two lines $x - 4y = 8$ and $x + y = 3$.

6.2. Find the equations of all lines which pass through the intersection point of the lines $x = 4$ and $y = 1$.

6.3. Given the lines $x + 2y = 3$ and $x - By = 1$. Choose B so that the two lines intersect at the point $P(1, 1)$.

6.4. Evaluate the determinants

$$(a)\begin{vmatrix} 1 & 9375 \\ 1 & 1 \end{vmatrix} \qquad (b)\begin{vmatrix} 0 & 1 \\ -1 & 10827 \end{vmatrix} \qquad (c)\begin{vmatrix} 526 & 2 \\ 1052 & 4 \end{vmatrix}$$

6.5. $\begin{vmatrix} a_{11} & a_{12} & a_{13} \\ a_{21} & a_{22} & a_{23} \\ a_{31} & a_{32} & a_{33} \end{vmatrix}$ is called a determinant of the third order.

The following rules are valid: $\begin{vmatrix} 1 & 0 & 0 \\ 0 & a_{22} & a_{23} \\ 0 & a_{32} & a_{33} \end{vmatrix} = \begin{vmatrix} a_{22} & a_{23} \\ a_{32} & a_{33} \end{vmatrix}$

and

$$\begin{vmatrix} a_{11} & a_{12} + na_{11} & a_{13} \\ a_{21} & a_{22} + na_{21} & a_{23} \\ a_{31} & a_{32} + na_{31} & a_{33} \end{vmatrix} = \begin{vmatrix} a_{11} & a_{12} & a_{13} \\ a_{21} & a_{22} & a_{23} \\ a_{31} & a_{32} & a_{33} \end{vmatrix}$$

for any positive or negative n. Utilizing these rules, evaluate the determinant

$$\begin{vmatrix} 1 & 4 & 0 \\ 0 & 3 & 2 \\ 0 & 9 & 8 \end{vmatrix}$$

(*Hint:* Let $n = -4$.)

7.1. Find the locus of all points $P(x, y)$ which are such that the sum of the distances from P to $F_1(-c, 0)$ and from P to $F_2(c, 0)$ is constant: $d_{PF_1} + d_{PF_2} = 2a$ where a is a constant. In the final result, substitute for c a constant b according to $a^2 - b^2 = c^2$ and simplify. (This locus is an *ellipse*.)

7.2. Find the locus of all points $P(x, y)$ which are such that the difference of its distances from $F_1(-c, 0)$ and $F_2(c, 0)$ is constant: $d_{PF_1} - d_{PF_2} = 2a$ where a is a constant. In the final result substitute for c a constant b according to $a^2 + b^2 = c^2$. (This locus is a *hyperbola*.)

7.3. Sketch the graph of the locus in Problem 7.1.

7.4. Sketch the graph of the locus in Problem 7.2.

7.5. Given a point $P(4, \frac{7}{2})$ and a line L: $x + y = 1$. Find the shortest distance from P to L by intersecting a line perpendicular to L through P with L and computing the distance from P to the intersection point.

7.6. Given the circle $x^2 + y^2 = 1$ and a point $P(0, 1)$ on the circumference of the circle. Find another point $Q(x, y)$ on the circumference of the circle at a distance $\frac{1}{2}$ from P.

8.1. Given $y = x^2$. Introduce a new coordinate system according to $\bar{x} = x + 4$, $\bar{y} = y - 3$ and find the equation of the parabola in the new coordinate system.

8.2. Introduce a new coordinate system so that the parabola $y = 4x^2 + 16x - 64$ assumes the form $\bar{y} = \bar{x}^2$.

8.3. Find the intersection points of the parabola $y = x^2 + 2$ with the line $y = x + 3$. Introduce a new coordinate system according to $\bar{x} = x + 3$, $\bar{y} = y - 2$. Find the coordinates of the intersection points of the line with the parabola in the new coordinate system by two different methods.

8.4. Given two lines $y = 3x + 4$ and $\bar{y} = 3\bar{x} - 1$ in two different coordinate systems. Find a and b in $\bar{x} = x + a$, $\bar{y} = y + b$ so that the two lines coincide in the $\bar{x}, \bar{y}$-coordinate system.

8.5. Find the quadratic equation which has the x-coordinates of the intersection points of the parabola $y = x^2$ with the circle $x^2 + y^2 = 4$ as solutions.

9.1. Show that the sum of the two solutions of a quadratic equation is always real, whether the solutions are real or not.

9.2. Given the quadratic equation $ax^2 + bx + c = 0$. Show that, if x_1, x_2 are two (real or complex) numbers such that $-a(x_1 + x_2) = b$ and $ax_1x_2 = c$, then x_1 and x_2 are solutions of the quadratic equation.

9.3. Multiplication of complex numbers is defined as follows:

$$(a + ib)(c + id) = ac - bd + i(bc + ad).$$

Show that the product of two conjugate complex numbers is real.

9.4. Fractions with complex numerator and/or denominator are manipulated like ordinary fractions. Multiply numerator and denominator in the following fractions by a suitable complex number so that the denominator becomes real:

$$(a)\ \frac{1 - i2}{1 + i} \qquad (b)\ \frac{3 - i}{4 - i3} \qquad (c)\ \frac{i}{1 - i5}$$

9.5. Given the parabola $y = x^2 + 1$ and the straight line $y = mx - 2$. Determine the slope $m < \infty$ so that the line has only one intersection point with the parabola.

10.1. A triangle has one vertex at $A(-1, 0)$ and the other two vertices at the points at which the two lines through A are tangent to the parabola $y = x^2$. Find the lengths of the three sides of the triangle.

10.2. Given the parabola $y = x^2 + 3x + 1$. Find the values of x for which the tangent to this parabola has the slopes 1, 2, 3, $\cdots$, 10. Call these values $x_1, x_2, x_3, \cdots, x_{10}$. Find $x_{k+1} - x_k$ for all $k = 1, 2, 3, \cdots, 9$.

10.3. Show by geometric inspection that $y = x^2 + bx + c$ assumes the smallest value at that point at which the slope of the tangent line is zero.

10.4. Given two parabolas $y = ax^2 + bx + c$ and $y = Ax^2 + Bx + C$. Show that, if both parabolas intersect the x-axis in the same two points, then $a = nA$, $b = nB$, $c = nC$ for some constant n.

10.5. Consider the two parabolas in Problem 10.4. Show that the one can be transformed into the other one via a transformation of the type $\bar{y} = \alpha y$. Find α.

10.6. Consider the two parabolas in Problem 10.4. Show that the slope of the tangent line to the one parabola is at any given point a multiple of the slope of the tangent line to the other parabola.

11.1. For what values of x does the function $y = \sqrt{1 - x^2}$ have real values? (Use inequalities.)

11.2. Same as in Problem 11.1 for the function $y = \sqrt{x^2 - 1}$.

11.3. For what values of x is the function $y = x(x - 1)(x + 2)(x + 3)$ positive?

11.4. Represent the following regions geometrically:

(*a*) $-1 \leq x \leq 1,\ -1 \leq y \leq 1$ (*b*) $-2 < x - 1 < 2, y > 0$

(*c*) $x^2 + y^2 \leq 1$ (*d*) $x^2 < 4,\ -1 < y < 3$

12.1. Sketch the function $y = |x + 2|$.

12.2. Sketch the function $|y| = |x|$.

12.3. Sketch the function $y = [x - [x]]$.

12.4. Sketch the function $y = \dfrac{1}{x^2 - 1}$.

12.5. Sketch the function $y = x^2$ for $0 \leq x < 1, f(x + 1) = f(x)$.

13.1. Given $f(x) = 4x^2 - 1$. Find a δ_ε so that $|f(x_1) - f(x_2)| < \varepsilon$ for all $|x_1 - x_2| < \delta_\varepsilon$ in $0 \leq x \leq 2$.

13.2. Show that the function $y = |x|$ is uniformly continuous in the interval $-1 \leq x \leq 1$.

13.3. Show by inspection that the function

$$y = \begin{cases} x & \text{for } -1 \leq x < 1 \\ -x + 2 & \text{for } 1 \leq x < 3 \end{cases}$$

where $f(x + 4) = f(x)$, has no discontinuities.

CHAPTER II

AREAS

Sections 1 and 2 of this chapter deal with areas of rectangles and triangles. It is the purpose of these sections to establish the familiar formulas for the area of a rectangle of dimensions a and b as the product ab and for the area of a triangle of base c and height h as $\frac{1}{2}ch$. The following principle is stressed throughout these sections and frequently is made use of in the sequel: *Congruent regions have the same area, and if one region R_1 is entirely contained in another region R_2, then the area of R_1 is smaller than the area of R_2.*

▶1. AREA OF RECTANGLES

In this section we will enter a preliminary discussion of what will eventually lead us to the concept of an *area measure* of planar regions which are bounded by closed curves.

However, before we start working toward this end, we have to clarify what such an area measure is supposed to accomplish. So suppose we apply a coat of (pink) paint to a certain planar region and measure the quantity of paint that is required to accomplish this task. Clearly, congruent regions will require the same amount of paint to be covered with one coat. But suppose we now paint two regions, one of which can be entirely submerged in the other one. Then it turns out that we need more paint for the containing region than the one which can be submerged in it. In such a case we will say that the "area" (area in quotes shall stand for the intuitive concept of area) of the one region is larger than the other one, while in the first case, where the same amount of paint was required, we will say that the "areas" are equal (congruent regions have the same area). Moreover, if we have two regions, one of which requires an amount p of paint and the other an amount q of paint, then it is intuitively clear that the combined region will require an amount of $p + q$ of paint.

So it appears that an area measure which is sensibly defined should be consistent with the "paint measure" as we discussed it here. It seems that the system of paint measure is logically satisfactory although quite impractical, since in order to make a statement about the sizes of two regions with respect to each other, we would have to apply a coat of paint first to each of them. This is certainly very impractical, even though this task could be somewhat simplified by introducing a specific test region and defining the amount of paint required for this particular region as 1 ppu (pink-paint unit).

In addition to the properties of the paint measure which we discussed above, let us state two properties which are quite trivial but nevertheless important for what is to follow. Any region will require a positive amount of paint and any *degenerate* region (either a point or a curve) will require no paint at all.

In order to arrive at a satisfactory mathematical definition of an area measure, we will proceed essentially along the same lines as is done in establishing a length measure. We will try to establish a correlation between regions and positive numbers which has, in terms of our example with the paint, the following properties: Two regions for which the same amount of paint is required shall correspond to the same number; if one region requires less paint than another, then the number corresponding to the first region shall be less than the number corresponding to the second region, and finally if the number a corresponds to the region which requires the amount p of paint and the number b corresponds to the region which requires the amount q of paint, then the number $a + b$ shall correspond to the combined region that requires the amount $p + q$ of paint.

In order to accomplish our goal, i.e., the establishment of a satisfactory area measure, we will first discuss a region with a very simple boundary, namely, a rectangular region (see Fig. II.1). A rectangle is uniquely determined by its dimensions a and b, i.e., given the dimensions a and b, then all the rectangles with these given dimensions are congruent.

Thus we rightfully expect that the area of a rectangle will also depend only on a and b, and we write for the area

$$A[r(a, b)] \cdots \text{ Area of rectangle with dimensions } a \text{ and } b.$$

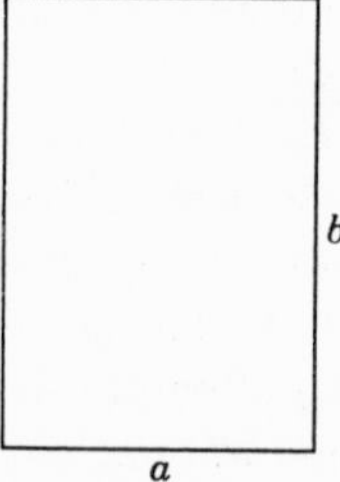

Fig. II.1

Clearly, the size (i.e., the amount of ppu's required) will depend on the length of a and the length of b. Suppose a is fixed; the larger b, the larger the size of the rectangle. Likewise, let b be fixed, then the larger a, the larger the size of the rectangle. So we see it is certainly sensible to postulate that the area measure should be an increasing function of a, if b is fixed and an increasing function of b if a is fixed. The simplest increasing function which we are acquainted with is the linear function. Therefore, we try the following definition

$$A[r(a, \underline{b})] = f(b)\, a \tag{II.1}$$

$$A[r(\underline{a}, b)] = g(a)\, b \tag{II.2}$$

where the underline indicates that the dimension so designated is to be considered as fixed and where $f(b)$ and $g(a)$ are proportionality factors, the values of which depend on b and a, respectively. If (II.1) and (II.2) both give a measure for the same area, then the quantities on the right side have to be equal:

$$f(b)\, a = g(a)\, b.$$

Let us divide this equation by the product ab. Then we obtain

$$\frac{f(b)}{b} = \frac{g(a)}{a}.$$

The left side depends on b only, the right side depends on a only; hence, if this is to be a true equation, both sides have to be equal to the same constant C which is independent of a and b but can otherwise be chosen quite arbitrarily.

Thus we obtain from

$$\frac{f(b)}{b} = C, \qquad \frac{g(a)}{a} = C$$

that

$$f(b) = Cb \text{ and } g(a) = Ca. \tag{II.3}$$

If we substitute these expressions into (II.1) and (II.2), we obtain in both cases

$$A[r(a, b)] = Cab. \tag{II.4}$$

The constant C is quite arbitrary and we can choose its value any way we wish. However, its value will be uniquely determined if we choose an *area measure unit*. It is customary to choose a square of sidelength 1 unit (rectangle with $a = 1$, $b = 1$) as measure unit for areas and call it *square unit*. (If the measure unit for length is 1 inch, then the measure unit for area is 1 square inch (1 sq in. or 1 in.^{2}); if the measure unit for length is 1 cm, then the measure unit for area would be 1 sq cm (or 1 cm^2), etc. . . .)

It now follows from (II.4) that

$$1 = A[r(1, 1)] = C.1.1$$

and from this, $C = 1$.

However, if we choose a square of sidelength 1 ft as unit for area measure, and still measure length in inches, then we have

$$1 = A[r(a, b)] = C.12.12$$

and, consequently, $C = \frac{1}{144}$. So we see that C plays in a sense the role of a *conversion factor* that converts square inches into square feet, etc. . . .

For reasons of simplicity, we will henceforth assume that $C = 1$, i.e., the measure unit for areas will always be a square of sidelength 1 unit.

Let us now discuss whether this definition of area measure as introduced by (II.4) has all the properties which we listed as desirable in the beginning of this section and which we can state now as follows—as far as rectangles are concerned:

(1) $$A[r(a, b)] > 0 \quad \text{if} \quad a > 0, b > 0,$$

(2) $$A[r(a, b)] = 0 \quad \text{if} \quad a = 0 \text{ or } b = 0 \text{ or both},$$

(3) $$A[r(a, b) \,\&\, r(c, d)] = A[r(a, b)] + A[r(c, d)]$$

where & shall mean "combined with," if this combination yields again a rectangle, and finally

(4) If $r(a, b)$ is contained in $r(c, d)$, then $A[r(a, b)] < A[r(c, d)]$.

To these conditions we may add the condition which determines the area measure unit

(5) $$A[r(1, 1)] = 1.$$

Properties (1) and (2) are clearly satisfied by (II.4) since the product of two positive numbers is again positive and a product is zero if, and only if, at least one factor is zero.

Property (3) requires some discussion. First, we can see easily that the combined region of the two rectangles $r(a, b)$ and $r(c, d)$ is a rectangle again only if they have one side in common, say, $b = c$. Thus we can piece the two rectangles together and obtain a rectangle with the dimensions $b, a + d$ (see Fig. II.2) which has, according to (II.4) with $C = 1$, the area

$$A[r(b, a + d)] = b(a + d) = ab + bd.$$

Since $A[r(a, b)] = ab$ and $A[r(b, d)] = bd$, we see thus that

(II.5) $$A[r(b, a + d)] = A[r(a, b) \,\&\, r(b, d)] = A[r(a, b)] + A[r(b, d)].$$

Finally, let us check on property (4). That this condition is satisfied can be checked directly but we will show here how this property can be deduced from (1) and (3).

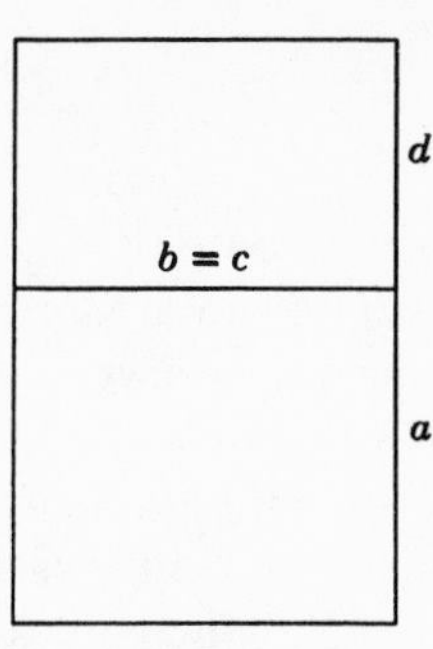

Fig. II.2

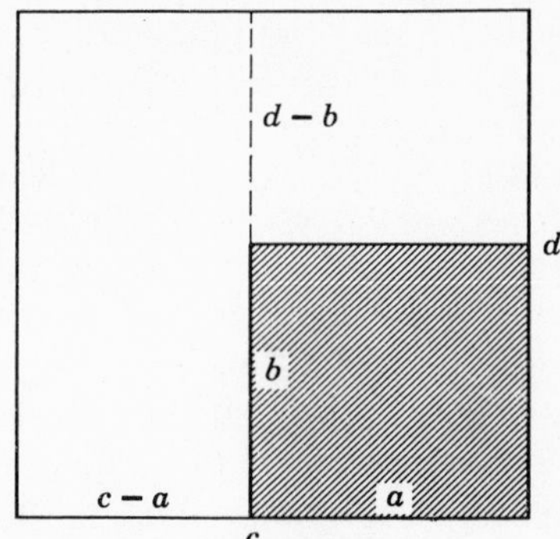

Fig. II.3

Suppose $r(a, b)$ is contained in $r(c, d)$ (see Fig. II.3). Consider the rectangles with dimensions a, d and $c - a, d$. From (II.5),

$$A[r(c, d)] = A[r(a, d) \,\&\, r(c - a, d)] = A[r(a, d)] + A[r(c - a, d)]$$

where the area of $r(a, d)$ is, again in view of (II.5),

$$A[r(a, d)] = A[r(a, b)] + A[r(a, d - b)].$$

Thus we obtain

$$A[r(c, d)] = A[r(a, b)] + A[r(a, d - b)] + A[r(c - a, b)].$$

Since all the terms on the right side are positive in view of (1), it follows that

$$A[r(c, d)] > A[r(a, b)].$$

Problems II.1–II.7

II.1. Consider the rectangles $r(a, b)$ and $r(c, d)$. Let $a < c$, $b \leq d$ or $a \leq c$, $b < d$ and show directly that

$$A[r(a, b)] < A[r(c, d)].$$

II.2. Let the units for length measurement be inches and the units of area measurement be square meters. Find the value of the conversion factor C. Same for meters and square yards.

II.3. Prove that $A[2r(a, b)] = 2A[r(a, b)]$ where $2r(a, b) = r(a, b) \,\&\, r(a, b)$.

II.4. Prove that $A[r(ca, b)] = cA[r(a, b)]$ and interpret geometrically.

II.5. Prove that

$$A[r(\alpha a, \beta b) \,\&\, r(\gamma c, \delta d)] = \alpha\beta A[r(a, b)] + \gamma\delta A[r(c, d)]$$

provided $\alpha a = \gamma c$ or $\beta b = \gamma c$ or $\beta b = \delta d$ or $\alpha a = \delta d$.

II.6. Given a rectangle with the side a fixed and the side b variable. The area is a function $f(b)$ of b. What is $f(x)$?

II.7. The side a of a rectangle with fixed dimension b is a function $f(A)$ of its area A. What is $f(x)$? ◀

▶2. AREA OF TRIANGLES

A configuration that receives considerable attention in plane geometry, as well as in social life, is the triangle, i.e., a figure that consists of three straight lines, each two of which meet in a point (vertex) (see Fig. II.4).

In this section we will try to generalize the concept of an area measure such that it becomes applicable to triangles. For this purpose we first consider a rectangle with dimensions a and b, and join two opposite vertices by a straight line (diagonal) (see Fig. II.5). We thus obtain two congruent triangles. We remember that one of our demands of an area measure is that two congruent figures must have the same area. Further, we require that the sum of the areas of two regions shall be equal to the area of the combined region.

Thus we have to consider the areas of the two triangles in Fig. II.5 as equal and assign to them a value such that the sum of the two areas is equal to the area of the rectangle with dimensions a and b. Since

$$A[r(a, b)] = ab,$$

we obtain for the area of either one of the two triangles

$$A(\text{triangle}) = \tfrac{1}{2}ab.$$

Note that we really did not have any choice in defining the area of a triangle, if we want to be consistent.

The triangle considered above is a very special one inasmuch as two of its sides are perpendicular to each other. We call such a triangle a *right triangle*. We will now proceed to free ourselves from this restriction and consider a general triangle which may or may not be a right triangle. In Fig. II.6 we have drawn such a triangle. We denote the vertices by capital letters, starting with the lower left vertex and proceeding in the enumeration

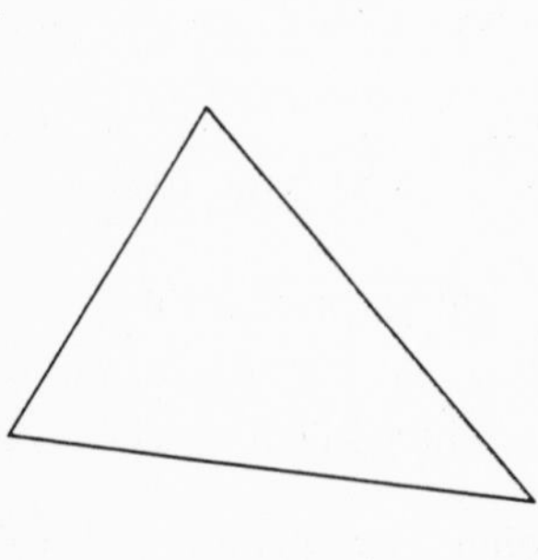

Fig. II.4

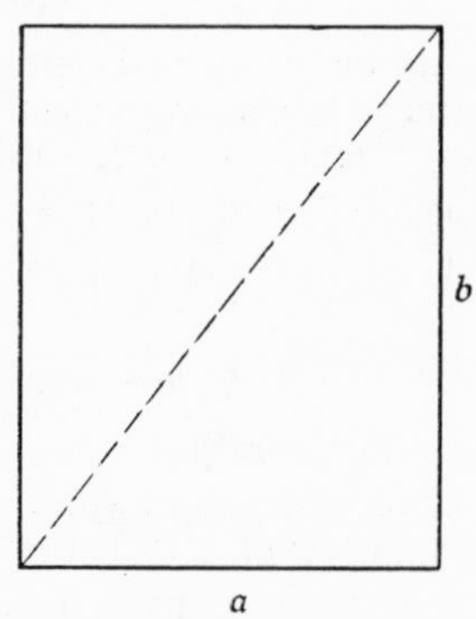

Fig. II.5

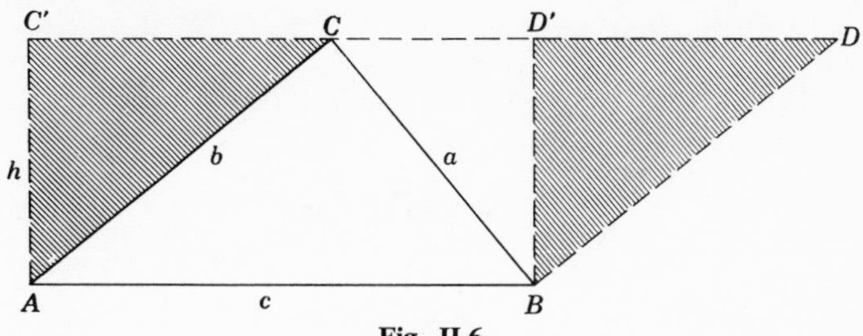

Fig. II.6

counterclockwise. We denote each side by the small letter corresponding to the vertex opposite it. Now we draw a line through C parallel to c, and a line through B parallel to b. These two lines will meet at a point D. The figure $(ABDC)$ is called a parallelogram because it consists of two pairs of parallel lines. (Clearly, if the triangle we began with had had a right angle at A, then $(ABDC)$ would have turned out to be a rectangle, which indeed is a special case of a parallelogram.)

We consider the line through C and D continued to the left and draw two lines through A and B which are perpendicular to c. The result is a rectangle $ABD'C'$ which has the area ch, if we use h to denote the length of the side AC' (or BD'). The two triangles ACC' and BDD' are congruent (right) triangles, and hence have the same area. In order to obtain from the parallelogram region $(ABDC)$ the rectangular region $(ABD'C')$, we have to add the triangular region (ACC') and take the triangular region (BDD') away, i.e., add and subtract at the same time regions of equal area. Thus it appears that the parallelogram $(ABDC)$ has the same area as the rectangle $(ABD'C')$, namely, ch. Therefore, it follows that the triangle (ABC), being obviously congruent to the triangle (BDC), has the area

$$A(\text{triangle}) = \tfrac{1}{2}ch. \tag{II.6}$$

We call c the *base* and h the *height* (*altitude*) of the triangle, forming the mental image of the base lying flat and the two sides b, a towering over it.

Having arrived at an area measure for triangles, we can now generalize this concept immediately to any region which is encompassed by a closed polygon ($\pi o\lambda v'$ = many, $\gamma o v v'$ = angle), i.e., a boundary with many angles. What we really mean by this expression is a boundary that consists of many line segments, as illustrated in Fig. II.7. Such a closed polygon can be subdivided into a number of triangles (in more than one way—see Fig. II.8) and the area of every triangle can be computed by formula (II.6). We define the area of the polygon to be the sum of the areas of the component figures, and then arrive at the area of the polygonal region by adding all the areas of the component triangles. It can be shown that we will arrive

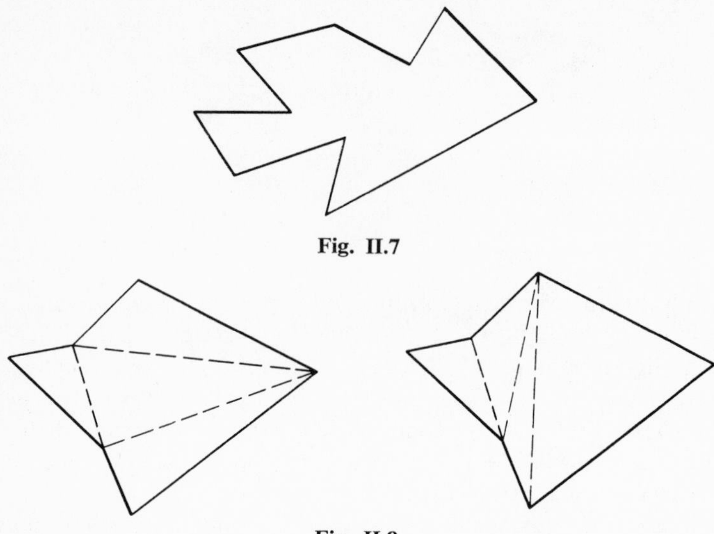

Fig. II.7

Fig. II.8

at the same result in whatever way we subdivide the polygonal region into triangles.

Problems II.8–II.14

II.8. Find the area of the irregular pentagon ($ABCDE$) where the vertices have the coordinates $A(2, 0)$, $B(2, 1)$, $C(5, 1)$, $D(2, 3)$, $E(0, 2)$.

II.9. Find the area of the equilateral triangle of side length 1.

II.10. Find the area of the regular hexagon of side length 1.

II.11. Find the area of the irregular octagon with the vertices $A(1, 0)$, $B(1, 2)$, $C(4, 2)$, $D(5, 4)$, $E(4, 5)$, $F(1, 5)$, $G(1, 4)$, $H(0, 3)$, by partitioning it into triangles in at least two different ways.

II.12. Find the area of a trapezoid. (A trapezoid is a quadrangle, two sides of which are parallel to each other. Let the dimensions of these two sides be a and b, and denote their distance apart by h.)

II.13. Given a triangle with fixed base b and variable height h. The area is a function $f(h)$ of h. What is $f(x), f(t^2), f\left(\frac{1}{u}\right)$?

II.14. Given a triangle of fixed height h and variable base b. b is a function $f(A)$ of the area. What is $f(x)$? ◀

3. SERIES AND SEQUENCES

Let us consider a geometrical configuration which consists of a square of sidelength 1 with an isosceles right triangle of sidelength 1 surmounted on it, as indicated in Fig. II.9. We proceed to inscribe a sequence of squares in this triangle, also shown in Fig. II.9. The sidelength of each square is half the sidelength of the preceding square. We can see that no matter how many squares we inscribe, there is still an isosceles triangle left in which we can continue the process. In other words, there is no last square or, as we may say, there are infinitely many squares which can thus be inscribed in the triangle under consideration—or, for that matter, in any triangle. Let us denote the area of the basic square of sidelength 1 by a_0, the area of the next smaller square by a_1, the area of the next one by a_2, etc. . . .

We have infinitely many squares at our disposal. We can never draw them all, but we can draw as many as we please. If we combine any number of such consecutive squares, we obtain a region which is encompassed by a polygon. The area of this region is equal to the sum of the areas of its square components. Thus, the area of the region which is obtained by

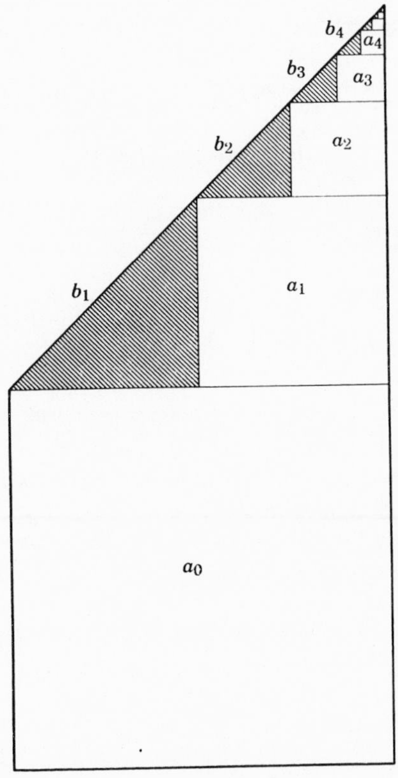

Fig. II.9

a combination of the squares with areas $a_0, a_1, a_2, \cdots, a_n$ is given by

$$a_0 + a_1 + a_2 + \cdots + a_n.$$

This sum can be found whether we consider 5 squares ($n = 5$) or 100 million squares ($n = 100000000$). (In the latter case, it may take a little longer.)

We are now about to take a very bold step. Let us pose the question: Is it reasonable to assign an area measure to the region consisting of the totality of *all* squares with the areas $a_0\ a_1, a_2, \cdots$? We remember that we demanded in Section 1 of this chapter that the area measure be such that if a region is contained in another region, then its area measure shall be smaller than the area measure of the region in which it is contained. Clearly, the region consisting of as many consecutive squares as we care to consider is contained in the region bounded by the bold polygon in Fig. II.9. If we keep inscribing in this region additional squares, we will never leave the region, no matter how far we go, as is quite obvious from the construction process.

Thus, if we consider the totality of all the squares as a region at all, it will certainly be sensible to assign to it an area measure which is smaller than the area measure of the circumscribed region, which in turn is $\frac{3}{2}$. This means that

$$a_0 + a_1 + a_2 + \cdots < \frac{3}{2}$$

where the three dots on the left of this inequality indicate that this summation is to be continued ad infinitum.

Admitting that a region may consist of infinitely many portions, the areas of which add up to the area of the total region, really involves a generalization of our concept of area measure as follows:

If a region R consists of infinitely many regions $R_0, R_1, R_2, \cdots$ which do not overlap, and if there exists a region $\bar{R}$ which has a finite area measure such that it contains all the infinitely many non-overlapping regions R_k ($k = 0, 1, 2, 3, \cdots$), then the area measure $A(R)$ of the region R shall be defined as follows:

$$A(R) = A(R_0) + A(R_1) + A(R_2) + A(R_3) + \cdots$$

where the $A(R_k)$ ($k = 0, 1, 2, 3, \cdots$) are the area measures of the regions R_k.

We call this property the *total additivity* of the area measure.

Now let us return to the evaluation of our sum $a_0 + a_1 + a_2 + \cdots$. Since it is always awkward to write out a number of terms in order to indicate a summation process, we introduce an abbreviating notation. The word *sum* starts with an S, so we could write Sa_k for $a_0 + a_1 + a_2 + \cdots$ and indicate somehow that the summation is to be extended from $k = 0$ to ∞. This is not the way it is done, however, since too many people read the roman script and mathematicians do not want just anybody to read what they produce. Therefore, we use the Greek equivalent of S, namely Σ (*read:* sigma) to indicate a summation as follows:

The finite sum $s_n = a_0 + a_1 + a_2 + \cdots + a_n$ is denoted as follows

$$a_0 + a_1 + a_2 + \cdots + a_n = \sum_{k=0}^{n} a_k$$

and if the summation is to be extended to infinity as encountered above, we indicate this by writing

$$a_0 + a_1 + a_2 + \cdots = \sum_{k=0}^{\infty} a_k.$$

We call k the *summation subscript* and note that it is in a way a dummy, because it can be replaced by any other letter without changing the sum at all—provided it is replaced in all instances in which it occurs. So, instead of $\sum_{k=0}^{\infty} a_k$, we could also write $\sum_{i=0}^{\infty} a_i$ or $\sum_{j=0}^{\infty} a_j$ and it would still represent the same sum. The numbers below and above the Σ symbol we call the *summation limits* for obvious reasons.

In this new notation, our problem is to evaluate the sum

$$\sum_{k=0}^{\infty} a_k.$$

Inspection of Fig. II.9 shows that the region which is bounded by the bold polygon consists of the region which is made up of all the squares together with the shaded region which, in turn, consists of infinitely many isosceles right triangles. To this shaded region we can also assign an area measure and justify this by the same argument we employed in assigning an area measure to the region consisting of infinitely many squares. If $b_1, b_2, b_3, \cdots$ are the areas of the triangles, then

$$\sum_{k=1}^{\infty} b_k$$

will be the area measure of the shaded region and, if our generalization of the area measure to infinitely many regions is senseful at all, the result has to be consistent with all the basic properties of the area measure—in particular, with the property that the area of a region which is obtained by the combination of two nonoverlapping regions is equal to the sum of the areas of the two regions. Since the area of the polygonal region in Fig. II.9 is, as we previously remarked, $\frac{3}{2}$ we have

$$\sum_{k=0}^{\infty} a_k + \sum_{k=1}^{\infty} b_k = \frac{3}{2}. \tag{II.7}$$

We observe that

$$b_k = \tfrac{1}{2}a_k \text{ for all } k = 1, 2, 3, \cdots.$$

Hence it appears that

$$\sum_{k=1}^{\infty} b_k = \sum_{k=1}^{\infty} \tfrac{1}{2}a_k = \tfrac{1}{2} \sum_{k=1}^{\infty} a_k$$

and we can write (II.7) as

$$a_0 + \sum_{k=1}^{\infty} a_k + \tfrac{1}{2} \sum_{k=1}^{\infty} a_k = \frac{3}{2}$$

and, consequently,

$$a_0 + \frac{3}{2} \sum_{k=1}^{\infty} a_k = \frac{3}{2}. \tag{II.8}$$

Since a_0 is the area of the square with side length 1, we have $a_0 = 1$ and we obtain from (II.8)

$$\sum_{k=1}^{\infty} a_k = \frac{1}{3}$$

and therefore

$$a_0 + \sum_{k=1}^{\infty} a_k = \sum_{k=0}^{\infty} a_k = \frac{4}{3}. \tag{II.9}$$

This result can just as well be obtained without reference to geometric inspection and area measure. We note that the side lengths of the squares which are involved in our process are $1, \frac{1}{2}, \frac{1}{4}, \frac{1}{8}, \cdots$. The sidelength of the $(n + 1)$th square is clearly $\frac{1}{2^n}$ (note that the side length of the first square is obtained for $n = 0$). Hence, we obtain for the areas

$$a_0 = 1$$
$$a_1 = \frac{1}{4}$$
$$a_2 = \frac{1}{16} = \frac{1}{4^2}$$
$$a_3 = \frac{1}{64} = \frac{1}{4^3}$$
$$a_4 = \frac{1}{256} = \frac{1}{4^4}$$
$$\vdots$$
$$a_n = \frac{1}{(2^n)^2} = \frac{1}{4^n}$$
$$\vdots$$

Thus our problem boils down to the purely arithmetical problem of evaluating the sum

$$1 + \frac{1}{4} + \frac{1}{4^2} + \frac{1}{4^3} + \frac{1}{4^4} + \cdots = \sum_{k=0}^{\infty} \left(\frac{1}{4}\right)^k. \tag{II.10}$$

Let us evaluate the finite sums s_n for several values of n. We have

$$s_0 = a_0 = 1$$
$$s_1 = a_0 + a_1 = \tfrac{5}{4} = 1.25$$
$$s_2 = a_0 + a_1 + a_2 = 1.3125$$
$$s_3 = a_0 + a_1 + a_2 + a_3 = 1.328 \cdots$$
$$s_4 = a_0 + a_1 + a_2 + a_3 + a_4 = 1.332 \cdots$$

We observe that this sequence of values $s_0, s_1, s_2, s_3, \cdots$ comes closer to the value $\frac{4}{3} = 1.3333 \cdots$ of the sum, the larger n is. We call these sums s_n the *partial sums* of $\sum_{k=0}^{\infty} a_k$ which, in turn, is called an *infinite series* (or simply *series*). Specifically, we call s_n the nth partial sum, and it appears quite obvious that the value of the series $\sum_{k=0}^{\infty} a_k$, provided such a value exists, is the value which is approached by the sequence of partial sums as n grows beyond bounds or, as we say, as n tends to infinity.*

We call the value that is approached by the elements of a sequence s_n, as n tends to infinity, the *limit* of the sequence and employ the following notation

$$\lim_{n \to \infty} s_n = S.$$

As we observed earlier, this limit is the value of the series of which the s_k's are partial sums:

$$\sum_{k=0}^{\infty} a_k = \lim_{n \to \infty} s_n \tag{II.11}$$

where $s_n = a_0 + a_1 + a_2 + \cdots + a_n$.

Thus far we really have not established that $\lim_{n \to \infty} s_n = \frac{4}{3}$. All we have done is evaluate a few partial sums and observe the trend of these partial sums towards $\frac{4}{3}$. To find this limit in a more systematic manner, let us consider the more general problem of adding up the infinite series

$$\sum_{k=0}^{\infty} q^k$$

which is clearly a generalization of the case we just considered where $q = \frac{1}{4}$.

In evaluating the partial sums, we can see that, provided $q \neq 1$, we have the following:

$$\begin{aligned}
s_0 &= 1 \\
s_1 &= 1 + q = (1 + q)\frac{(1 - q)}{(1 - q)} = \frac{1 - q^2}{1 - q} \\
s_2 &= 1 + q + q^2 = \frac{1 - q^2}{1 - q} + q^2 = \frac{1 - q^3}{1 - q} \\
s_3 &= 1 + q + q^2 + q^3 = \frac{1 - q^3}{1 - q} + q^3 = \frac{1 - q^4}{1 - q} \\
s_4 &= 1 + q + q^2 + q^3 + q^4 = \frac{1 - q^4}{1 - q} + q^4 = \frac{1 - q^5}{1 - q^4},
\end{aligned}$$

etc. . . . The reader can already see how the pattern develops and make the intelligent conjecture that

$$s_n = 1 + q + q^2 + \cdots + q^n = \frac{1 - q^{n+1}}{1 - q}, \qquad q \neq 1. \tag{II.12}$$

* Customarily, the value of an infinite series is *defined* as the value that is approached by the partial sums as n tends to infinity.

In order to verify this relation, let us multiply both sides by $(1 - q)$:

$$(1 - q)(1 + q + q^2 + q^3 + \cdots + q^{n-1} + q^n) = 1 - q^{n+1}.$$

If we carry out the multiplication on the left side, we obtain

$$\begin{aligned} 1 + q + q^2 + q^3 + \cdots + q^n& \\ - q - q^2 - q^3 - \cdots - q^n - q^{n+1} &= 1 - q^{n+1} \end{aligned}$$

and we see that (II.12) is indeed correct.

Thus we have now a closed representation of the nth partial sum of the series $\sum_{k=0}^{\infty} q^k$, which is called the *geometric series*, namely

$$s_n = \frac{1 - q^{n+1}}{1 - q},$$

and we can now undertake to investigate its limit. If we consider

$$\lim_{n\to\infty} s_n = \lim_{n\to\infty} \frac{1 - q^{n+1}}{1 - q}$$

we see that the only term on the right which depends on n at all is q^{n+1}. So it appears reasonable to expect that once we know the limit of q^{n+1} as n tends to infinity, we will also know the limit of s_n.

Let us examine increasing powers of q for several values of q. Let $q = \frac{1}{4}$: then we obtain for the first, second, third, fourth, and fifth powers of q:

$$0.25, 0.0625, 0.015625, 0.00390625, 0.00097656, \cdots$$

Let $q = \frac{1}{3}$: then we obtain for the first, second, $\cdots$, fifth powers of q:

$$0.\dot{3}, 0.\dot{1}, 0.0370370\cdots, 0.0123456\cdots, 0.00411522\cdots, \cdots$$

Let $q = \frac{9}{10}$: then we obtain for $q^1, q^2, \cdots, q^5$:

$$0.9, 0.81, 0.729, 0.6561, 0.59049, \cdots$$

For $q = 2$, we obtain

$$2, 4, 8, 16, 32, \cdots$$

For $q = 1.1$, we have

$$1.1, 1.21, 1.331, 1.4641, 1.61051, \cdots$$

and finally, let us consider $q = 1$. Then we obtain

$$1, 1, 1, 1, 1, \cdots$$

We can see quite clearly that in the first three cases with $q = \frac{1}{4}, \frac{1}{3}, \frac{9}{10}$ the powers of q decrease as the exponent increases. In the two cases where $q = 2$ and $q = 1.1$ we see that the powers of q increase steadily as n increases and, in the last case, we see that all powers of q have the same value 1. We can also see that, if q is very small, the powers of q decrease very rapidly (see the case with $q = \frac{1}{4}$). If q is close to 1 but still less than 1, the powers of q still decrease but not so rapidly anymore. $q = 1$ appears to be the turning point, i.e., for all q which are less than 1, the sequence q^n decreases and for all values of q which are larger than 1, the sequence of the powers of q increases.

If q is some positive number which is less than 1, then we can write it as $\frac{1}{r}$, where r is some number that is larger than 1, and we have

$$q^n = \frac{1}{r^n}.$$

Since r is larger than 1, r^n will increase beyond bound as n tends to infinity and we obtain

$$\text{(II.13)} \qquad \lim_{n\to\infty} q^n = \lim_{n\to\infty} \frac{1}{r^n} = 0 \text{ for } 0 < q < 1 \quad (r > 1).$$

As the reader can easily convince himself, this relation holds true also if q is a number between -1 and 0.

In view of (II.13) we can see that

$$\text{(II.14)} \qquad \lim_{n\to\infty} s_n = \lim_{n\to\infty} \frac{1 - q^{n+1}}{1 - q} = \frac{1}{1 - q}$$

for all q which are in the interval $-1 < q < 1$ or, as we may state, for all q for which $|q| < 1$.

Thus, in view of (II.11)

$$\text{(II.15)} \qquad \sum_{k=0}^{\infty} q^k = \frac{1}{1 - q} \text{ for } |q| < 1.$$

It is quite clear from the above discussion that the series in (II.15) is quite senseless for $|q| > 1$.

Now, if we substitute $q = \frac{1}{4}$ in (II.15), we see that

$$\sum_{k=0}^{\infty} \left(\frac{1}{4}\right)^k = \frac{4}{3}$$

confirming the value we arrived at earlier by geometric inspection.

Let us summarize the content of this section:

We considered sums with infinitely many terms

$$\sum_{k=0}^{\infty} a_k = a_0 + a_1 + a_2 + a_3 + \cdots$$

which are called *infinite series*. If such a sum has a value at all, then its value is given by the limit

$$\sum_{k=0}^{\infty} a_k = \lim_{n\to\infty} s_n$$

of its partial sum $s_n = a_0 + a_1 + a_2 + \cdots + a_n$.

In particular, we considered the case where $a_k = q^k$ for $|q| < 1$. This particular series is called the *geometric series*. The limit of its partial sums

$$s_n = \frac{1 - q^{n+1}}{1 - q}$$

turned out to be $\dfrac{1}{1-q}$ for all $|q| < 1$. Thus we could conclude that

$$\sum_{k=0}^{\infty} q^k = \frac{1}{1-q} \text{ for } |q| < 1.$$

Problems II.15–II.24

II.15. Write the following sums using the sigma notation:

(*a*) $1 + 2 + 3 + 4 + \cdots + 100$

(*b*) $1 + \frac{1}{2} + \frac{1}{3} + \frac{1}{4} + \cdots + \frac{1}{99}$

(*c*) $0.1 + 0.01 + 0.001 + \cdots + 0.0000000000000000000001$

(*d*) $1 - q + q^2 - q^3 + \cdots + (-1)^n q^n$

(*e*) $1 + \frac{1}{4} + \frac{1}{9} + \frac{1}{16} + \frac{1}{25} + \frac{1}{36} + \cdots$

(*f*) $1 - \frac{1}{8} + \frac{1}{27} - \frac{1}{64} + \cdots$

(*g*) $x - \dfrac{x^2}{2} + \dfrac{x^3}{3} - \dfrac{x^4}{4} + \cdots$

(*h*) $1 - x^2 + x^4 - x^6 + x^8 - \cdots$

II.16. Evaluate the following sums:

(*a*) $\sum_{k=1}^{8} k$ (*b*) $\sum_{k=1}^{4} \dfrac{1}{k}$

(*c*) $\sum_{k=1}^{5} k^2$ (*d*) $\sum_{k=1}^{3} (k^3 - k)$

(*e*) $\sum_{k=0}^{\infty} (0.9)^k$ (*f*) $\sum_{k=0}^{\infty} \dfrac{2^{k-1}}{3^k}$

II.17. Find the limits of the following sequences:

$$(a)\ s_n = \frac{n+1}{n} \qquad (b)\ s_n = \frac{n^2-1}{2n^2}$$

$$(c)\ s_n = \frac{n(n-1)}{2n^2} \qquad (d)\ s_n = \frac{n(n-1)(2n-1)}{6n^3}$$

II.18. What is the limit of the sequence 0.3, 0.33, 0.333, 0.3333, $\cdots$?

II.19. Evaluate the sum in Problem II.15(*g*) for $x = 0.1$, using the first four terms only. What do you think is an estimate of the error which you committed by chopping off the series after four terms?

II.20. Given

$$s_n = \frac{(-1)^n n}{2n+3}.$$

Find s_0, s_1, s_2, s_3, and s_4. What is the limit as n tends to infinity?

II.21. Show that $\sum_{k=0}^{n} Ca_k = C\sum_{k=0}^{n} a_k$.

II.22. Show that $\sum_{k=0}^{n} (a_k + b_k) = \sum_{k=0}^{n} a_k + \sum_{k=0}^{n} b_k$.

II.23. Find $\sum_{k=1}^{n} 1$ and $\sum_{k=1}^{n-1} 1$.

II.24. Write

$$\frac{1}{1-x^4}, \quad |x| < 1$$

as an infinite series.

4. MANIPULATIONS WITH LIMITS

Let us evaluate the following limit

$$\lim_{n\to\infty} \frac{n^2+2n}{3n^2-4}.$$

First, we divide numerator and denominator of the quotient under the limit sign by n^2, thus leaving the value of the fraction unchanged but making it more easily accessible to our investigation:

$$\lim_{n\to\infty} \frac{n^2+2n}{3n^2-4} = \lim_{n\to\infty} \frac{1+\dfrac{2}{n}}{3-\dfrac{4}{n^2}}.$$

Now we can see quite easily that the expression $\frac{2}{n}$ in the numerator and the expression $\frac{4}{n^2}$ in the denominator approach zero as n tends to infinity and it appears that the entire fraction approaches the value $\frac{1}{3}$:

$$\lim_{n\to\infty} \frac{1 + \frac{2}{n}}{3 - \frac{4}{n^2}} = \frac{1}{3}.$$

If we write down symbolically what we have actually done in evaluating this limit, we obtain

$$\lim_{n\to\infty} \frac{1 + \frac{2}{n}}{3 - \frac{4}{n^2}} = \frac{\lim_{n\to\infty}\left(1 + \frac{2}{n}\right)}{\lim_{n\to\infty}\left(3 - \frac{4}{n^2}\right)} = \frac{\lim_{n\to\infty} 1 + \lim_{n\to\infty} \frac{2}{n}}{\lim_{n\to\infty} 3 - \lim_{n\to\infty} \frac{4}{n^2}}.$$

We evaluated each one of the four limits by itself and then put the results together again in the indicated order. But is such a procedure permissible? This question, fortunately, can be answered in the affirmative under certain slight restrictions. Since we introduced the concept of a limit from a purely intuitive standpoint, we are not able to analyze this problem in any detail, but it will certainly appear quite reasonable and "intuitively clear" to the reader that the following rules, which govern the manipulation with limits, hold true.

The limit of a sum of two sequences is equal to the sum of the limits of the two sequences, provided that both limits exist. If $\lim_{n\to\infty} a_n = A$ and $\lim_{n\to\infty} b_n = B$, then

(II.16) $$\lim_{n\to\infty} (a_n + b_n) = A + B.$$

This is the rule which we actually applied in our problem to evaluate the limit of the numerator. Let us consider still another example.

Let $a_n = \dfrac{n+1}{n}$ and $b_n = \dfrac{1}{n}$. Clearly, $\lim_{n\to\infty} a_n = \lim_{n\to\infty} \dfrac{n+1}{n} = 1$ and $\lim_{n\to\infty} b_n = \lim_{n\to\infty} \dfrac{1}{n} = 0$. Hence we obtain in view of (II.16)

$$\lim_{n\to\infty} (a_n + b_n) = \lim_{n\to\infty} \left(\frac{n+1}{n} + \frac{1}{n}\right) = 1 + 0.$$

This can be checked directly as follows:

$$a_n + b_n = \frac{n+1}{n} + \frac{1}{n} = \frac{n+2}{n}$$

and hence, $\lim_{n\to\infty} \dfrac{n+2}{n} = 1.$

A rule which is analogous to (II.16) holds for the limit of the difference of two sequences. *The limit of the difference of two sequences is equal to the difference of the limits of the two sequences, provided that both limits exist.* If $\lim_{n\to\infty} a_n = A$ and $\lim_{n\to\infty} b_n = B$, then

$$\lim_{n\to\infty} (a_n - b_n) = A - B. \tag{II.17}$$

The reader will notice that this rule was used to evaluate the limit of the denominator in our problem. So let us work another problem which will demonstrate that the condition that both limits have to exist is quite essential. Suppose we have

$$a_n = n + 1 \text{ and } b_n = n.$$

Then neither $\lim_{n\to\infty} a_n$, nor $\lim_{n\to\infty} b_n$ exist, i.e., $\lim_{n\to\infty} a_n = \lim_{n\to\infty} (n + 1) = \infty$ and $\lim_{n\to\infty} b_n = \lim_{n\to\infty} n = \infty$. If we would nevertheless apply our rule, we would obtain

$$\lim_{n\to\infty} (a_n - b_n) = \infty - \infty$$

which is quite meaningless. However, we see that $a_n - b_n = n + 1 - n = 1$ and we have consequently

$$\lim_{n\to\infty} (a_n - b_n) = 1.$$

Now we have to discuss two more rules which deal with the limits of products and quotients.

The limit of a product is equal to the product of the limits, provided that both limits exist. If $\lim_{n\to\infty} a_n = A$ and $\lim_{n\to\infty} b_n = B$, then

$$\lim_{n\to\infty} (a_n b_n) = AB. \tag{II.18}$$

As an example, let us consider

$$a_n = \frac{n}{n+1}, \; b_n = \frac{n+3}{n}.$$

Then $\lim_{n\to\infty} a_n = \lim_{n\to\infty} \frac{n}{n+1} = 1$ and $\lim_{n\to\infty} b_n = \lim_{n\to\infty} \frac{n+3}{n} = 1$ and according to (II.18)

$$\lim_{n\to\infty} a_n b_n = \lim_{n\to\infty} \frac{n}{n+1} \cdot \frac{n+3}{n} = 1$$

which can also be checked directly.

Rules (II.16) and (II.18) actually hold for a sum of any number of terms or a product of any number of factors.

Finally, we have: *The limit of a quotient is equal to the quotient of the limits, provided that both limits exist, and the elements of the sequence in the denominator are different from zero and tend to a limit which is different from zero.* If $\lim_{n\to\infty} a_n = A$ and $\lim_{n\to\infty} b_n = B \neq 0$, where $b_n \neq 0$ for all n, then

$$\lim_{n\to\infty} \frac{a_n}{b_n} = \frac{A}{B}. \tag{II.19}$$

This rule was finally used in our example above to express the limit as the quotient of the limits.

We wish to point out to the reader that we cheated a little in the examples that served to illustrate our rules. Specifically, we assumed without further discussion that

$$\lim_{n\to\infty} \frac{n+1}{n} = 1, \quad \lim_{n\to\infty} \frac{n}{n+1} = 1 \quad \text{and} \quad \lim_{n\to\infty} \frac{n+3}{n} = 1.$$

Let us apply the appropriate rules toward the evaluation of these limits after dividing numerator and denominator by n.

In the first case we have

$$\lim_{n\to\infty} \frac{n+1}{n} = \lim_{n\to\infty} \frac{1+\frac{1}{n}}{1} = \frac{\lim_{n\to\infty}\left(1+\frac{1}{n}\right)}{\lim_{n\to\infty} 1} = \lim_{n\to\infty} 1 + \lim_{n\to\infty} \frac{1}{n}.$$

We see that the whole problem boils down to the evaluation of the limit of the sequence $\frac{1}{n}$ as n tends to infinity. (The same thing occurs in the two other cases, as the reader can easily see for himself.)

If we had based the concept of a limit on a rigorous mathematical foundation, we would have had no difficulty in proving that this limit is zero. We introduced the limit from a purely intuitive standpoint however, and thus have to accept at faith that

$$\lim_{n\to\infty} \frac{1}{n} = 0 \tag{II.20}$$

which should be plausible and will certainly not strain the imagination. It is *not possible*, no matter how hard we may try, to obtain this result by a manipulation of the four rules which we have stated in the preceding discussion.

Our results enable us to establish a simple recipe for the evaluation of limits of quotients with polynomials of n in numerator and denominator (for definition of *polynomial*, see Appendix I). Consider, for example,

$$\lim_{n\to\infty} \frac{n^4 - 3n^2 + 4n + 7}{2n^4 + 4n^2 + 3n - 10037}.$$

Let us divide numerator and denominator by n^4 to obtain

$$\lim_{n\to\infty} \frac{1 - \dfrac{3}{n^2} + \dfrac{4}{n^3} + \dfrac{7}{n^4}}{2 + \dfrac{4}{n^2} + \dfrac{3}{n^3} - \dfrac{10037}{n^4}}.$$

We see that all terms in numerator and denominator tend to zero as n tends to infinity *except* for the coefficients of n^4, and we therefore have the limit $\frac{1}{2}$, i.e., the ratio of the coefficients of n^4.

It is now easy to see that this rule applies in general: *If we have a quotient of two polynomials in n of the same degree, say, k, then the limit is equal to the ratio of the coefficients of n^k.* The validity of this rule can even be extended to the case where the degree of the numerator polynomial is different from the degree of the denominator polynomial, as we will see in the following two examples.

First we consider

$$\lim_{n\to\infty} \frac{n^2 + 3n - 1}{n^3 + 4n^2 + n}.$$

The coefficient of n^3 in the numerator is 0 and the coefficient of n^3 in the denominator is 1. Hence, if our rule applies, the limit will be $\frac{0}{1} = 0$ which is indeed the case as this direct check will show:

$$\lim_{n\to\infty} \frac{n^2 + 3n - 1}{n^3 + 4n^2 + n} = \lim_{n\to\infty} \frac{\dfrac{1}{n} + \dfrac{3}{n^2} - \dfrac{1}{n^3}}{1 + \dfrac{4}{n} + \dfrac{1}{n^2}} = \frac{0}{1} = 0.$$

Finally, we consider

$$\lim_{n\to\infty} \frac{n^4 - 3n^2 + 4n}{n^3 + 1}.$$

The coefficient of n^4 in the numerator is 1, in the denominator it is 0. Hence, by our recipe, the limit would be $\frac{1}{0}$, i.e., does not exist, which is indeed the case as a direct check shows.

In the preceding discussion we accepted on faith the rather obvious fact that $\dfrac{1}{n}$ tends to zero as n tends to infinity. It is equally obvious that n has to tend to infinity as $\dfrac{1}{n}$ tends to zero. Thus we can certainly write the limit which we considered in the beginning of this section, namely,

$$\lim_{n\to\infty} \frac{n^2 + 2n}{3n^2 - 4}$$

which turned out to be equivalent to

$$\lim_{n\to\infty} \frac{1 + \frac{2}{n}}{3 - \frac{4}{n^2}}$$

in the form

$$\lim_{\frac{1}{n}\to 0} \frac{1 + 2\left(\frac{1}{n}\right)}{3 - 4\left(\frac{1}{n}\right)^2}.$$

Now, could we not avoid this awkward notation by writing x instead of $\frac{1}{n}$ with the understanding that x has to approach zero, namely,

$$\lim_{x\to 0} \frac{1 + 2x}{3 - 4x^2}?$$

The answer is yes, although there are some reservations to it. If we look at this limit in terms of x, conveniently forgetting its past history, then the question arises as to how x is to approach zero. It could approach zero as $\frac{1}{n}$ as $n \to \infty$, or as $\frac{1}{n^2}$ as $n \to \infty$, or as $\frac{1 + n^3}{4n - 3n^2 + 10n^4}$ as $n \to \infty$, or, as a matter of fact, in any other manner. Now, if the result we obtain is the same, no matter how x approaches zero, there is no problem. Fortunately, this is the case in our example and in all other examples that are likely to arise in this treatment.

However, there are cases where the manner in which x approaches zero does make a difference as far as the limit is concerned. Take, for example, the pathological function

$$f(x) = \begin{cases} 1 \text{ for all rational values of } x \\ 0 \text{ for all irrational values of } x \end{cases}$$

and consider

$$\lim_{x\to 0} f(x).$$

If we let x approach zero as $\frac{1}{n}$ where $n \to \infty$, and since it follows from the definition of this function that $f\left(\frac{1}{n}\right) = 1$ for all integers n, we obtain 1 as the limit. On the other hand, if we let x approach zero as $\frac{\sqrt{2}}{n}$ where $n \to \infty$, then $f\left(\frac{\sqrt{2}}{n}\right) = 0$ because $\frac{\sqrt{2}}{n}$ is irrational for all integers n and we obtain 0 as the limit. In such a case we say that the limit does not exist because the value obtained clearly depends on the selected sequence through which we let x go to zero.

In general, we say that

$$\lim_{x \to 0} f(x)$$

for some given function $f(x)$ exists if, and only if,

$$\lim_{n \to \infty} f(x_n)$$

has the same value, no matter what sequence $x_1, x_2, x_3, \cdots$ with $\lim_{n \to \infty} x_n = 0$ we select. This criterion is, of course, anything but practical because it is humanly impossible to check all possible sequences that tend to zero. Although, there is a more practical alternative, we need not go into this matter any further because all the limits of this nature that we will encounter in this treatment exist, i.e., are independent of the sequence selected and can thus be evaluated by letting x run through the sequence $\frac{1}{n}$ with $n \to \infty$.

This means that the rules which we have discussed in the first portion of this section also apply to limits of the type $\lim_{x \to 0} f(x)$, as far we will encounter them in this treatment.

We warn the reader that the argument which we put forth here is by no means a justification of this procedure, but it will suffice for our purpose.

Problems II.25–II.30

II.25. Evaluate the following limits:

(*a*) $\lim_{n \to \infty} \dfrac{2n^2 + 1}{8642 - n^2}$ (*b*) $\lim_{n \to \infty} \dfrac{n - 3}{12n}$

(*c*) $\lim_{n \to \infty} \dfrac{9n^5 - 6n + 111}{n^5 + 1000000}$ (*d*) $\lim_{n \to \infty} \dfrac{n^3 - 3n^2 + 4n + 12}{4n^4 - 3n}$

(*e*) $\lim_{n \to \infty} \dfrac{n^3 + 4}{n(n^2 - 1)}$ (*f*) $\lim_{n \to \infty} \dfrac{n - 4}{4n^2 + 1}$

II.26. Which of the following limits exists?

(*a*) $\lim_{n \to \infty} \dfrac{n}{n^5 - 3n^2 + 4n + 1}$ (*b*) $\lim_{n \to \infty} \dfrac{(n^2 + 1)\sqrt{n}}{n^3 + 4n + 3}$

(*c*) $\lim_{n \to \infty} \dfrac{n^4 + 4n}{n^3 - 12}$ (*d*) $\lim_{n \to \infty} \dfrac{n^5 + 4n^2 - 1}{\sqrt{n}(n^4 + 3)}$

II.27. Evaluate:

(*a*) $\lim_{x\to 0} \dfrac{x^2 + 4x}{3x^2 - 1}$ (*b*) $\lim_{x\to 0} \dfrac{x^3 + 2x + 12}{x^2 - 6}$

(*c*) $\lim_{x\to 0} \dfrac{2x^4 + 3}{x^4 - 1}$ (*d*) $\lim_{x\to 0} \dfrac{2x^2 + 4x + 4}{(x + 1)^2}$

II.28. Find the following limits, provided they exist, using rule (II.17) wherever it is applicable:

(*a*) $\lim_{n\to\infty} \left(\dfrac{n}{n + 1} - \dfrac{n^2 + 3}{2n^2 + 1}\right)$ (*b*) $\lim_{n\to\infty} \left(\dfrac{1}{n} - \dfrac{4n}{n + 12}\right)$

(*c*) $\lim_{n\to\infty} \left(n - \dfrac{n^2 + 1}{n + 4}\right)$ (*d*) $\lim_{n\to\infty} \left(n^2 - \dfrac{4n^4}{3n^2 - 1}\right)$

II.29. Show by rule (II.18) that

$$\lim_{n\to\infty} Ca_n = C \lim_{n\to\infty} a_n$$

provided that $\lim_{n\to\infty} a_n$ exists.

II.30. Suppose that $\lim_{n\to\infty} a_n = A$ and $\lim_{n\to\infty} b_n = B \neq 0$. Show that if $\lim_{n\to\infty} \dfrac{a_n}{b_n} = 1$, then $A = B$. (*Hint:* Assume that $A \neq B$ and show that this leads to a contradiction. It then follows that it is not possible that $A \neq B$; hence, the contrary has to be true, i.e., $A = B$.)

5. THE AREA OF A CIRCLE*

We proceed now to define the area of a circle. All we have at our disposal is the definition of the area of a rectangle and the consequent formulas for areas of regions which are bounded by straight line segments (polygons). Clearly, we cannot give an arbitrary definition of the area of a circle because that might have the consequence that we will get stuck with two inconsistent concepts of area. In order to arrive at a satisfactory definition of the area of a circle we proceed according to a method which was first developed by *Archimedes of Syracuse* (287–212 B.C.), the greatest mathematician of ancient times. His method is really the basis of what we call nowadays the *Integral Calculus*.

The basic idea of Archimedes' method is a generalization of postulate (4), p. 76, for the area measure which, generalized to closed (not necessarily rectangular) regions, says that whenever one region is entirely contained in another region, the area-measure of the enclosed region is smaller than the area measure of the enclosing region.

On the basis of this idea we assign to the circle an area measure that is larger than the area measure of *all possible* inscribed polygons and smaller

* The reader who is *not* familiar with trigonometry is referred to Appendix III which he should study at this time before continuing with the regular text.

than the area measure of *all possible* circumscribed polygons. In practice, we obtain increasingly better "approximations" to what ultimately will be called the area of the circle, if we consider a sequence of inscribed regular polygons with an increasing number of vertices and a sequence of circumscribed regular polygons with an increasing number of vertices.

Suppose we have a circle of radius r (see Fig. II.10) and consider an inscribed and a circumscribed square. Let A_4 be the area of the circumscribed square and a_4 the area of the inscribed square. If we denote the area of the circle (i.e., the number which is larger than the area of all inscribed polygons and smaller than the area of all circumscribed polygons, if such a number exists at all) by A, then the inequality

$$a_4 < A < A_4$$

holds.

If, instead of squares, we consider now an inscribed regular octagon and a circumscribed regular octagon (see dotted lines in Fig. II.10) with the areas a_8 and A_8, respectively, we see by inspection that $A_8 < A_4$ and $a_8 > a_4$. At the same time $A_8 > A$ and $a_8 < A$. Hence, it follows that

$$a_4 < a_8 < A < A_8 < A_4.$$

Thus, it appears that a_8 and A_8 are better approximations to A than A_4 and a_4. The reader can already see from this short account that it seems that a continuation of this process will yield increasingly better approximations as the number of vertices of the polygons becomes larger. At the same time it is clear that there is no end to this process, i.e., no matter how many vertices a polygon has, there is always one with more vertices that will yield a still better approximation. The following question, however, remains

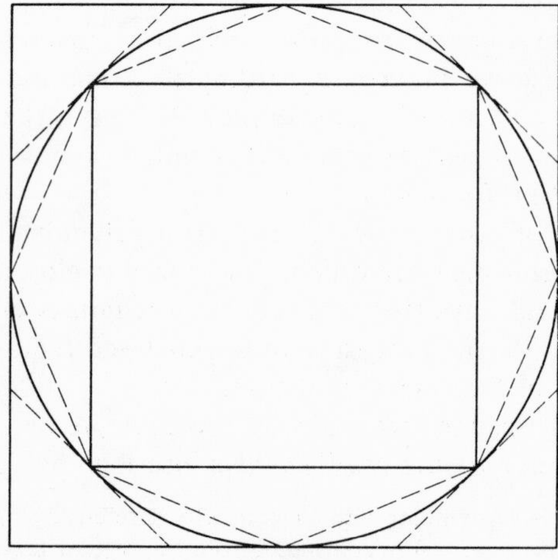

Fig. II.10

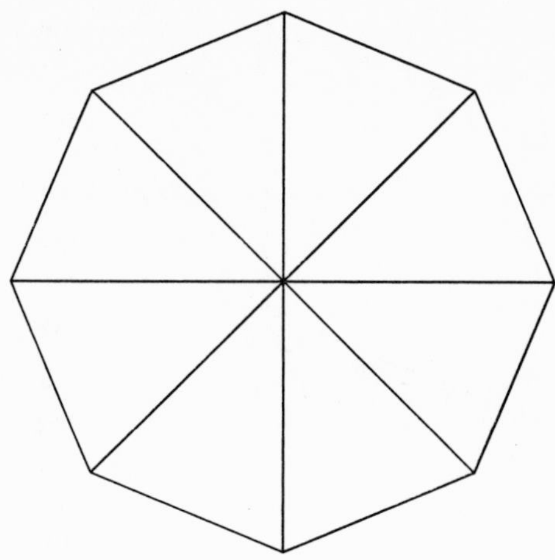

Fig. II.11

unsettled: does the difference between the areas of two corresponding polygons—the one inscribed and the other one circumscribed—become less than any finite positive number, no matter how small, or does it not as n becomes large? We will see at the end of this section that this difference does, indeed, tend to zero.

In order to carry out the indicated process numerically, we have first to derive formulas for the areas of the inscribed and circumscribed polygons. These areas can be expressed in terms of the radius of the circle and the number of vertices. First, we note that every regular polygon with n vertices can be subdivided into n congruent isosceles triangles (see Fig. II.11).

For the following discussion we refer to Fig. II.12. The triangle $0AB$ is part of an inscribed regular polygon. Its area a is given by

$$a = \frac{rh}{2}.$$

Clearly,

$$\frac{h}{r} = \sin \alpha, \qquad h = r \sin \alpha.$$

Hence

(II.21) $$a = \tfrac{1}{2} r^2 \sin \alpha$$

where α is the angle between the two equal sides measured in degrees.

The triangle $0CD$ is part of a circumscribed regular polygon. Its area A_c is given by

$$A_c = \frac{rb}{2}.$$

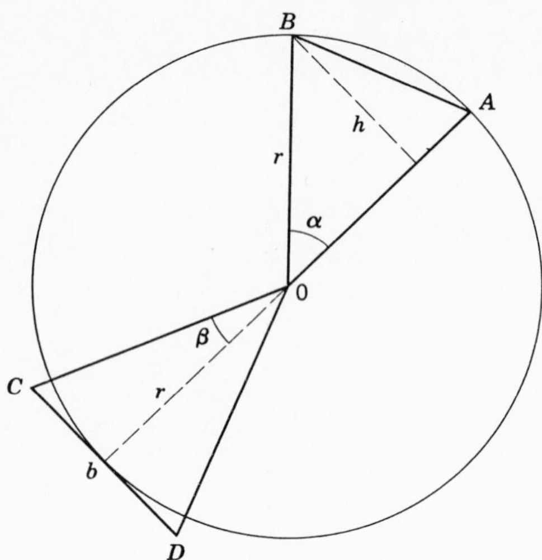

Fig. II.12

Now,

$$\frac{b}{2r} = \tan \beta, \qquad b = 2r \tan \beta.$$

Hence

$$A_c = r^2 \tan \beta \tag{II.22}$$

where β is half the angle between the two equal sides.

Suppose we now consider regular polygons with n vertices. Then the angle α at the center of each isosceles triangular component of the inscribed regular polygon is given by

$$\alpha = \frac{360}{n}$$

and the angle β, which is half the angle at the center of each triangular component of the circumscribed polygon, is given by

$$\beta = \frac{180}{n}.$$

Thus we obtain for the area a_n of the inscribed regular polygon with n vertices, according to (II.21)

$$a_n = \tfrac{1}{2} n r^2 \sin \frac{360}{n} \tag{II.23}$$

and for the area A_n of the circumscribed regular polygon with n vertices, according to (II.22),

$$A_n = n r^2 \tan \frac{180}{n}. \tag{II.24}$$

Since

$$a_n < A < A_n$$

we arrive at the important inequality

$$\text{(II.25)} \qquad \tfrac{1}{2}r^2 n \sin\frac{360}{n} < A < r^2 n \tan\frac{180}{n}.$$

Let us now evaluate this inequality for various values of n, using five-place tables for the values of the trigonometric functions.*

Letting $n = 4$,

$$2r^2 < A < 4r^2$$

Letting $n = 16$,

$$3.06144r^2 < A < 3.18252r^2$$

Letting $n = 32$,

$$3.12144r^2 < A < 3.15168r^2.$$

We observe that the lower bound and the upper bound agree with each other in the first decimal place. Hence, the area of a circle of radius r, accurate to one decimal place, is given by $3.1r^2$. Now, let $n = 128$; then

$$3.14112r^2 < A < 3.1424r^2.$$

We see that the approximations agree in the first two decimal places. Hence, the area accurate to two decimal places is given by $3.14r^2$.

There is no use going any further if we use five-place tables, because the fifth place is already inaccurate (rounded off) and becomes, after multiplication by a number greater than 100, the third decimal place. Indeed, if we would evaluate (II.25) for $n = 256$, using five-place tables, we would not obtain a better result than the one we obtained already for $n = 128$.

We observe that inasmuch as the area of the circle is smaller than the area of the circumscribed polygon and larger than the area of the inscribed polygon, we get an approximation to the area of the circle which is better than the one given by either upper or lower bound, if we take the arithmetical mean of upper and lower bound. We obtain

for $n = 4$: $A \cong 3r^2$,

for $n = 16$: $A \cong 3.12198r^2$,

for $n = 32$: $A \cong 3.13656r^2$,

for $n = 128$: $A \cong 3.14176r^2$.

However, we can not tell directly from these results, how much better approximations they really are.

* Standard Mathematical Tables, CRC, 12th ed. p. 93. Observe that these values of the trigonometric functions which we use can be found without knowledge of the length of the unit circle (see Appendix III, Section 4).

Now let us shortly recapitulate what we have done: We squeezed the area of the circle in between an upper and a lower bound. We still do not know what the area of the circle is. All we can tell is that it is larger than the lower bound and smaller than the upper bound. It is intuitively clear that upper and lower bound come closer to each other as n becomes large. However, all we can say for sure is that the lower bound never exceeds a certain finite number because the inscribed polygons have an area which is smaller than the area of any circumscribed polygon and the area of the circumscribed polygons is always greater than a certain finite positive number which is different from zero, because it is always greater than the area of any inscribed polygon which is always greater than zero for $n \geq 3$.

In order to show that upper and lower bound both approach the same number as n becomes large, i.e., the gap between them approaches zero, we have to show that the quotient of upper and lower bound approaches 1. This means, obviously, that numerator and denominator both approach the same limit* (see Problem II.30). Now,

$$Q_n = \frac{a_n}{A_n} = \frac{\frac{1}{2}r^2 n \sin\dfrac{360}{n}}{r^2 n \tan\dfrac{180}{n}} = \frac{1}{2}\,\frac{\sin\dfrac{360}{n}}{\tan\dfrac{180}{n}}.$$

Since

$$\sin 2\alpha = 2 \sin \alpha \cos \alpha$$

(see Appendix III, formula (AIII, 13), we have

$$\sin\frac{360}{n} = 2 \sin\frac{360}{2n} \cos\frac{360}{2n} = 2 \sin\frac{180}{n} \cos\frac{180}{n}$$

and, consequently,

$$Q_n = \frac{1}{2}\,\frac{2 \sin\dfrac{180}{n} \cos\dfrac{180}{n}}{\tan\dfrac{180}{n}}.$$

Since

$$\tan\frac{180}{n} = \frac{\sin\dfrac{180}{n}}{\cos\dfrac{180}{n}},$$

* This argument is valid if the numerator sequence as well as the denominator sequence have a limit and the limit of the denominator sequence is different from zero. This is here the case. The numerator sequence is an increasing sequence which is bounded above and the denominator sequence is a decreasing sequence which is bounded below (away from zero). According to a famous theorem of *Bolzano*, such sequences have limits and the limit in the latter case is different from zero (see Problem II.35).

we obtain

$$Q_n = \frac{\sin \dfrac{180}{n} \cos^2 \dfrac{180}{n}}{\sin \dfrac{180}{n}} = \cos^2 \frac{180}{n}.$$

Now, as $n \to \infty$ we see that

$$\lim_{n \to \infty} Q_n = \lim_{n \to \infty} \cos^2 \frac{180}{n}.$$

Because

$$\lim_{n \to \infty} \frac{180}{n} = 0,$$

it appears that

$$\lim_{n \to \infty} \cos \frac{180}{n} = \cos 0 = 1$$

and we have

$$\lim_{n \to \infty} Q_n = \lim_{n \to \infty} \cos \frac{180}{n} \lim_{n \to \infty} \cos \frac{180}{n} = 1.$$

Thus we see that A_n and a_n both approach the same limit and this limit is some finite number because a_n is finite for all n and A_n is never 0.

With the notation

(II.26) $$\lim_{n \to \infty} \frac{n}{2} \sin \frac{360}{n} = \pi$$

we can write

(II.27) $$A = r^2\pi$$

for the area of a circle with radius r, where $\pi = 3.14 \cdots$.

Problems II.31–II.35

II.31. Find upper and lower bounds for the area of a circle with radius 1 (unit circle), using regular polygons with 6, 12, 24, 96 vertices. Use five-place tables.

II.32. Find $\sin \alpha$ for the following values of α:

$$\alpha = 45°, \frac{45°}{4}, \frac{45°}{8}.$$

(Use half-angle formulas, Appendix III, Section 4.)

II.33. Same as in Problem II.32 for $\tan \alpha$.

II.34. Evaluate the ratio $\dfrac{a_n}{A_n}$ where a_n is the area of a regular inscribed polygon and A_n is the area of a regular circumscribed polygon with n vertices for $n = 4$, $n = 16$, $n = 32$, $n = 64$, $n = 96$, $n = 128$. (Note that the radius of the circle is immaterial for this computation.)

II.35. Suppose you have infinitely many numbers and they are arranged so that $a_0 < a_1 < a_2 < \cdots < a_n < \cdots$. Suppose you know that $a_n < A$ for *all n*. Illustrate with examples that the sequence a_n approaches a limit which is less than or equal to A.

6. CIRCUMFERENCE OF A CIRCLE

We will now employ the Archimedean method which we developed in the preceding section to find a suitable definition for the length of the circumference of a circle. As the concept of area in the preceding section was based on the concept of area of a polygonal region, the concept of length will be based on the concept of length of a line segment and, in turn, the length of a polygon.

Again we will consider inscribed polygons with the idea in mind that the larger the number of vertices, the closer the length of the polygon will be to what we will ultimately call the length of the circumference of the circle.

Let us refer to Fig. II.13 for the following developments. We see that

$$\frac{b}{2r} = \sin\frac{\alpha}{2}.$$

Hence,

$$b = 2r\sin\frac{\alpha}{2}$$

and, consequently, the length l_n of an inscribed regular polygon with n vertices is given by

$$l_n = 2rn\sin\frac{180}{n},$$

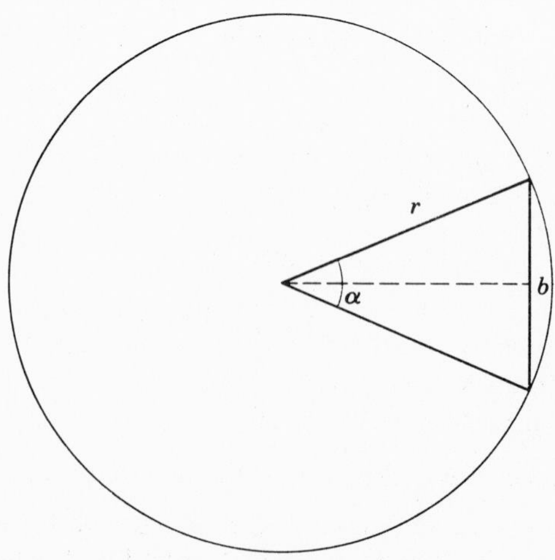

Fig. II.13

since $\alpha = 360/n$ is the central angle subtended by one side of a regular polygon with n vertices.

From

$$\sin 2\beta = 2 \sin \beta \cos \beta$$

it follows with $\beta = 180/n$ that

$$\sin \frac{360}{n} = 2 \sin \frac{180}{n} \cos \frac{180}{n}$$

and, consequently,

$$\sin \frac{180}{n} = \frac{\sin \dfrac{360}{n}}{2 \cos \dfrac{180}{n}}.$$

Hence,

$$l_n = rn \frac{\sin \dfrac{360}{n}}{\cos \dfrac{180}{n}}, \qquad n \geq 3.$$

We have seen in the preceding section [see (II.26)] that

$$\lim_{n\to\infty} \frac{n}{2} \sin \frac{360}{n}$$

exists and have denoted its value by π.

Hence,

$$\lim_{n\to\infty} l_n = 2r \lim_{n\to\infty} \frac{n}{2} \frac{\sin \dfrac{360}{n}}{\cos \dfrac{180}{n}} = 2r \frac{\lim\limits_{n\to\infty} \dfrac{n}{2} \sin \dfrac{360}{n}}{\lim\limits_{n\to\infty} \cos \dfrac{180}{n}} = 2r \frac{\pi}{\cos 0} = 2r\pi.$$

Therefore, we can define the circumference C of a circle as

$$C = 2r\pi \tag{II.28}$$

where r is the radius and $\pi = 3.14 \cdots$.

This definition is, of course, only justified if the perimeter L_n of the circumscribed polygons tends to the same limit as the perimeter l_n of the inscribed polygons as n becomes large. This is indeed the case as can be seen as follows.

We see from Fig. II.14 that

$$\frac{a}{2r} = \tan \frac{\beta}{2}.$$

Hence

$$a = 2r \tan \frac{\beta}{2}$$

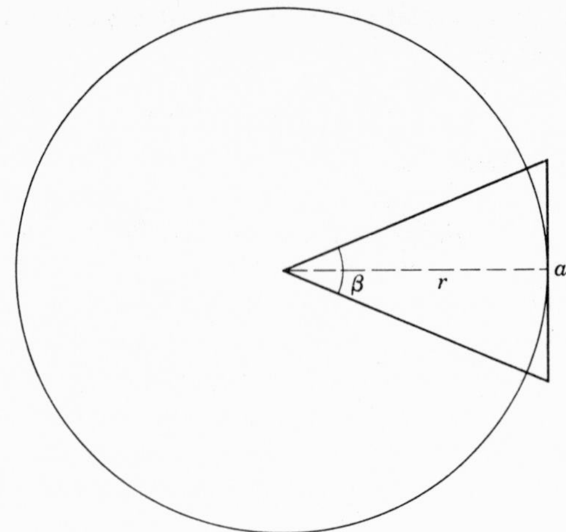

Fig. II.14

and the perimeter L_n of the circumscribed regular polygon with n vertices is given by

$$L_n = 2rn \tan \frac{180}{n}$$

since $\beta = 360/n$ for a regular polygon with n vertices.

We have seen in the preceding section that

$$\lim_{n\to\infty} n \tan \frac{180}{n} = \lim_{n\to\infty} \frac{n}{2} \sin \frac{360}{n} = \pi.$$

Hence,

$$\lim_{n\to\infty} l_n = \lim_{n\to\infty} L_n = 2r\pi.$$

Problems II.36–II.40

II.36. Consider inscribed and circumscribed regular polygons of a unit circle. Find l_3, L_3, l_4, L_4, l_6, L_6, l_{36}, L_{36} and evaluate the differences

$$L_k - l_k \text{ for } k = 3, 4, 6, 36.$$

II.37. Given a circle with radius r. Express the area A of the circle as a function $f(C)$ of its circumference. What is $f(x)$?

II.38. Express the circumference C of a circle as a function $f(A)$ of its area.

II.39. Find approximations for π from the values l_k and L_k in Problem II.36 and compare them with the approximations which we found in Section 5.

II.40. Find approximations of π by evaluating $n \tan \frac{180}{n}$ for $n = 90$ and $n = 180$. Use five-place tables.

7. RADIAN MEASURE

Now that we know it is senseful to assign a length measure to the circumference of a circle, we are in a position to introduce a new measure for angles which proves to be more adequate for most mathematical investigations than the degree measure.

For the following discussion we refer to Fig. II.15. If the point P moves on the circumference of the circle with radius 1 (unit circle) from T in the *counterclockwise* (*positive*) direction through a distance x, then the segment $0P$ will sweep an angle of $\alpha°$. It is obvious that there is a one to one correspondence between $\alpha°$ and x, i.e., with every angle α there corresponds one distance x measured on the circumference of the unit circle and with every distance x there corresponds one angle α provided that $0 \leq \alpha < 360°$. Hence the distance x along the circumference of the unit circle is suitable for the measurement of angles. We call this new measurement of angles the *radian measure*. Since the length of the unit circle is 2π, as we have seen in the preceding section, we see that an angle of 360° corresponds to the radian measure 2π radians, an angle of 180 degrees corresponds to π radians, and angle of 90 degrees to $\pi/2$ radians, etc. $\cdots$

In general, we have

$$\alpha = \frac{360x}{2\pi} = \frac{180x}{\pi}$$

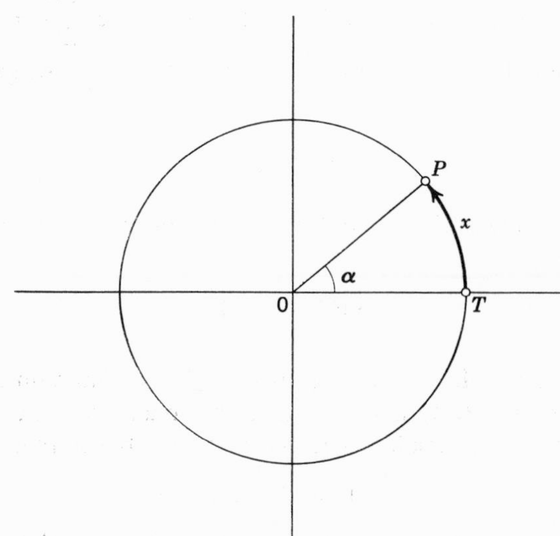

Fig. II.15

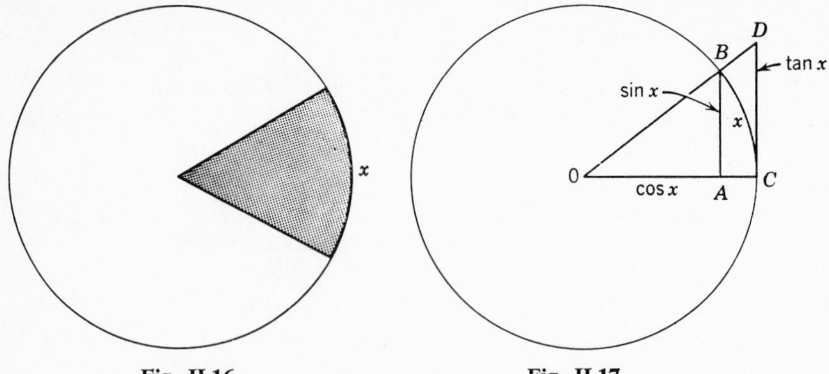

Fig. II.16 Fig. II.17

for the conversion of x radians into α degrees and

$$x = \frac{\pi\alpha}{180}$$

for the conversion of α degrees into x radians.

The relation between circumference of a circle and its area with π as the connecting link as developed in Sections 5 and 6 will enable us to find a formula for the area of a circular sector which is such that its circular boundary has the length x, where $0 \leq x < 2\pi$. Now, the entire circle of length $2r\pi$ has the area $r^2\pi$. Hence, a circular sector (see Fig. II.16), which has a circular boundary of length 1, has the area $\frac{r^2\pi}{2r\pi} = \frac{r}{2}$ and, consequently, a circular sector with a circular boundary of length x has the area

(II.29) $$S_x = \frac{xr}{2}.$$

This result will now enable us to derive an important and interesting limit relation, namely,

(II.30) $$\lim_{x\to 0} \frac{\sin x}{x} = 1.$$

To show this, we refer to the unit circle in Fig. II.17 and observe that the area a of the triangle OAB is smaller than the area $\mathscr{A}$ of the circular sector $0CB$ which, in turn, is smaller than the area A of the triangle $0CD$:

(II.31) $$a \leq \mathscr{A} \leq A$$

where we assume that $0 \leq x < \pi/2$. [Since x is allowed to assume the value 0, we have to include the equal signs in the inequality (II.31).]

Now,

$$a = \frac{1}{2} \sin x \cos x$$

(II.32)
$$\mathscr{A} = \frac{x}{2}$$

$$A = \frac{1}{2} \tan x$$

and if we substitute for a, $\mathscr{A}$, A in (II.31) according to (II.32), we have

$$\frac{1}{2} \sin x \cos x \leq \frac{x}{2} \leq \frac{1}{2} \tan x.$$

Multiplying this inequality by 2 and dividing it by $\sin x$, yields

$$\cos x \leq \frac{x}{\sin x} \leq \frac{1}{\cos x}.$$

Now, we let $x \to 0$ and obtain

$$1 \leq \lim_{x \to 0} \frac{x}{\sin x} \leq 1$$

since $\cos x \to 1$ as $x \to 0$.

Thus $\dfrac{x}{\sin x}$ as $x \to 0$ is less than or equal to 1 and at the same time greater than or equal to 1. This is only possible if

$$\lim_{x \to 0} \frac{x}{\sin x} = 1.$$

It follows that the same has to be true for the reciprocal value and thus proves relation (II.30) (see Problem II.47).

We wish to observe that in most Calculus texts this fundamental formula, which is derived on the basis of the knowledge of the relation between circumference and area of a circle, is then used to derive a certain relation (differentiation of the sine function) which, in turn, is used to establish an integration formula which ultimately is used to find the area and circumference of a circle. This is a beautiful example of a vicious circle.

Problems II.41–II.47

II.41. (*a*) Convert the following angles in degrees into radians: 270, 225, 60, 30, 22.5, 135, 345

(*b*) Convert the following radian measures into degree measures: $\frac{5\pi}{6}$, $\frac{7\pi}{4}$, $\frac{3\pi}{2}$, $\frac{\pi}{12}$, $\frac{11\pi}{6}$, $\frac{5\pi}{3}$, $\frac{5\pi}{3}$.

II.42. Evaluate $\dfrac{\sin x}{x}$ for $x = 1, \dfrac{\pi}{4}, \dfrac{\pi}{6}, \dfrac{\pi}{16}, \dfrac{\pi}{64}$. Use tables.

II.43. Suppose you want the value of $\sin x$ to five decimal places. Use tables to determine for what values of x we can substitute x for $\sin x$ without noticing the difference in the fifth decimal place. Do the same for four and three decimal places.

II.44. Find $\lim_{x\to 0} \dfrac{\tan x}{x}$. $\left(\textit{Hint:} \text{ Note that } \tan x = \dfrac{\sin x}{\cos x} \text{ and hence, } \dfrac{\tan x}{x} = \dfrac{1}{\cos x} \cdot \dfrac{\sin x}{x}\right)$.

II.45. Find

$$\lim_{x\to 0} \frac{\sin^2 x}{x^2}.$$

II.46. Find $\lim_{x\to 0} \dfrac{\sin 2x}{x}$.

II.47. Prove that if $\lim_{x\to 0} \dfrac{x}{\sin x} = 1$, then $\lim_{x\to 0} \dfrac{\sin x}{x} = 1$.

$\left(\textit{Hint:} \text{ Note that } \dfrac{\sin x}{x} = \dfrac{1}{\dfrac{x}{\sin x}}.\right)$

8. AREA UNDER A CURVE

We will now generalize the idea of Section 5 to define the area of a region which is bounded on one side by a curve, represented by a function $y = f(x)$, and on the remaining sides by the x-axis and the vertical lines at $x = a$ and $x = b$ (see Fig. II.18). We will assume for the following that $f(x) \geq 0$ in the interval $a \leq x \leq b$ and that $y = f(x)$ does not have any discontinuities. We defined the area of a circle in Section 5 as the limit of a sum of areas of triangles. To chop up the area in Fig. II.18 into triangles would be highly impractical. Since the only other polygonal region of which we already know the area is the rectangle, we will try to make use of rectangles for our purpose. This is really quite simple. We subdivide the interval $a \leq x \leq b$ into n equal subintervals by introducing the division points

$$x_1, x_2, x_3, \cdots x_{n-1}$$

with the understanding that

$$x_1 - a = x_2 - x_1 = x_3 - x_2 = \cdots = b - x_{n-1} = \Delta x$$

where $\Delta x = \dfrac{b-a}{n}$. To obtain a unified notation, let us set

$$a = x_0, b = x_n.$$

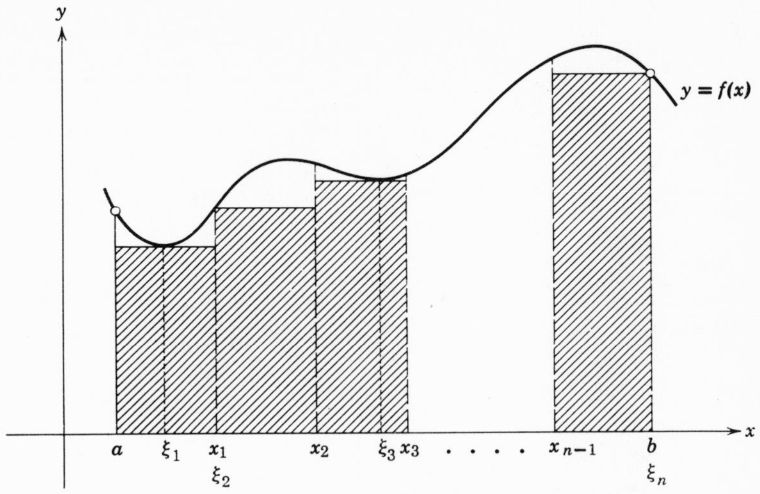

Fig. II.18

Now we locate in every subinterval $x_{k-1} \leq x \leq x_k$ $(k = 1, 2, \cdots n)$ the value ξ_k for which the function $f(x)$ assumes the smallest value:

$$f(\xi_k) = \min f(x) \text{ in } x_{k-1} \leq x \leq x_k.$$

We erect the ordinates at all division points x_k and at all points ξ_k and draw horizontal segments through $f(\xi_k)$ for all $k = 1, 2, 3, \cdots, n$. We thus obtain a collection of rectangles which are indicated by the shaded areas in Fig. II.18. We will denote the sum of these areas by $\underline{S}_n$ where n indicates the number of subintervals. We have

$$\text{(II.33)} \qquad \underline{S}_n = f(\xi_1)\,\Delta x + f(\xi_2)\,\Delta x + \cdots + f(\xi_n)\,\Delta x$$

$$= \Delta x \sum_{k=1}^{n} f(\xi_k).$$

If $A_{a,b}$ stands for the yet to be defined area measure of the region that is bounded by $y = f(x)$, the x-axis and the lines $x = a$ and $x = b$, then it is intuitively clear that

$$\underline{S}_n \leq A_{a,b}.$$

Let us take, for example,

$$f(x) = x(1 - x) + 1, a = 0, b = 1$$

and let $n = 4$, hence $\Delta x = \frac{1}{4}$.

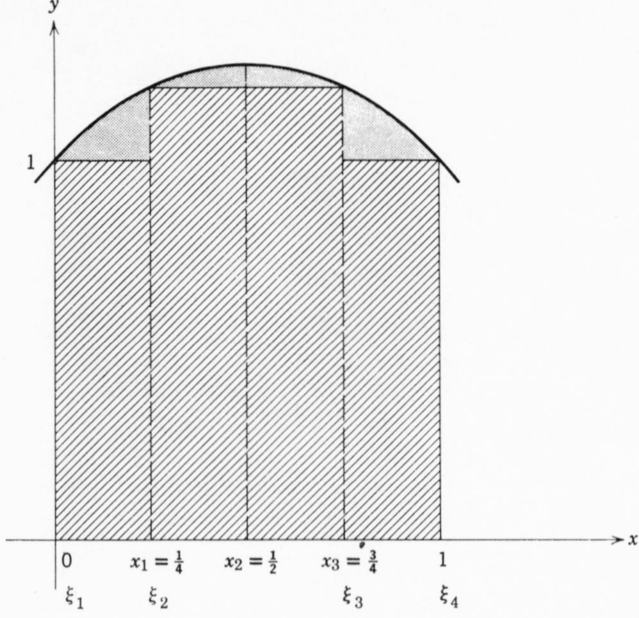

Fig. II.19

We obtain (see Fig. II.19) $\xi_1 = 0, \xi_2 = \frac{1}{4}, \xi_3 = \frac{3}{4}, \xi_4 = 1$, and, consequently,

$$\underline{S}_4 = \frac{1}{4}\left(1 + \frac{19}{16} + \frac{19}{16} + 1\right) = 1.093 \cdots$$

It is obvious from Fig. II.19 that $\underline{S}_4$ is smaller than the area we are interested in. The difference is indicated by the dotted region. Suppose we increase the number of subintervals to $n = 8$ for the purpose of decreasing this difference. Then we obtain (see Fig. II.20)

$$\underline{S}_8 = \frac{1}{8}\left(1 + \frac{71}{64} + \frac{19}{16} + \frac{79}{64} + \frac{79}{64} + \frac{19}{16} + \frac{71}{64} + 1\right) = 1.132 \cdots$$

Clearly,

$$\underline{S}_8 > \underline{S}_4$$

but still

$$\underline{S}_8 < A_{a,b}.$$

Again the difference is indicated by the dotted region in Fig. II.20.

Now let us go a step further and double the number of subintervals again, taking $n = 16$ and, consequently, $\Delta x = \frac{1}{16}$ (see Fig. II.21). We obtain

$$\underline{S}_{16} = \frac{1}{16}\left(1 + \frac{271}{256} + \frac{71}{64} + \frac{295}{256} + \frac{19}{16} + \frac{311}{256} + \frac{79}{64} + \frac{319}{256} + \frac{319}{256} + \frac{79}{64} + \frac{311}{256} + \frac{19}{16} + \frac{295}{256} + \frac{71}{64} + \frac{271}{256} + 1\right) = 1.150\cdots$$

and we can see again that

$$\underline{S}_8 < \underline{S}_{16} < A_{a,b}.$$

(We will see later, on p. 141, that this area $A_{a,b}$ is found to be $\frac{7}{6} = 1.1\dot{6}$).

We can see from Figs. II.19, 20, and 21 that the discrepancy between the sum of the areas of the inscribed rectangles and the yet to be defined area of the region under the curve $y = f(x)$ (error) as indicated by the dotted regions becomes smaller as the number n of subintervals increases. It is intuitively clear that this error can still be made smaller by further increasing the number of subintervals. This is our motivation to define the area under the curve $y = f(x)$ if $f(x)$ has no discontinuities in $a \leq x \leq b$ between $x = a$ and $x = b$ as

(II.34) $$A_{a,b} = \lim_{n\to\infty} \sum_{k=1}^{n} f(\xi_k)\,\Delta x$$

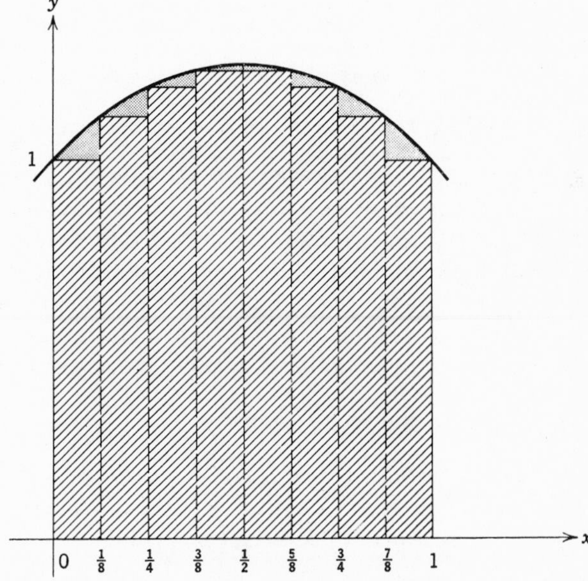

Fig. II.20

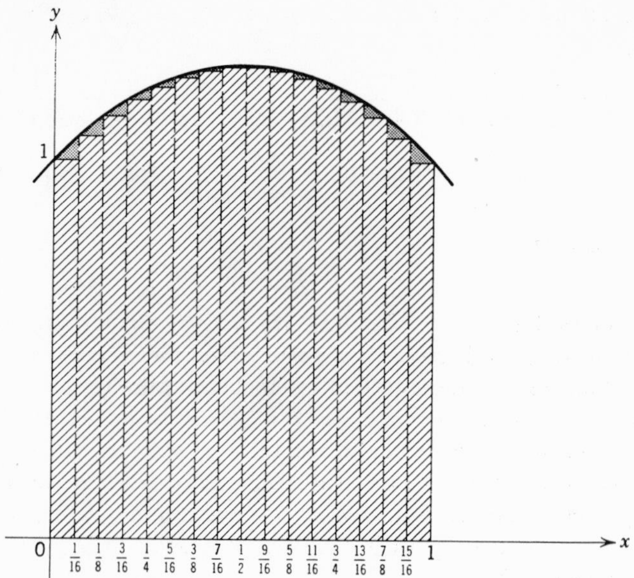

Fig. II.21

where the limit is to be understood in the following sense: The number of subintervals has to increase beyond bound ($n \to \infty$) while at any given stage of the process all subintervals have to have the same length $\dfrac{b-a}{n}$. It is clear that as $n \to \infty$, the length of each subinterval $\dfrac{b-a}{n} \to 0$.

As in Section 5, we have to show now that this definition is senseful. We will proceed for this purpose as in Section 5 where we first considered the sum of the areas of the inscribed triangles and then the sum of the areas of the circumscribed triangles, showing that the difference of the two approaches zero as $n \to \infty$. In order to obtain the sum of the areas of the circumscribed rectangles in our case, we have to locate all points η_k in $x_{k-1} \leq x \leq x_k$ for which the function $f(x)$ assumes its largest value:

$$f(\eta_k) = \max f(x) \text{ in } x_{k-1} \leq x \leq x_k.$$

Clearly, the rectangles with the widths $\Delta x = x_k - x_{k-1}$ and the heights $f(\eta_k)$ are circumscribed rectangles (see Fig. II.22). We denote the sum of the areas of all the circumscribed rectangles by $\bar{S}_n$:

$$\bar{S}_n = f(\eta_1)\,\Delta x + f(\eta_2)\,\Delta x + \cdots + f(\eta_n)\,\Delta x = \Delta x \sum_{k=1}^{n} f(\eta_k).$$

Clearly,

$$\bar{S}_n \geq A_{a,b}$$

for all n.

Now we consider the difference (see Fig. II.23) $\bar{S}_n - \underline{S}_n$ and obtain

$$\begin{aligned}\bar{S}_n - \underline{S}_n &= [f(\eta_1) - f(\xi_1)]\,\Delta x + [f(\eta_2) - f(\xi_2)]\,\Delta x \\ &\quad + \cdots + [f(\eta_n) - f(\xi_n)]\,\Delta x = \Delta x \sum_{k=1}^{n} [f(\eta_k) - f(\xi_k)] \\ &= \frac{b-a}{n} \sum_{k=1}^{n} [f(\eta_k) - f(\xi_k)].\end{aligned}$$

It can be shown that this difference approaches zero, if $f(x)$ is uniformly continuous in $a \leq x \leq b$. (This is the case, if $f(x)$ is continuous in every point of the interval $a \leq x \leq b$.)

From this and the fact that both limits exist, it follows that

$$\lim_{n\to\infty} \underline{S}_n = \lim_{n\to\infty} \bar{S}_n = A_{a,b}.$$

We call this limit, which serves to define the area measure of the region encompassed by $y = 0$, $x = a$, $x = b$, and $y = f(x)$, the *definite integral* of $f(x)$ between the limits a and b:

$$\lim_{n\to\infty} \Delta x \sum_{k=1}^{n} f(\xi_k) = \lim_{n\to\infty} \Delta x \sum_{k=1}^{n} f(\eta_k) = \int_a^b f(x)\,dx.$$

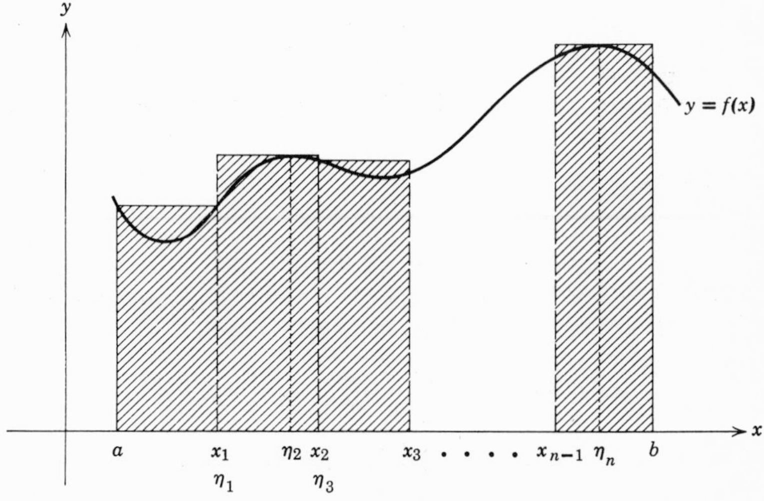

Fig. II.22

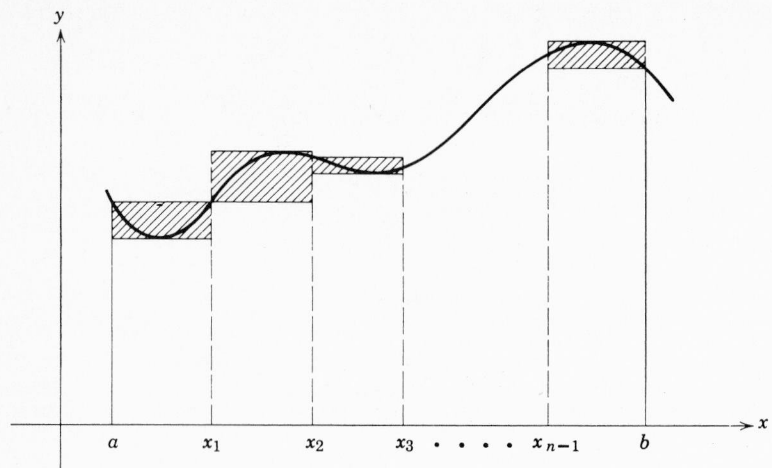

Fig. II.23

▶If $f(x)$ is uniformly continuous* in $a \leq x \leq b$, then there exists for any arbitrary small $\varepsilon > 0$ a δ_ε so that

$$|f(\eta_k) - f(\xi_k)| < \varepsilon$$

provided that

$$|\eta_k - \xi_k| < \delta_\varepsilon$$

(see Chapter I, Section 13).

Now let us choose an arbitrary small $\varepsilon > 0$. Then δ_ε is determined by this ε [and the function $f(x)$] and we take n sufficiently large so that

$$\Delta x = \frac{b - a}{n} < \delta_\varepsilon. \tag{II.35}$$

Since η_k and ξ_k are both located in the same subinterval of length Δx, we have

$$|\eta_k - \xi_k| \leq \Delta x$$

and because of (II.35)

$$|\eta_k - \xi_k| < \delta_\varepsilon.$$

Hence,

$$f(\eta_k) - f(\xi_k) < \varepsilon$$

[we can omit the absolute value signs because from the definition of $f(\eta_k)$ and $f(\xi_k)$ follows that $f(\eta_k) \geq f(\xi_k)$] and we obtain

$$0 \leq \bar{S}_n - \underline{S}_n = \frac{b - a}{n} \sum_{k=1}^{n} [f(\eta_k) - f(\xi_k)]$$

$$< \frac{b - a}{n} \sum_{k=1}^{n} \varepsilon = \frac{b - a}{n} n\varepsilon = (b - a)\varepsilon$$

* See Chapter I, Section 13.

where ε can be chosen as small as we please, provided we choose n sufficiently large. $\left(\text{Clearly, } \sum_{k=1}^{n} \varepsilon = \varepsilon \sum_{k=1}^{n} 1 = \varepsilon n. \text{ See Problem II.23}\right)$.

This means that we can make the difference $\bar{S}_n - \underline{S}_n$ as small as we please if we choose n large enough, and this is obviously equivalent with the statement

$$\lim_{n\to\infty} (\bar{S}_n - \underline{S}_n) = 0. \tag{II.36}$$

Since

$$\underline{S}_n \leq A_{a,b} \leq \bar{S}_n$$

we obtain

$$0 \leq A_{a,b} - \underline{S}_n \leq \bar{S}_n - \underline{S}_n$$

and as $n \to \infty$, in view of (II.36)

$$\lim_{n\to\infty} (A_{a,b} - \underline{S}_n) = \lim_{n\to\infty} (\bar{S}_n - \underline{S}_n) = 0.$$

It is quite obvious that $\underline{S}_n$ is an increasing sequence, i.e., $\underline{S}_n$ becomes larger if we add additional division points (increase n). Furthermore, it seems intuitively clear that $\underline{S}_n$ is always less than or at most equal to any one of the $\bar{S}_n$—no matter how large n is. Therefore, we conclude again—as we did already in Section 5—that $\lim_{n\to\infty} \underline{S}_n$ exists. Now, $\lim_{n\to\infty} A_{a,b}$ exists, of course, because $A_{a,b}$ is a constant number. Hence, by our rule according to which the limit of a difference of two sequences is equal to the difference of the limits of the two sequences, provided that both limits exist (see Section 4), we obtain

$$\lim_{n\to\infty} (A_{a,b} - \underline{S}_n) = \lim_{n\to\infty} A_{a,b} - \lim_{n\to\infty} \underline{S}_n = A_{a,b} - \lim_{n\to\infty} \underline{S}_n$$

and since

$$\lim_{n\to\infty} (A_{a,b} - \underline{S}_n) = 0,$$

we have

$$A_{a,b} = \lim_{n\to\infty} \underline{S}_n.$$

◀

Problems II.48–II.53

II.48. $f(x) = x(1 - x) + 1$, $a = 0$, $b = 1$. Find $\bar{S}_n$ for $n = 4$, 8, and 16. Find $\bar{S}_n - \underline{S}_n$ for $n = 4$, 8, and 16, using the values for $\underline{S}_n$ which were found in the text.

II.49. $\dfrac{\bar{S}_n + \underline{S}_n}{2}$ is a better approximation to the area than either $\bar{S}_n$ or $\underline{S}_n$. Evaluate this average for $n = 4$, 8, and 16 for the function in Problem II.48.

II.50. Find $\underline{S}_n$ and $\bar{S}_n$ for $n = 4$, 8, 16 for the function $f(x) = 1/x$, $a = 1$, $b = 2$. ($A_{a,b} = 0.69315 \cdots$)

II.51. Same as in Problem II.49 for the function in Problem II.50.

II.52. Same as in Problem II.48 for the function $f(x) = \sqrt{1 - x^2}$, $a = 0$, $b = 1$. The area bounded by this curve, the x-axis, and the lines $x = 0$ and $x = 1$ is a quadrant of a unit circle. Multiply your results for $\bar{S}_n$ and $\underline{S}_n$ by 4 and compare them with the results which we obtained for π in Section 5 where we used regular polygons to approximate the area of a circle.

II.53. Take again $f(x) = \sqrt{1 - x^2}$, $a = 0$, $b = 1$. Instead of dividing the interval into equal subintervals, use the following division points:

$$x_1 = \frac{1}{8}, x_2 = \frac{1}{4}, x_3 = \frac{3}{8}, x_4 = \frac{1}{2}, x_5 = \frac{5}{8}, x_6 = \frac{11}{16}, x_7 = \frac{3}{4},$$

$$x_8 = \frac{13}{16}, x_9 = \frac{7}{8}, x_{10} = \frac{29}{32}, x_{11} = \frac{15}{16}, x_{12} = \frac{31}{32}.$$

Compare your results with the results of Problem II.52 as well as with the results for π of Section 5.

9. THE DEFINITE INTEGRAL

In the preceding section, we defined the area under a curve $y = f(x)$ between $x = a$ and $x = b$ and bounded below by the x-axis to be the limit of a sum $\underline{S}_n$ (and, in view of (II.36), the limit of $\bar{S}_n$ as well).

Since $\underline{S}_n$ is the sum of inscribed rectangles and thus its value always below the value which is to be assigned to the region under consideration, we call it a *lower sum*. $\bar{S}_n$, for analogous reasons, is called an *upper sum*. The definition of area which we gave in the preceding section (and the subsequent proof we presented to establish the existence of the limit of $\underline{S}_n$) only applies to a very special case, namely, to the case where $f(x)$ is uniformly continuous in $a \leq x \leq b$ and $f(x) \geq 0$ in the entire interval.

Let us postpone a discussion of the possibility of $f(x)$ being negative in at least some portions of the interval for later and focus our attention on the assumption of uniform continuity. It is quite obvious that we can assign an area measure to a region which is bounded above by the step function

$$y = [x]$$

and on the sides by $x = 1$, $x = 5$ and below by the x-axis as depicted in Fig. II.24 (see also Chapter I, Section 12, Fig. I.40). Even though this function is certainly not uniformly continuous in $1 \leq x \leq 5$ (there are three jumps each of saltus 1 in the interval), it follows quite easily, since the shaded area in Fig. II.24 consists of four rectangles, that the area measure to be assigned to this region is 10.

In order to cover this case—and even others— by a general definition, we proceed as outlined in the following. First of all, we consider the function $y = f(x)$ of which we do not know anything except that it is uniquely

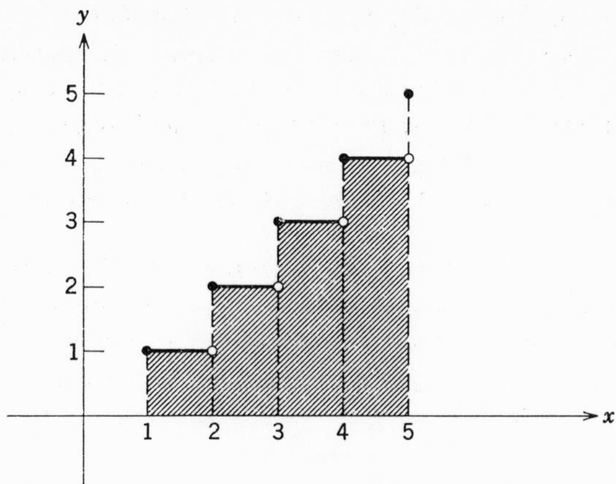

Fig. II.24

defined on the interval $a \leq x \leq b$, i.e., with every x in the interval there corresponds one value y. Then we subdivide the interval $a \leq x \leq b$ into n equal or unequal subintervals and compute the corresponding upper and lower sums. (A function may not always have a largest and a smallest value in each subinterval. In that case, we take, instead of the largest value, the smallest number which is larger than or equal to the values of the function in the subinterval, and instead of the smallest value of the function, we take the largest number which is smaller or equal to the values of the function in the subinterval.)

We do this for all possible subdivisions and then let $n \to \infty$ with the understanding that the length of each subinterval approaches zero in this process. If upper and lower sums for all possible subdivisions tend to the same limit, then we call this common limit the *definite integral* of $f(x)$ between the limits $x = a$ and $x = b$ and write

$$\lim_{n\to\infty} \sum_{k=1}^{n} f(\xi_k)\, \Delta x_k = \int_a^b f(x)\, dx \tag{II.37}$$

where $\Delta x_k = x_k - x_{k-1}$. We call a the *lower integration limit* and b the *upper integration limit*. The integral sign is really a degenerated (or hybrid, depending on the point of view) S which signifies that a summation process is involved in obtaining the integral, even though not an ordinary summation process.

The function $f(x)$ under the integral sign is called the *integrand* and dx plays essentially the role of a taillight. In the case that $f(x) \geq 0$, the integral in (II.37) defines the area under the curve $y = f(x)$ between $x = a$, $x = b$

and above $y = 0$. Specifically, we can show that if $f(x)$ is uniformly continuous in $a \leq x \leq b$, then the definite integral as defined in (II.37) exists and its value is to be found as the limit of a lower sum using a subdivision of equal subintervals, because the limits of all such sums are equal in case of the existence of the integral. Thus, the definition we gave in the preceding section appears as a special case of the definition (II.37) of this section.

▶We wish to point out that the definition (II.37) is not only general enough to cover cases where the function $f(x)$ has finitely many discontinuities in the interval of integration but also certain cases where the function has infinitely many discontinuities. We will give here two examples, in one of which the integral exists, and in the other of which it does not exist.

Let us consider the function

$$f(x) = \begin{cases} 1 \text{ for } \dfrac{1}{2} \leq x \leq 1 \\ 0 \text{ for } \dfrac{1}{3} \leq x < \dfrac{1}{2} \\ 1 \text{ for } \dfrac{1}{4} \leq x < \dfrac{1}{3} \\ 0 \text{ for } \dfrac{1}{5} \leq x < \dfrac{1}{4} \\ 1 \text{ for } \dfrac{1}{6} \leq x < \dfrac{1}{5} \\ \cdot \\ \cdot \\ \cdot \end{cases}$$

The reader can easily see how the definition of this function is to be continued (see Fig. II.25).

We can see that this function has infinitely many jumps of saltus 1 in the interval $0 \leq x \leq 1$. Still, it can be shown that the integral as defined in (II.37) exists and has the value

$$\int_0^1 f(x)\, dx = 0.69315 \cdots.$$

However, if we consider the function

$$f(x) = \begin{cases} 1 \text{ for } x \text{ irrational} \\ 0 \text{ for } x \text{ rational} \end{cases}$$

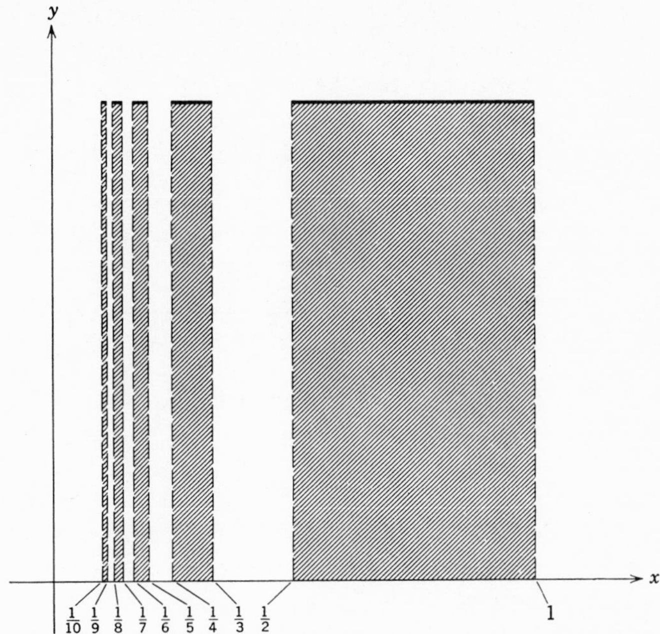

Fig. II.25

then we see easily that the integral from 0 to 1 (or over any other interval for that matter) does not exist. Since

$$\min f(x) = 0$$

in any subinterval (because any subinterval, no matter how small, contains rational points), and

$$\max f(x) = 1$$

in any subinterval (because any interval contains irrational points), we have

$$\underline{S}_n = 0 \text{ for all } n$$

and

$$\bar{S}_n = 1 \text{ for all } n.$$

Thus, $\lim \underline{S}_n \neq \lim \bar{S}_n$, i.e., not all limits of upper and lower sums are equal and, consequently, the integral does not exist, since one of the basic conditions is not met. ◀

Now we turn to the question of what happens if $f(x)$ is negative in the entire integration interval or in parts thereof.

Let us refer to Fig. II.26. We wish to find the area which is enclosed by $y = f(x)$, $x = a$, $x = b$ and the x-axis. The function $y = f(x)$ in Fig. II.26

intersects the x-axis in two points, namely, at $x = c$ and at $x = d$. In the interval $c \leq x \leq d$ we have $f(x) \leq 0$. Clearly, we obtain the area under the curve $y = f(x)$ between a and c and d and b by integration as follows

$$A_{a,c} = \int_a^c f(x)\,dx, \qquad A_{d,b} = \int_d^b f(x)\,dx.$$

What happens between c and d? Clearly, the values of $f(x)$ in this interval are negative. Hence, in order to obtain the heights of the rectangles in upper and lower sum, we have to take the absolute values of $f(x)$. Specifically, we take

$$\min |f(x)| = |f(\xi_k)| \text{ in } x_{k-1} \leq x \leq x_k$$

and

$$\max |f(x)| = |f(\eta_k)| \text{ in } x_{k-1} \leq x \leq x_k$$

and obtain

$$A_{c,d} = \lim_{n\to\infty} \sum_{k=1}^{n} |f(\xi_k)|\,\Delta x = \int_c^d |f(x)|\,dx,$$

i.e., instead of integration the function $f(x)$ in the interval in which the function $f(x)$ is negative, we integrate the absolute value of the function.

Thus we obtain in case

$f(x) \geq 0$ in $a \leq x \leq c$, $f(x) \leq 0$ in $c \leq x \leq d$ and $f(x) \geq 0$ in $d \leq x \leq b$

the following formula for the area

$$A_{a,b} = \int_a^c f(x)\,dx + \int_c^d |f(x)|\,dx + \int_d^b f(x)\,dx.$$

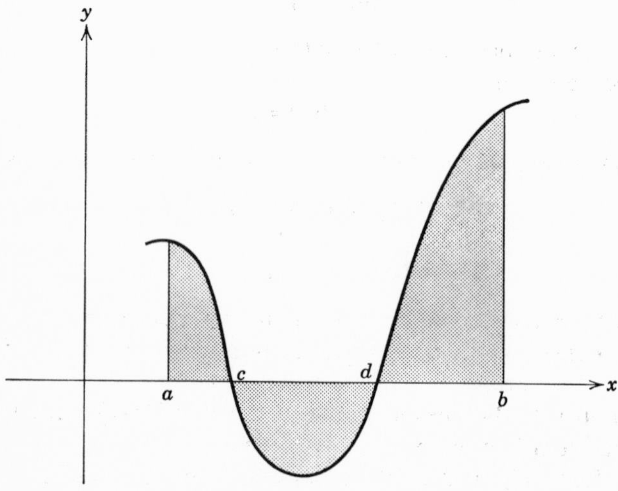

Fig. II.26

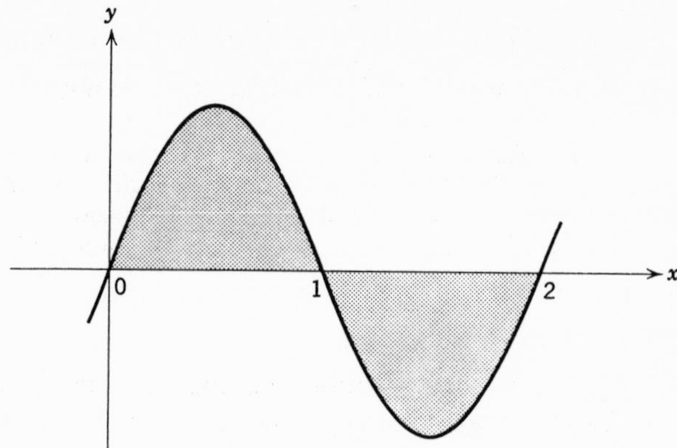

Fig. II.27

Suppose we have the function

$$y = x(x - 1)(x - 2)$$

(see Fig. II.27) and we wish to find the area which is enclosed by this curve and the x-axis. Clearly, we have to take

$$\begin{aligned} A_{0,2} &= \int_0^1 x(x-1)(x-2)\,dx + \int_1^2 |x(x-1)(x-2)|\,dx \\ &= \int_0^1 x(x-1)(x-2)\,dx - \int_1^2 x(x-1)(x-2)\,dx. \end{aligned}$$

The reader can easily generalize this idea to the case where $f(x)$ has any finite number of sign changes in the integration interval.

Problems II.54–II.59

II.54. Show that

$$\int_0^2 x(x-1)(x-2)\,dx = 0.$$

II.55. Show by geometric inspection that

$$\int_a^b f(x)\,dx = \int_a^c f(x)\,dx + \int_c^b f(x)\,dx$$

where $f(x) \geq 0$ in $a \leq x \leq b$ and c is some number between a and b.

II.56. Show that the formula in Problem II.55 is also true if $a \leq b \leq c$ and $f(x) \geq 0$ in $a \leq x \leq c$.

II.57. Show that the formula in Problem II.55 is true regardless of the sign of $f(x)$.

II.58. Show that $\int_a^b Cf(x)\,dx = C\int_a^b f(x)\,dx$ where C is a constant. Assume that $f(x)$ is such that the definition of the integral in (II.34) applies, and use this definition to prove the above formula.

II.59. Consider the function $y = f(x)$ which is represented in Fig. I.48 (Chapter I, Section 13). Find the area of the region which is bounded above by $y = f(x)$, below by $y = -1$ and on the sides by $x = 1/2n$ and $x = 1$. This area A_n depends on n. Does $\lim_{n\to\infty} A_n$ exist? If so, what is this limit and what does it represent?

10. THE TRAPEZOIDAL RULE

We have seen in the preceding sections that the area under a curve can be approximated by lower sums or upper sums, depending on whether we want an approximation from below or above. The error at each subinterval is indicated in Fig. II.28 by the shaded area in case we take the lower sum, and by the dotted area in case we use the upper sum, as an approximation. Even though this error becomes small and ultimately vanishes as $\Delta x = x_{k+1} - x_k \to 0$ for all k, in case the function is well behaved in the interval in which the area is sought, there is no reason why we shouldn't look for a better approximation, i.e., an approximation that yields for the same subdivision a smaller error than either the upper or the lower sum.

Let us consider Fig. II.29. If we join the beginning point P_1 of the curve in the interval $x_k \leq x \leq x_{k+1}$ with its endpoint P_2 by a straight line and approximate the area under the curve by the shaded trapezoid, then we can expect to obtain in general a more accurate result than the one obtainable from an approximation by an upper or a lower sum. Of course, there are cases where upper or lower sums do yield better results for a given subdivision than the trapezoidal approximation would yield. We depict two such cases in Fig. II.30.

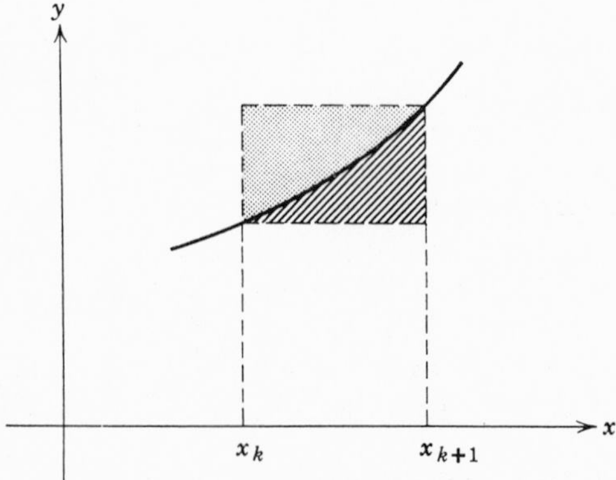

Fig. II.28

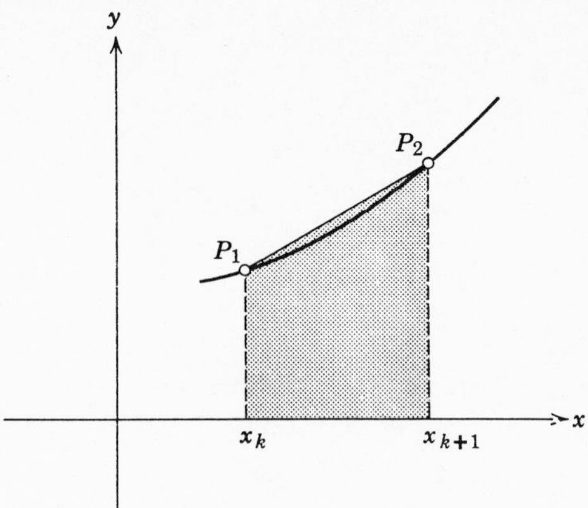

Fig. II.29

In Fig. II.30(a) the shaded area represents the error that is committed if the trapezoidal approximation is used, and the dotted area represents the error resulting from an approximation by the lower sum (inscribed rectangle). In Fig. II.30(b) the dotted area represents the error due to an upper sum approximation and the shaded area again indicates the error produced by a trapezoidal approximation. It is obvious that, in both cases, the dotted area is smaller than the shaded area, i.e., the error due to the trapezoidal approximation is larger than the error committed by the lower and upper sum approximations, respectively. However, the introduction of additional division points will, in general, reverse this situation.

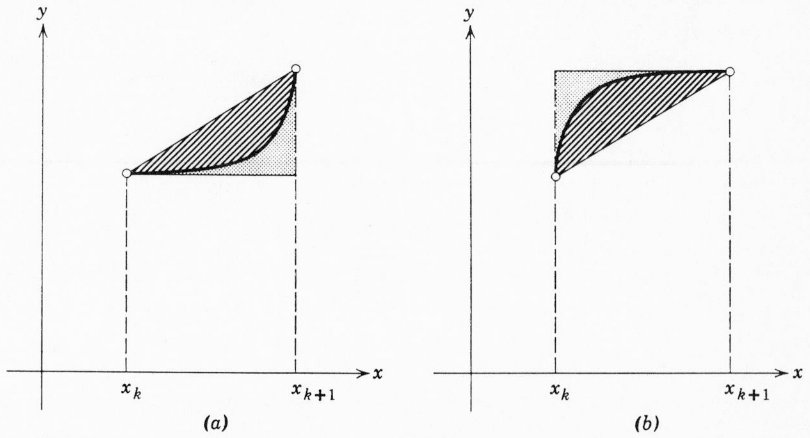

Fig. II.30

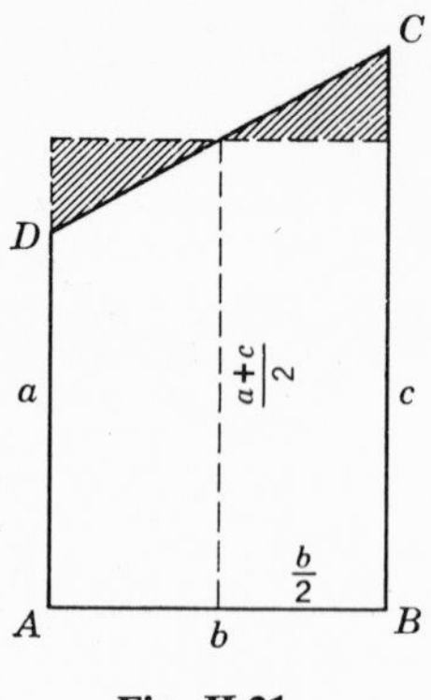

Fig. II.31

Let us now derive a general formula for the approximation of an area under a curve by a sum of areas of trapezoids.

First, we note that the area of the trapezoid $ABCD$ in Fig. II.31 is given by

(II.38) $$\text{Area of trapezoid} = b\,\frac{a + c}{2}$$

(see Problem II.12). This formula is quite obvious if we notice that the shaded triangles in Fig. II.31 are congruent.

Now we consider a function $y = f(x)$ of which we assume that it has no discontinuities in $a \leq x \leq b$ (see Fig. II.32). We divide the interval $a \leq x \leq b$ into n equal subintervals of length

$$\Delta x = \frac{b - a}{n}$$

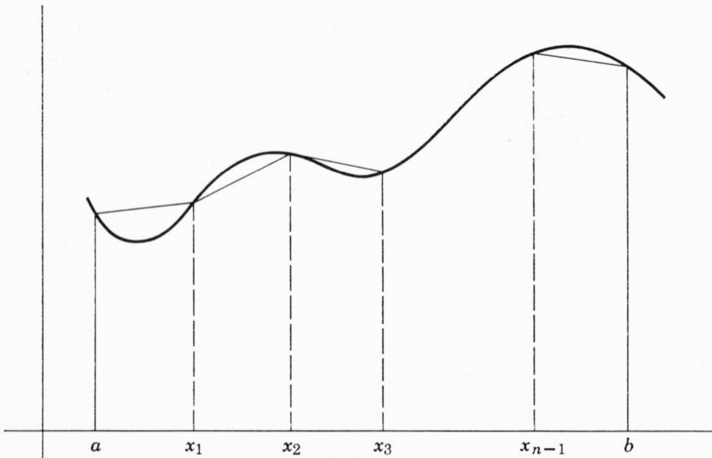

Fig. II.32

and call the division points $x_1, x_2, x_3, \cdots, x_{n-1}$, putting $x_0 = a, x_n = b$. Clearly,

$$x_k = a + k\frac{b-a}{n} \qquad \text{for } k = 0, 1, 2, \cdots, n.$$

At each one of these division points we erect the ordinate

$$y_k = f(x_k),$$

join each pair of adjacent points $(x_k, y_k), (x_{k+1}, y_{k+1})$ for all $k = 0, 1, 2, \cdots n - 1$, by a straight line and compute the area of every one of the trapezoids thus obtained (see Fig. II.33). Clearly, we obtain for the area A_k of the $(k + 1)$th trapezoid according to (II.38)

$$A_k = \Delta x \frac{y_{k+1} + y_k}{2}$$

for all $k = 0, 1, 2, \cdots, n - 1$, where we agree that $f(a) = f(x_0) = y_0$ and $f(b) = f(x_n) = y_n$.

Now we sum all these areas and obtain

$$\Delta x\left(\frac{y_1 + y_0}{2} + \frac{y_2 + y_1}{2} + \cdots + \frac{y_n + y_{n-1}}{2}\right)$$
$$= \Delta x\left(\frac{y_0}{2} + y_1 + y_2 + \cdots + y_{n-1} + \frac{y_n}{2}\right).$$

Since $\Delta x = \dfrac{b-a}{n}$, we obtain the following approximation for the area

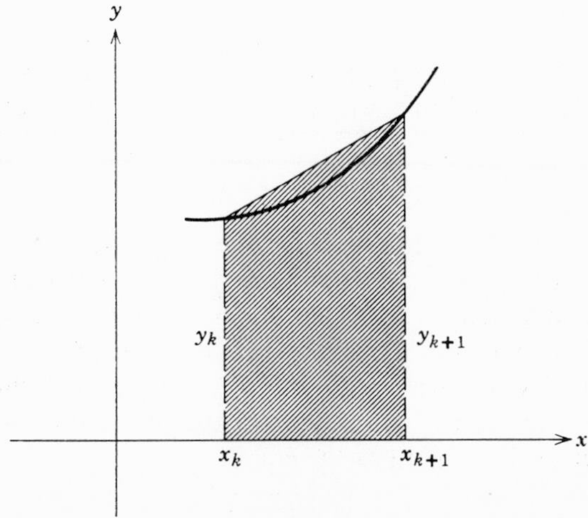

Fig. II.33

under the curve $y = f(x)$ between $x = a$ and $x = b$:

$$\text{(II.39)}\quad \int_a^b f(x)\,dx \cong \frac{b-a}{2n}(y_0 + 2y_1 + 2y_2 + \cdots + 2y_{n-1} + y_n).$$

This formula is called the *trapezoidal rule* for quite obvious reasons.

In Section 8 we approximated the area under the curve

$$y = x(1 - x) + 1$$

between $x = 0$ and $x = 1$ by a lower sum with 16 subintervals and obtained $\underline{S}_{16} = 1.150\cdots$. Let us now use the trapezoidal rule with the same number of subintervals for the same problem.

We have

$$x_0 = 0,\ x_1 = \frac{1}{16},\ x_2 = \frac{1}{8},\ x_3 = \frac{3}{16},\ x_4 = \frac{1}{4},\ x_5 = \frac{5}{16},$$

$$x_6 = \frac{3}{8},\ x_7 = \frac{7}{16},\ x_8 = \frac{1}{2},\ x_9 = \frac{9}{16},\ x_{10} = \frac{5}{8},\ x_{11} = \frac{11}{16},$$

$$x_{12} = \frac{3}{4},\ x_{13} = \frac{13}{16},\ x_{14} = \frac{7}{8},\ x_{15} = \frac{15}{16},\ x_{16} = 1$$

and, accordingly,

$$y_0 = 1,\ y_1 = \frac{271}{256},\ y_2 = \frac{284}{256},\ y_3 = \frac{295}{256},\ y_4 = \frac{304}{256},\ y_5 = \frac{311}{256},$$

$$y_6 = \frac{316}{256},\ y_7 = \frac{319}{256},\ y_8 = \frac{320}{256},\ y_k = y_{16-k} \text{ for } k = 0, 1, 2, \cdots 16.$$

Hence, we obtain

$$\int_0^1 [x(1-x)+1]\,dx$$

$$\cong \frac{1}{32}\left[1 + 2\left(\frac{\begin{matrix}271 + 284 + 295 + 304 + 311 + 316 + 319 + 320\\ + 319 + 316 + 311 + 304 + 295 + 284 + 271\end{matrix}}{256}\right) + 1\right]$$

$$= 1.16601.$$

We will see in Section 13, Problem II.81, that the true value of this integral is found to be $1.1\dot{6}$. Thus we see that the approximation 1.16601 which we just obtained is considerably better than the approximation $1.150\cdots$ as obtained from the lower sum in Section 8.

Let us now find as another application of the trapezoidal rule an approximation to the value of π, i.e., the area of the unit circle. The unit circle with the center in the origin has the equation

$$y = \sqrt{1 - x^2}.$$

We consider one quadrant of this circle above the x-axis between $x = 0$ and $x = 1$ and choose $n = 32$.

We have

$$x_k = k\tfrac{1}{32},\ k = 0, 1, 2, \cdots 32$$

and obtain accordingly the following values for y_k.

$y_0 = 1$	$2y_9 = 1.91927$	$2y_{17} = 1.69443$	$2y_{25} = 1.24844$
$2y_1 = 1.99902$	$2y_{10} = 1.89984$	$2y_{18} = 1.65359$	$2y_{26} = 1.16592$
$2y_2 = 1.99609$	$2y_{11} = 1.87812$	$2y_{19} = 1.60930$	$2y_{27} = 1.07347$
$2y_3 = 1.99119$	$2y_{12} = 1.85405$	$2y_{20} = 1.56125$	$2y_{28} = 0.96825$
$2y_4 = 1.98431$	$2y_{13} = 1.82752$	$2y_{21} = 1.50908$	$2y_{29} = 0.84779$
$2y_5 = 1.97543$	$2y_{14} = 1.79844$	$2y_{22} = 1.49217$	$2y_{30} = 0.69597$
$2y_6 = 1.96453$	$2y_{15} = 1.76666$	$2y_{23} = 1.39054$	$2y_{31} = 0.35903$
$2y_7 = 1.95156$	$2y_{16} = 1.73205$	$2y_{24} = 1.32288$	$y_{32} = 0.$
$2y_8 = 1.94849$			

Hence, we obtain with (II.39)

$$\frac{\pi}{4} = \int_0^1 \sqrt{1 - x^2}\, dx \cong \frac{1}{64}\, 50.06768 = 0.78231$$

and, therefore,

$$\pi \cong 3.12924.$$

This result deviates from the true value of $\pi = 3.1415 \cdots$ by $0.0123 \cdots$ which is not as accurate as we might have expected it to be. The reason is that the trapezoidal approximations to the circle do not yield very good results in the neighborhood of the point (1, 0).

Problems II.60–II.64

II.60. Find an approximation to $\int_0^1 x^{10}\, dx$ by using the trapezoidal rule with $n = 4$ and compare it to the result that is obtained from an approximation by the lower sum $\underline{S}_4$. (True value of the integral is $\frac{1}{11}$.)

II.61. A function $f(x)$ is said to be monotonically increasing if, for any pair of values $x_1 < x_2$, the relation $f(x_1) \leq f(x_2)$ holds. Show that the trapezoidal rule applied to a monotonically increasing function is obtained by taking the arithmetic mean of lower sum and upper sum. (*Hint:* Note that, if $f(x)$ is monotonically increasing, then $\max f(x) = y_{k+1}$ in $x_k \leq x \leq x_{k+1}$, $\min f(x) = y_k$ in $x_k \leq x \leq x_{k+1}$.)

II.62. Find an approximation to $\int_0^1 x^2\, dx$ by using the trapezoidal rule. Start with $n = 2$ and continue doubling the number of subintervals until no more changes of the result in the third decimal place can be expected.

II.63. Prove that the trapezoidal rule yields the exact result if applied to the integration of all linear functions, i.e., functions of the type $y = ax + b$.

II.64. Use the trapezoidal rule to find an approximation to $\pi = 4\int_0^1 \sqrt{1 - x^2}\,dx$ taking 16 subintervals between 0 and $\frac{1}{2}$ and 32 subintervals between $\frac{1}{2}$ and 1. Compare your result with the one obtained in this section and the one obtained in Section 5.

11. INTEGRATION BY A LIMIT OF A SUM PROCESS

We will devote this section to the discussion of two very simple examples, in which we will compute the area of a rectangle and a triangle by an integration process, i.e., by the evaluation of the appropriate limits of lower sums, and thus demonstrate how the formulas for the area of these basic geometric configurations now appear as special cases of our general definition of area as given in (II.34) (Section 8). (It would be awkward, indeed, if this were not so. After all, the general definition of area as given in Section 8 was based on the formula for the area of a rectangle, and the formula for the area of a triangle, in turn, was developed from the formula for the area of a rectangle—see Section 2.)

First, let us consider a rectangle with the dimensions a and b. We choose our coordinate system so that the rectangle takes the position as indicated in Fig. II.34. We can interpret this problem as the problem of finding the area of a region which is bounded above by $y = b$ (the line parallel to the x-axis at distance b from the x-axis) between $x = 0$, $x = a$ and above the x-axis.

If we subdivide the interval $0 \leq x \leq a$ into n subintervals of length $\Delta x = \dfrac{a}{n}$, we obtain in every one of these subintervals

$$\min f(x) = f(\xi_k) = b$$

and

$$\max f(x) = f(\eta_k) = b,$$

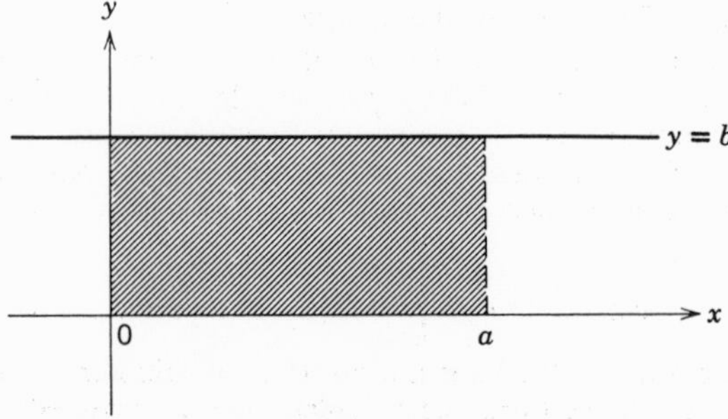

Fig. II.34

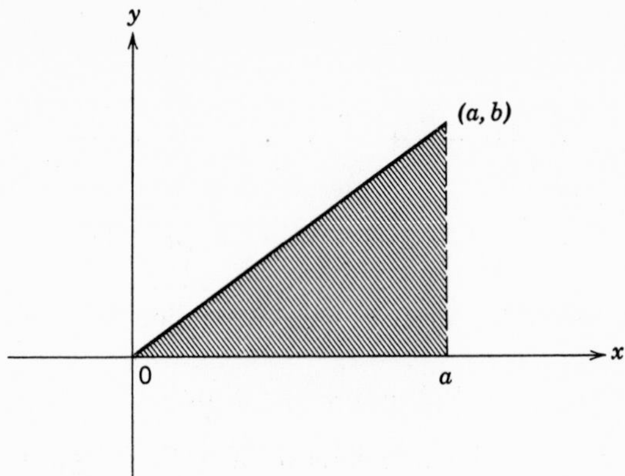

Fig. II.35

i.e., $f(\xi_k) = f(\eta_k) = b$ and, consequently,

$$\underline{S}_n = \bar{S}_n = \sum_{k=1}^{n} b\,\Delta x = \frac{ba}{n}\sum_{k=1}^{n} 1 = ab.$$

Therefore,

$$\int_0^a b\,dx = \lim_{n\to\infty} \underline{S}_n = \lim_{n\to\infty} \bar{S}_n = \lim_{n\to\infty} ab = ab, \tag{II.40}$$

as was to be expected.

Next, we consider a right triangle where the two sides forming the right angle have the dimensions a and b. We choose our coordinate system in such a way that the triangle will take the position as indicated in Fig. II.35. The line through (0, 0) and (a, b), forming the hypothenuse of the triangle, has the equation

$$y = \frac{b}{a}\,x.$$

Thus we face the problem of finding the area under the curve $y = \frac{b}{a}x$ between $x = 0$, $x = a$ and above the x-axis. A subdivision of the interval $0 \le x \le a$ into n equal subintervals will yield an undersum (lower sum), as indicated for $n = 6$ in Fig. II.36. In general, we have clearly

$$\xi_1 = 0, \quad \xi_2 = \frac{a}{n}, \quad \xi_3 = \frac{2a}{n}, \cdots, \xi_n = \frac{n-1}{n}\,a$$

and, consequently,

$$f(\xi_1) = 0, \quad f(\xi_2) = \frac{b}{n}, \quad f(\xi_3) = \frac{2b}{n}, \cdots, f(\xi_n) = \frac{(n-1)b}{n}.$$

Thus with $\Delta x = \frac{a}{n}$, we have

$$\underline{S}_n = \frac{a}{n}\left[0 + \frac{b}{n} + \frac{2b}{n} + \frac{3b}{n} + \cdots + \frac{(n-1)b}{n}\right]$$

$$= \frac{ab}{n^2}[1 + 2 + 3 + \cdots + (n-1)].$$

In order to discover the limit of this expression as $n \to \infty$, we have to evaluate the sum

$$1 + 2 + 3 + \cdots + (n-1)$$

for any n and represent this sum in terms of n. For this purpose, we rewrite the sum in the more elaborate form

$$1 + 2 + 3 + 4 + \cdots + (n-4) + (n-3) + (n-2) + (n-1).$$

If we add the first and the last term, we obtain n. If we add the second and the next to the last term, we obtain n. If we add the third term and the term preceding the next to the last, we obtain n again, etc. . . .

Now, if n is odd, we obtain exactly $\frac{n-1}{2}$ such sums, i.e, the sum of this series is given by

$$1 + 2 + 3 + \cdots + (n-1) = \frac{n(n-1)}{2}.$$

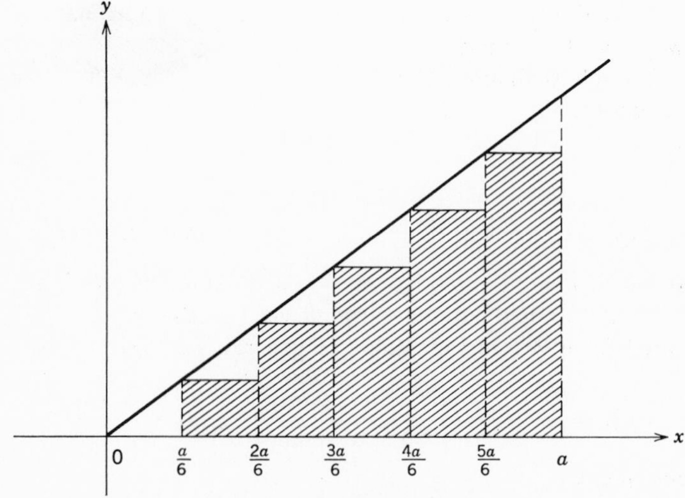

Fig. II.36

Suppose n is even. Then we obtain $\frac{n-2}{2}$ such sums and the term $\frac{n}{2}$ in the middle is left out. Thus we obtain altogether

$$1 + 2 + 3 + \cdots + (n-1) = \frac{n-2}{2}n + \frac{n}{2} = \frac{n(n-1)}{2},$$

which is the same formula as the one obtained above for odd n. Thus we can state that

$$1 + 2 + 3 + \cdots + (n-1) = \frac{n(n-1)}{2}$$

for any integer n.

Hence, we obtain

$$\underset{=}{S}_n = \frac{ab}{n^2}\frac{n(n-1)}{2} = \frac{ab}{2}\frac{n^2-n}{n^2} = \frac{ab}{2}\left(1 - \frac{1}{n}\right)$$

and we see easily that

$$\text{(II.41)} \quad \int_0^a \frac{b}{a} x\,dx = \lim_{n\to\infty} \underset{=}{S}_n = \lim_{n\to\infty} \frac{ab}{2}\left(1 - \frac{1}{n}\right) = \frac{ab}{2}\lim_{n\to\infty}\left(1 - \frac{1}{n}\right) = \frac{ab}{2}$$

as we expected to obtain.

Next we consider the general case where the triangle is not necessarily a right triangle. We choose our coordinate system so that the origin coincides with the vertex A at which the triangle has an obtuse angle, if it has an obtuse angle at all (note that a triangle has at most one obtuse angle). If there is no obtuse angle, then we let the origin coincide with just any vertex.

Further, we choose the x-axis so that it coincides with the height of the triangle through A (see Fig. II.37). With the notation introduced in Fig. II.37, we have $p + q = a$. The equation of the line through AC is given by

$$y = \frac{p}{h}x$$

where $h = \sqrt{b^2 - p^2}$ by the theorem of Pythagoras and the equation of the line through AB is given by

$$y = -\frac{q}{h}x.$$

Therefore, the area of the triangle (ABC) is given by

$$\int_0^h \frac{p}{h}x\,dx + \int_0^h \left|-\frac{q}{h}x\right| dx.$$

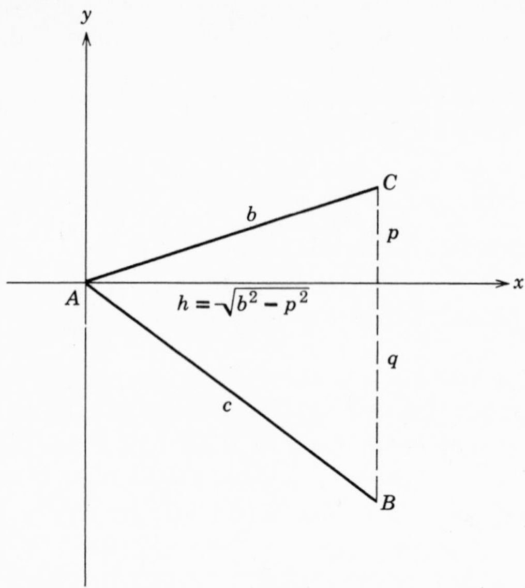

Fig. II.37

In view of (II.41), where we now write h instead of a and p instead of b in case of the first integral, and h instead of a and q instead of b in case of the second integral, the area of the triangle (ABC) is given by

$$\frac{hp}{2} + \frac{hq}{2} = \frac{h(p+q)}{2} = \frac{ha}{2}.$$

Since a is the base of our triangle, we thus obtain the well known formula

$$\text{Area of triangle} = \frac{1}{2}\,\text{base} \times \text{height}.$$

Problems II.65–II.69

11.65. Evaluate the following sums:

(a) $\sum_{k=1}^{12} k$ (b) $\sum_{k=2}^{10} k$

(c) $\sum_{k=1}^{10000} k$ (d) $\sum_{k=1}^{100} \left(k + \frac{k}{2}\right)$

II.66. Find the area of a right triangle with sides 3, 4, 5 by a limit of a sum process.

II.67. Find the area of a triangle with sides 3, 5, 7 by a limit of a sum process.

II.68. Find the area of a region bounded by $y = [x]$, the x-axis, $x = 0$ and $x = 10$ by a limit of a sum process.

II.69. Consider $f(x) = x^2$ in the interval $0 \leq x \leq 1$. Find $\underline{S}_n$ for the area under $y = x^2$, between $x = 0, x = 1$ and above the x-axis. Use equal subintervals and evaluate the lower sum for $n = 4, 8, 32$. Make a conjecture about the limit.

12. FINITE SUMS

In the preceding section we found that

$$\sum_{k=1}^{n-1} k = 1 + 2 + 3 + \cdots + (n-1) = \frac{n(n-1)}{2}$$

by a method which *C. F. Gauss* (1777–1855) purportedly invented in grade school when his incompetent teacher required the class to add up all the numbers from 1 to 100 in the hope that this would keep the class busy for a while. It is almost needless to say that Gauss had the last laugh.

In the following section we will need a formula for the sum

$$\sum_{k=1}^{n-1} k^2 = 1 + 4 + 9 + \cdots + (n-1)^2.$$

In order to evaluate this sum, we consider the following two sums, which appear to pose a more complicated problem (and do, as a matter of fact, if we were out to evaluate them), namely,

$$\sum_{k=1}^{n-1} k^3 = 1 + 8 + 27 + \cdots + (n-1)^3$$

and

$$\sum_{k=1}^{n-1} (k-1)^3 = 0 + 1 + 8 + 27 + \cdots + (n-2)^3.$$

Clearly,

$$\sum_{k=1}^{n-1} k^3 - \sum_{k=1}^{n-1} (k-1)^3 = (n-1)^3. \tag{II.42}$$

On the other hand

$$\begin{aligned} \sum_{k=1}^{n-1} k^3 - \sum_{k=1}^{n-1} (k-1)^3 &= \sum_{k=1}^{n-1} [k^3 - (k-1)^3] \\ &= \sum_{k=1}^{n-1} (k^3 - k^3 + 3k^2 - 3k + 1) \\ &= \sum_{k=1}^{n-1} (3k^2 - 3k + 1). \end{aligned} \tag{II.43}$$

Since

$$\sum_{k=1}^{n-1} (3k^2 - 3k + 1) = 3\sum_{k=1}^{n-1} k^2 - 3\sum_{k=1}^{n-1} k + \sum_{k=1}^{n-1} 1$$

and

$$\sum_{k=1}^{n-1} k = \frac{n(n-1)}{2}, \qquad \sum_{k=1}^{n-1} 1 = (n-1), \qquad \text{(See Problem II.23)},$$

we have in view of (II.42) and (II.43)

$$3\sum_{k=1}^{n-1} k^2 - 3\,\frac{n(n-1)}{2} + (n-1) = (n-1)^3$$

and, consequently, after shifting of terms and dividing by 3,

$$\begin{aligned}\sum_{k=1}^{n-1} k^2 &= \frac{(n-1)^3}{3} + \frac{3n(n-1)}{6} - \frac{n-1}{3}\\ &= (n-1)\left[\frac{2(n-1)^2 + 3n - 2}{6}\right]\\ &= (n-1)\left[\frac{2n^2 - 4n + 2 + 3n - 2}{6}\right] = \frac{(n-1)n(2n-1)}{6}.\end{aligned}$$

Let us list all the summation formulas which we obtained so far for later reference purposes:

(II.44) $$\sum_{k=1}^{n-1} 1 = (n-1)$$

(II.45) $$\sum_{k=1}^{n-1} k = \frac{n(n-1)}{2}$$

(II.46) $$\sum_{k=1}^{n-1} k^2 = \frac{(n-1)n(2n-1)}{6}$$

Problems II.70–II.74

II.70. Evaluate

(*a*) $\sum_{k=1}^{101} \frac{k}{3}$ (*b*) $\sum_{k=1}^{1000} (k+1)$

(*c*) $\sum_{k=1}^{51} k^2$ (*d*) $\sum_{k=1}^{100} k^2$

II.71. Find a formula for $\sum_{k=1}^{n-1} k^3$. [*Hint:* Consider the sums $\sum_{k=1}^{n-1} k^4$ and $\sum_{k=1}^{n-1} (k-1)^4$ and proceed as in the text.]

II.72. Find a formula for

$$1 + 3 + 5 + \cdots + (2m+1).$$

[*Hint:* Observe that $1 + 2 + 3 + \cdots + 2m + (2m+1) - (2 + 4 + 6 + \cdots + 2m) = 1 + 3 + 5 + \cdots + (2m+1)$ and $2 + 4 + 6 + \cdots + 2m = 2(1 + 2 + 3 + \cdots + m)$.]

II.73. Evaluate

$$\frac{a}{n}\left(\frac{a}{n}\right)^2 + \frac{a}{n}\left(\frac{2a}{n}\right)^2 + \cdots + \frac{a}{n}\left(\frac{(n-1)a}{n}\right)^2.$$

II.74. Evaluate

$$\frac{8r^3\pi}{n^3}\sum_{k=1}^{n-1} k^2 + \frac{8r^3\pi}{n^2}\sum_{k=1}^{n-1} k$$

and take the limit as $n \to \infty$.

13. AREA UNDER A PARABOLIC ARC

Let us consider the problem of finding the area A which is bounded by an open rectangle with a parabolic arc being the supplementary boundary.

First, we consider the problem of finding the area under the parabola

$$y = x^2$$

between $x = 0$, $x = a$ and above the x-axis (see Fig. II.38). We subdivide the interval $0 \leq x \leq a$ into n equal subintervals of length $\frac{a}{n}$. Then the coordinates of the division points are

$$x_1 = \frac{a}{n}, \quad x_2 = \frac{2a}{n}, \quad x_3 = \frac{3a}{n}, \cdots, x_{n-1} = \frac{(n-1)a}{n}$$

and for the sake of uniformity we put

$$0 = x_0 \text{ and } a = x_n.$$

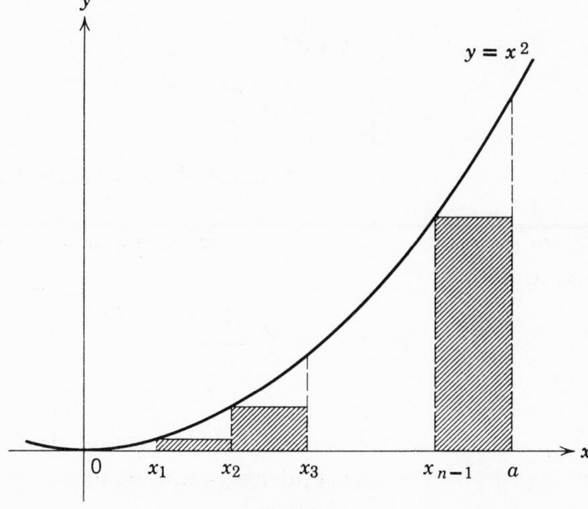

Fig. II.38

We note that

$$\min f(x) = f(x_k) \text{ in } x_k \leq x \leq x_{k+1}$$

and obtain, therefore, for the lower sum in view of

$$f(x_k) = f\left(\frac{ka}{n}\right) = \frac{k^2a^2}{n^2}, \qquad k = 0, 1, 2, \cdots (n-1),$$

the following expression

$$\begin{aligned} \underline{S}_n &= 0 + \frac{a}{n}\left(\frac{a}{n}\right)^2 + \frac{a}{n}\left(\frac{2a}{n}\right)^2 + \cdots + \frac{a}{n}\left(\frac{(n-1)a}{n}\right)^2 \\ &= \frac{a^3}{n^3}[1 + 2^2 + 3^2 + \cdots + (n-1)^2] = \frac{a^3}{n^3}\frac{(n-1)n(2n-1)}{6} \\ &= \frac{a^3}{6n^3}(2n^3 - 3n^2 + n) \end{aligned}$$

or, as we may write,

$$\underline{S}_n = \frac{a^3}{3}\left(1 - \frac{3}{2n} + \frac{1}{2n^2}\right).$$

Since

$$\lim_{n\to\infty}\left(1 - \frac{3}{2n} + \frac{1}{2n^2}\right) = 1$$

we have

(II.47) $$A = \int_0^a x^2\,dx = \frac{a^3}{3}.$$

It follows from (II.47) right away that

$$\int_0^b x^2\,dx = \frac{b^3}{3}$$

which represents the area under the parabola $y = x^2$, between $x = 0$, $x = b$, and above the x-axis.

Hence, we obtain for the area under the parabola $y = x^2$ between $x = a$, $x = b$, and above the x-axis

(II.48) $$\int_a^b x^2\,dx = \frac{b^3 - a^3}{3}$$

(see Fig. II.39).

This formula, together with the formulas (II.40) and (II.41) of Section 11, will enable us to find the area under a parabolic arc

(II.49) $$y = Ax^2 + Bx + C$$

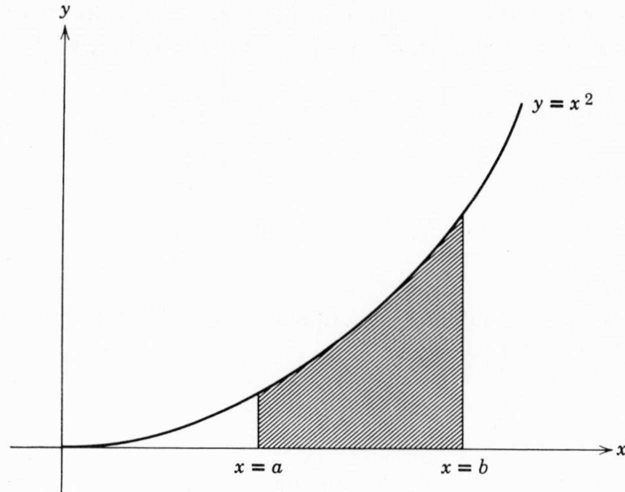

Fig. II.39

between any point $x = a$ and any other point $x = b$, if we also assume that the function in (II.49) is positive between a and b. (Otherwise, we would have to divide the integration interval as we have demonstrated in Section 9.)

We need for this purpose a property of the definite integral which can be easily established, namely, that

$$\text{(II.50)} \qquad \int_a^b [f(x) + g(x)]\, dx = \int_a^b f(x)\, dx + \int_a^b g(x)\, dx.$$

We will prove this relation for monotonically increasing functions $f(x)$ and $g(x)$ only, but we wish to point out that it is true in general—provided that the two integrals on the right exist.

If $f(x)$ and $g(x)$ are monotonically increasing (for definition of monotonically increasing functions, see Problem II.61), it is clear that

$$\min\,[f(x) + g(x)] = f(x_k) + g(x_k)[= \min f(x) + \min g(x)]$$

in any interval $x_k \leq x \leq x_{k+1}$. Therefore,

$$\underline{S}_n = \Delta x \sum_{k=0}^{n-1} [f(x_k) + g(x_k)] = \Delta x \sum_{k=0}^{n-1} f(x_k) + \Delta x \sum_{k=0}^{n-1} g(x_k).$$

If the limits of both sums on the right side of this relation exist as $n \to \infty$, which we will assume, then invoking our rule according to which the limit of a sum of two sequences is equal to the sum of the limits of the two sequences, provided that both limits exist (see Section 4), we have that

$$\lim_{n\to\infty} \underline{S}_n = \lim_{n\to\infty} \Delta x \sum_{k=0}^{n-1} f(x_k) + \lim_{n\to\infty} \Delta x \sum_{k=0}^{n-1} g(x_k) = \int_a^b f(x)\,dx + \int_a^b g(x)\,dx.$$

On the other hand,

$$\lim_{n\to\infty} \underline{S}_n = \int_a^b [f(x) + g(x)]\,dx$$

and (II.50) follows.

Now, if we wish to integrate the function in (II.49), we make use of the relation (II.50) as follows:

$$\int_a^b (Ax^2 + Bx + C)\,dx = \int_a^b Ax^2\,dx + \int_a^b (Bx + C)\,dx.$$

We apply (II.50) again to the last integral on the right and obtain

$$\int_a^b (Ax^2 + Bx + C)\,dx = \int_a^b Ax^2\,dx + \int_a^b Bx\,dx + \int_a^b C\,dx.$$

We have seen in Problem II.58 that

$$\int_a^b kf(x)\,dx = k\int_a^b f(x)\,dx$$

where k is a constant. Hence

$$\int_a^b (Ax^2 + Bx + C)\,dx = A\int_a^b x^2\,dx + B\int_a^b x\,dx + C\int_a^b dx.$$

From (II.48) it follows that

$$\int_a^b x^2\,dx = \frac{b^3 - a^3}{3}.$$

From (II.40) and (II.41) in Section 11 it follows that

$$\int_a^b x\,dx = \frac{b^2 - a^2}{2}, \qquad \text{and} \qquad \int_a^b dx = b - a$$

(see also Problems II.75 and II.76).

Thus we finally arrive at the formula

(II.51)

$$\int_a^b (Ax^2 + Bx + C)\,dx = A\,\frac{b^3 - a^3}{3} + B\,\frac{b^2 - a^2}{2} + C(b - a).$$

Problems II.75–II.83

II.75. We have seen in Section 11 that

$$\int_0^a b\,dx = ab.$$

Derive from this formula that $\int_0^b dx = b$ and, in turn, $\int_a^b dx = b - a$.

II.76. We have seen in Section 11 that $\int_0^a \frac{b}{a} x\,dx = \frac{ab}{2}$. Derive from this result that $\int_0^b x\,dx = \frac{b^2}{2}$ and, in turn, $\int_a^b x\,dx = \frac{b^2 - a^2}{2}$.

II.77. Evaluate:

(*a*) $\int_0^1 (4x^2 + 6x + 3)\,dx$ (*b*) $\int_{-3}^0 (x^2 - 12x + 1)\,dx$

(*c*) $\int_0^4 (3x^2 + 2x + 4)\,dx$ (*d*) $\int_{100}^{101} (x^2 - 500)\,dx.$

II.78. Find the area of the region between the curve $y = f(x)$, the x-axis, and $x = a$, $x = b$:

(*a*) $f(x) = x^2 - 1, \quad a = -2, \quad b = 2$

(*b*) $f(x) = x^2 - 3x + 2, \quad a = 0, \quad b = 4$

(*c*) $f(x) = x^2 + 3x + 2, \quad a = -5, \quad b = -1$

(*d*) $f(x) = x^2 - x, \quad a = -1, \quad b = 1$

Note that these functions change sign in the integration interval.

II.79. Determine A, B, C so that the parabola

$$y = Ax^2 + Bx + C$$

passes through the points (1, 1), (2, 2) and (3, 5).

II.80. Find the area under the parabola in Problem II.79 between $x = 1$ and $x = 3$.

II.81. Find $\int_0^1 [x(1 - x) + 1]\,dx$ and compare the result with the values which we obtained for the undersums in Section 8 and from the trapezoidal rule in Section 11.

II.82. Find the area of the region which is encompassed by the parabola $y = x^2$ and the line $y = x$. (Sketch the region.)

II.83. Find the area of the region which is encompassed by the two parabolas

$$y = x^2 \text{ and } y = \frac{3}{4}x^2 + 1.$$

(Sketch the region.)

14. SIMPSON'S RULE

In Section 10 we derived the so-called trapezoidal rule which yields for a given subdivision an approximate value to the definite integral. We arrived at this rule by approximating the function $y = f(x)$ to be integrated by a polygon and then, in turn, by approximating the area under the curve $y = f(x)$ by a sum of areas of trapezoids.

It seems quite obvious that we can obtain better approximations to the area, if we use a closer approximation to the curve than the one furnished by a polygon. This is exactly what we are going to do now.

Again we subdivide the interval $a \leq x \leq b$ by division points $x_1, x_2, x_3, \cdots, x_{n-1}$ into n equal subintervals of length $\Delta x = \frac{b - a}{n}$ but we will assume now that n is an *even* number for reasons which will soon become obvious. Now we erect the ordinates at all division points (see Fig. II.40). The ordinates at division points with an even subscript we represent by a solid line and the ordinates at division points with an odd subscript we represent by a broken line.

Now, instead of replacing the curve within each subinterval by a straight line, we will replace the curve between each two consecutive division points with an *even* subscript x_{2k}, x_{2k+2} by a parabola $y = Ax^2 + Bx + C$ which passes also through the point $[x_{2k+1}, f(x_{2k+1})]$. It seems quite apparent that a much better approximation is obtained in this manner. Now all we have to do is find the equation of the $\frac{n}{2}$ parabolas involved, apply formula

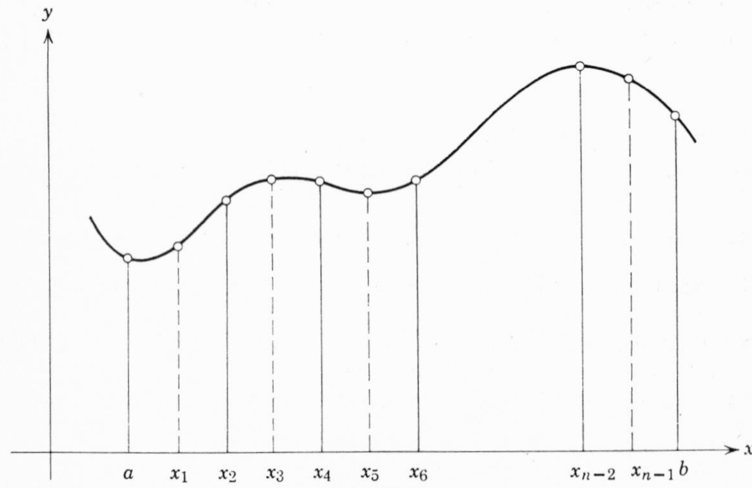

Fig. II.40

(II.51) from Section 13 to find the areas under those parabolas, and form the sum of all these areas.

Again, we let $a = x_0$, $b = x_n$ to unify the notation. Further, we let

$$f(x_k) = y_k,\ k = 0, 1, 2, 3, \cdots, n.$$

Now let us consider the subinterval $x_{2k} \le x \le x_{2k+2}$ (see Fig. II.41). We have to fit a parabola $y = Ax^2 + Bx + C$ through the three points

$$(x_{2k}, y_{2k}),\ (x_{2k+1}, y_{2k+1}),\ (x_{2k+2}, y_{2k+2})$$

and then find the area under the parabolic arc. We note that the area under this parabolic arc depends only on the distance Δx between consecutive division points and the lengths of y_{2k}, y_{2k+1} and y_{2k+2}. It is quite immaterial where x_{2k+1} is located relative to the origin. We can simplify our problem to some extent if we assume that $x_{2k+1} = 0$, i.e., shift the entire configuration in Fig. II.41 by x_{2k+1} units to the left (see Fig. II.42). Since $\Delta x = \dfrac{b-a}{n}$ we have now $x_{2k} = -\Delta x = -\dfrac{b-a}{n}$ and $x_{2k+2} = \Delta x = \dfrac{b-a}{n}$. Thus we obtain for the area under the parabolic arc $y = Ax^2 + Bx + C$ between x_{2k} and x_{2k+2} in view of (II.51),

(II.52)
$$\begin{aligned}\int_{-\Delta x}^{\Delta x} (Ax^2 + Bx + C)\,dx &= A\,\frac{(\Delta x)^3 - (-\Delta x)^3}{3} + B\,\frac{(\Delta x)^2 - (-\Delta x)^2}{2} \\ &\quad + C[\Delta x - (-\Delta x)] \\ &= 2A\,\frac{(\Delta x)^3}{3} + 2C\Delta x.\end{aligned}$$

We note that B has dropped out entirely due to the shift of x_{2k+1} into the origin of the coordinate system and thus only A and C are left to be determined so that $y = Ax^2 + Bx + C$ passes through the three points $(-\Delta x, y_{2k})$, $(0, y_{2k+1})$, $(\Delta x, y_{2k+2})$:

$$\begin{aligned} y_{2k} &= A(-\Delta x)^2 + B(-\Delta x) + C \\ y_{2k+1} &= C \\ y_{2k+2} &= A(\Delta x)^2 + B(\Delta x) + C. \end{aligned}$$

Addition of the first and the last equation yields

(II.53)
$$y_{2k+2} + y_{2k} = 2A(\Delta x)^2 + 2C.$$

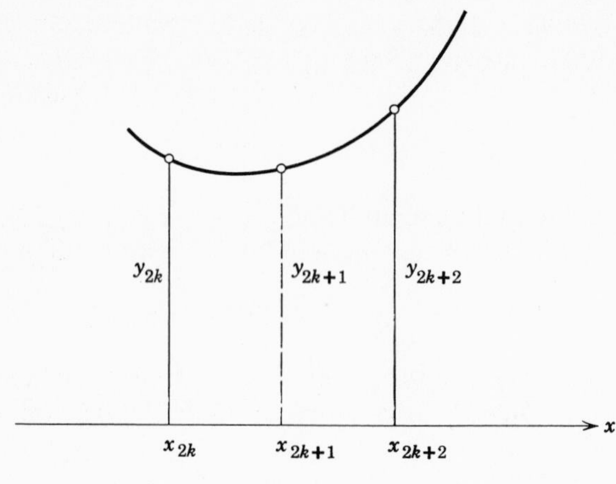

Fig. II.41

From the second equation we have

(II.54) $$C = y_{2k+1}$$

and hence, in view of (II.53),

(II.55) $$A = \frac{y_{2k+2} + y_{2k} - 2y_{2k+1}}{2(\Delta x)^2}.$$

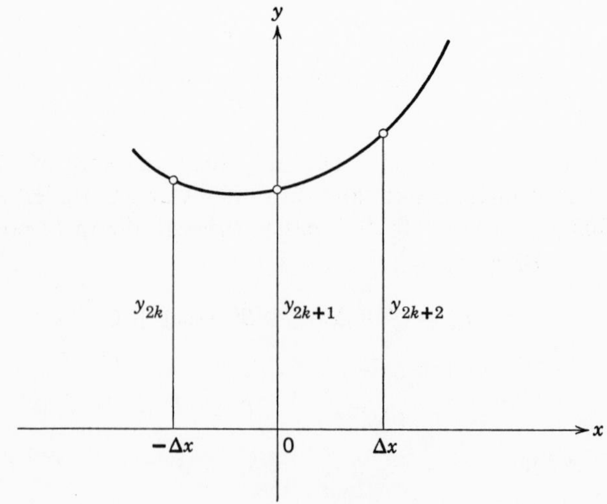

Fig. II.42

If we substitute the values for A and C from (II.55) and (II.54) into (II.52), we see that the area A_{2k} under the parabolic arc between x_{2k} and x_{2k+2} is

(II.56)

$$A_{2k} = \frac{y_{2k+2} + y_{2k} - 2y_{2k+1}}{2(\Delta x)^2} \cdot \frac{2(\Delta x)^3}{3} + 2y_{2k+1}\Delta x$$

$$= \left(\frac{y_{2k+2} + y_{2k} - 2y_{2k+1}}{3} + 2y_{2k+1}\right)\Delta x = \frac{y_{2k+2} + 4y_{2k+1} + y_{2k}}{3}\Delta x.$$

Now we sum all these areas $A_0, A_2, A_4, \cdots A_{n-2}$ and obtain

$$\sum_{k=0}^{\frac{n}{2}-1} A_{2k} = \frac{\Delta x}{3}[(y_0 + 4y_1 + y_2) + (y_2 + 4y_3 + y_4) + (y_4 + 4y_5 + y_6)$$
$$+ \cdots + (y_{n-4} + 4y_{n-3} + y_{n-2}) + (y_{n-2} + 4y_{n-1} + y_n)]$$
$$= \frac{\Delta x}{3}(y_0 + 4y_1 + 2y_2 + 4y_3 + 2y_4 + 4y_5 + 2y_6 + \cdots + 2y_{n-4}$$
$$+ 4y_{n-3} + 2y_{n-2} + 4y_{n-1} + y_n).$$

Thus we obtain the following approximation to the definite integral of the function $f(x)$ between a and b, if we also substitute for Δx its value $\Delta x = \dfrac{b-a}{n}$:

$$\text{(II.57)} \quad \int_a^b f(x)\,dx \cong \frac{b-a}{3n}(y_0 + 4y_1 + 2y_2 + 4y_3 + 2y_4 + \cdots$$
$$+ 2y_{n-2} + 4y_{n-1} + y_n).$$

This is called *Simpson's rule.*

This rule is easy to remember: the first and the last ordinate y_0 and y_n are each taken once, all other even-numbered ordinates are taken twice and all the odd-numbered ordinates are taken four times.

In order to obtain some insight into the effectiveness of this formula, we will try it out in computing an approximation of the area of one quadrant of the unit circle, which will yield an approximation to $\dfrac{\pi}{4}$. We will see that the approximation which we will thus obtain is better than the one we arrived at by using the trapezoidal rule in Section 11, but not as good as the one obtained in Section 5.

The unit circle has the equation

$$y = \sqrt{1 - x^2}.$$

We subdivide the interval $0 \leq x \leq 1$ into 32 subintervals and compute the values of y_k by making use of square root tables.*

* Standard Mathematical Tables, CRC, 12th ed. pp. 210–229.

We obtain:

$$
\begin{aligned}
y_0 &= 1 & 32y_1 &= 31.98437\\
32y_2 &= 31.93744 & 32y_3 &= 31.85906\\
32y_4 &= 31.74902 & 32y_5 &= 31.60696\\
32y_6 &= 31.43247 & 32y_7 &= 31.22499\\
32y_8 &= 30.98387 & 32y_9 &= 30.70831\\
32y_{10} &= 30.39737 & 32y_{11} &= 30.04996\\
32y_{12} &= 29.66479 & 32y_{13} &= 29.24038\\
32y_{14} &= 28.77499 & 32y_{15} &= 28.26569\\
32y_{16} &= 27.71281 & 32y_{17} &= 27.11088\\
32y_{18} &= 26.45751 & 32y_{19} &= 25.74879\\
32y_{20} &= 24.97999 & 32y_{21} &= 24.14539\\
32y_{22} &= 23.87467 & 32y_{23} &= 22.24860\\
32y_{24} &= 21.16601 & 32y_{25} &= 19.97498\\
32y_{26} &= 18.65470 & 32y_{27} &= 17.17556\\
32y_{28} &= 15.49193 & 32y_{29} &= 13.56466\\
32y_{30} &= 11.13553 & 32y_{31} &= 5.74456\\
y_{32} &= 0
\end{aligned}
$$

Thus,

$$2\sum_{k=1}^{k=15} y_{2k} = 24.02363, \quad 4\sum_{k=0}^{k=15} y_{2k+1} = 50.10675$$

and consequently, after elementary operations

$$\pi \cong 3.13043$$

as compared to the value 3.12981 which was obtained by the trapezoidal rule using the same number of subintervals.

Problems II.84–II.87

II.84. Use Simpson's rule to find

$$\int_0^1 (2x^2 + 3x + 1)\, dx.$$

Take $n = 2, 4, 8$. How do you always obtain the same result?

II.85. Use Simpson's rule to find an approximation for

$$\int_0^1 \frac{4}{1 + x^2}\, dx.$$

II.86. Use Simpson's rule to find an approximation to

$$\int_0^{\pi} \sin x \, dx.$$

Take $n = 4$. (For values of $\sin x$, see Appendix III, Section 2.)

II.87. Use the trapezoidal rule for the integral in Problem II.86 with the same number of division points. The true value of this integral is 2. Compare the results.

15. DEFINITE INTEGRAL WITH A VARIABLE UPPER LIMIT

We have seen in Section 13 that the area under a parabolic arc $y = x^2$ between $x = a$ and $x = b$ is given by

$$\int_a^b x^2 \, dx = \frac{b^3}{3} - \frac{a^3}{3}.$$

Let $a = 0$ in the following discussion for reasons of convenience. Now let us consider various values of b and evaluate this area in every instance.

First, let $b = 0$, then we obtain

$$\int_0^0 x^2 \, dx = 0.$$

Next we let $b = \frac{1}{2}$. Then

$$\int_0^{\frac{1}{2}} x^2 \, dx = \frac{1}{24}.$$

For $b = 1$, we obtain $\int_0^1 x^2 \, dx = \frac{1}{3}$.

For $b = 2$, $\int_0^2 x^2 \, dx = \frac{8}{3}$.

For $b = 3$, $\int_0^3 x^2 \, dx = 9$.

For $b = 9$, $\int_0^9 x^2 \, dx = 243$.

For $b = 12$, $\int_0^{12} x^2 \, dx = 576$, etc. $\cdots$

We see that the value of $\int_0^b x^2 \, dx$ depends on the value which we assign to b, or as we can say: $\int_0^b x^2 \, dx$ *is a function of* b. This is also quite clear from looking at Fig. II.43, where we have drawn three vertical lines at three

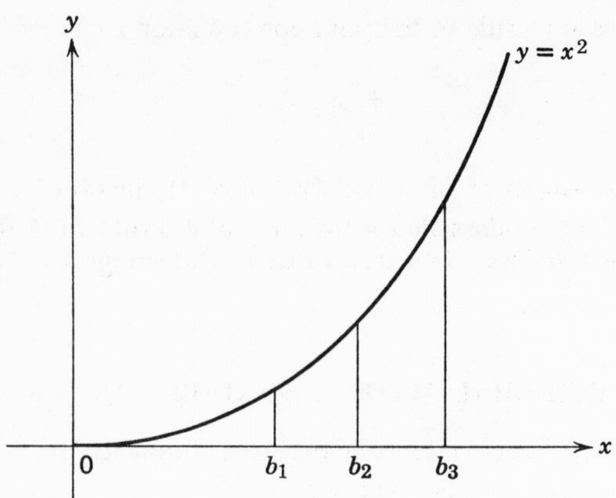

Fig. II.43

different points b_1, b_2, and b_3. Clearly, the areas from 0 to b_1, b_2, b_3 are all different.

We express the fact that $\int_0^b x^2\,dx$ is a function of b in the customary form

$$\int_0^b x^2\,dx = F(b).$$

Before we continue, let us note that it is really immaterial what letter we use to designate the integration variable. Instead of $\int_0^b x^2\,dx$ we might just as well write $\int_0^b u^2\,du$ or $\int_0^b t^2\,dt$ or use any other letter, for that matter, since the integration variable does not explicitly occur in the final result. (The integration variable is a "dummy" just as the summation subscript in a sum.) In general, we can see that

$$\int_a^b f(x)\,dx = \int_a^b f(u)\,du = \int_a^b f(t)\,dt = \cdots.$$

If we use u now instead of x for the integration variable, we have

$$\int_0^b u^2\,du = F(b)$$

Since it is customary to denote a variable by x, we write x instead of b and have

$$\int_0^x u^2\,du = F(x),$$

i.e., the area under the parabolic arc $y = x^2$ between the fixed lower limit 0 and the variable upper limit x is a function of x. (Note that we have denoted the integration variable by u so that we do not get it mixed up with the upper limit.)

In general, if we have some function $y = f(x)$ for which the integral exists, we can say that the area under the curve $y = f(x)$ between a fixed lower limit a and a variable upper limit x is a function of x:

$$\int_a^x f(u)\,du = F(x).$$

We will now investigate what happens to the area $F(x)$ as x increases. For example, in the case of the area under the parabolic arc which we discussed initially $[f(x) = x^2]$, we see that if x increases from 0 to 1, then the area increases from 0 to $\frac{1}{3}$. If x increases from 1 to 2, then $F(x)$ increases from $\frac{1}{3}$ to $\frac{8}{3}$. If x increases from 2 to 3, then $F(x)$ increases from $\frac{8}{3}$ to 9, etc. $\cdots$ We see that (at least in this case) even though x increases in all listed instances by the same amount, the corresponding increase of the area $F(x)$ differs from case to case.

We will now try to establish a general formula which will enable us to measure this increase for any x. For this purpose we consider a second point (see Fig. II.44) h units to the right of x which has the x-coordinate $x + h$ and consider the areas between a and x

$$\int_a^x f(u)\,du = F(x)$$

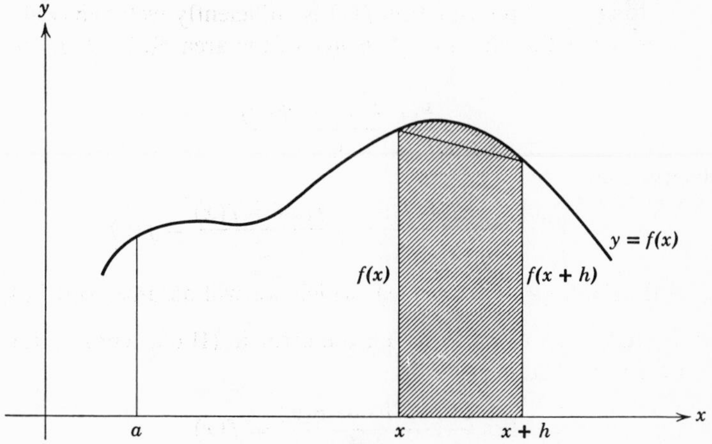

Fig. II.44

and between a and $x + h$

$$\int_a^{x+h} f(u)\,du = F(x + h).$$

Then, the corresponding increase (change) in area is given by

$$F(x + h) - F(x)$$

(per h units of x-axis).

Thus, the *approximate* increase of the area per unit increase of x is given by

$$\frac{F(x + h) - F(x)}{h}. \tag{II.58}$$

The numerator of this expression is represented by the shaded region in Fig. II.44. If h is very small, we can approximate this shaded region by a trapezoid as indicated in Fig. II.44. The area of this trapezoid is given by

$$A_{x,x+h}(\text{trapezoid}) = h\,\frac{f(x + h) + f(x)}{2}. \tag{II.59}$$

Hence, we can state that the change of area per unit increase of x is approximately given by

$$\frac{F(x + h) - F(x)}{h} \cong \frac{f(x + h) + f(x)}{2}. \tag{II.60}$$

Clearly, this approximation becomes more accurate the smaller h is because the error we make in approximating the curve $y = f(x)$ by a straight line segment in the interval between x and $x + h$ seems to decrease as h becomes smaller and it is intuitively clear that the error tends to zero as h tends to zero—if the function $f(x)$ is sufficiently well behaved.

Therefore, we define the *rate of change* of the area $F(x)$ *with respect to* x as

$$\lim_{h\to 0} \frac{F(x + h) - F(x)}{h}.$$

We observe that

$$\lim_{h\to 0} \frac{f(x + h) + f(x)}{2} = \frac{f(x) + f(x)}{2} = f(x)$$

provided that $\lim_{h\to 0} f(x + h) = f(x)$, which we will assume, and in view of our observation according to which the error in (II.60) tends to zero as h tends to zero, we obtain

$$\lim_{h\to 0} \frac{F(x + h) - F(x)}{h} = f(x) \tag{II.61}$$

for the *rate of change* of the area under $y = f(x)$ as a function of the upper integration limit.

We call the rate of change

$$\lim_{h\to 0} \frac{F(x+h) - F(x)}{h},$$

provided it exists, the *derivative* of the function $F(x)$ with respect to x and denote it by

$$F'(x) = \lim_{h\to 0} \frac{F(x+h) - F(x)}{h}. \tag{II.62}$$

We can now state our result in (II.62) in the following words: The rate of change of the area $F(x)$ under the curve $y = f(x)$ between a fixed lower limit a and a variable upper limit x is given by $f(x)$, or, if

$$F(x) = \int_a^x f(u)\,du,$$

then

$$F'(x) = f(x).$$

This relationship ties up the operation of integration between a fixed lower limit and a variable upper limit with a limit operation as defined in (II.62). This limit operation is called *differentiation.* If we integrate a function $f(x)$ between a fixed lower limit and a variable upper limit x, we obtain a function $F(x)$, and if we differentiate this function $F(x)$ again, we come back to $f(x)$. We therefore call the two operations *inverse* to each other, in the same way that we call squaring and extracting the square root inverse operations. (If we square the number 2, we obtain 4; then if we extract the positive square root of 4, we obtain 2 again, the number with which we started.)

Now, suppose we have a function $f(x)$. Then the area under the curve which represents this function between 0 and a variable upper limit x is given by

$$A_{0,x} = \int_0^x f(u)\,du = F(x)$$

where

$$F'(x) = f(x).$$

Let $x = a$, then

$$A_{0,a} = \int_0^a f(u)\,du = F(a);$$

let $x = b$, then

$$A_{0,b} = \int_0^b f(u)\,du = F(b)$$

and hence

$$A_{a,b} = A_{0,b} - A_{0,a} = \int_0^b f(u)\,du - \int_0^a f(u)\,du = F(b) - F(a)$$

or

(II.63) $$\int_a^b f(u)\,du = F(b) - F(a),$$

where $F'(x) = f(x)$.

The reader may get the impression that we have not been quite consistent with our notation. Originally, we called

$$\int_a^x f(u)\,du = F(x)$$

and now we used

$$\int_0^x f(u)\,du = F(x).$$

It seems that these two functions, both of which we called $F(x)$, cannot be the same. Still, a simple argument will reveal that they are "almost" the same in the following sense:

Since the area under $y = (fx)$ between 0 and x can be obtained by adding to the area between 0 and a the area between a and x (where $0 < a < x$), we have

$$\int_0^x f(u)\,du = \int_0^a f(u)\,du + \int_a^x f(u)\,du$$

because

$$\int_0^a f(u)\,du = A_{0,a} \qquad \text{and} \qquad \int_a^x f(u)\,du = A_{a,x}.$$

Now, $\int_0^a f(u)\,du$ is some constant number (the area under $y = f(x)$ between 0 and a). Therefore, the function which is represented by the integral $\int_a^x f(u)\,du$ which we called $F(x)$ at first differs from the function represented by $\int_0^x f(u)\,du$, which we called now $F(x)$ by some constant number $C = \int_0^a f(u)\,du$ only. So, if we want to be fussy, we could write

$$\int_0^x f(u)\,du = F(x) + C$$

for some constant number. Then

$$\int_0^a f(u)\,du = F(a) + C$$

$$\int_0^b f(u)\,du = F(b) + C$$

and, consequently, we obtain again formula (II.63):

$$\int_a^b f(u)\,du = \int_0^b f(u)\,du - \int_0^a f(u)\,du$$
$$= F(b) + C - F(a) - C = F(b) - F(a).$$

So we see that our little inconsistency did not have any harmful consequences at all. We will dwell on this problem in more detail in Chapter III, Section 5.

We recall now that we have already obtained the following integration formulas (see II.48 and Problems II.75 and II.76):

$$\int_a^b du = b - a$$
$$\int_a^b u\,du = \frac{b^2}{2} - \frac{a^2}{2}$$
$$\int_a^b u^2\,du = \frac{b^3}{3} - \frac{a^3}{3}.$$

Thus we find in the case of $f(x) = 1$ that $F(b) = b$, $F(a) = a$, i.e., $F(x) = \int_0^x du = x$ and we see that

$$(x)' = 1.$$

For $f(x) = x$, we have $F(x) = \int_0^x u\,du = \frac{x^2}{2}$ and, consequently,

$$\left(\frac{x^2}{2}\right)' = x$$

and, finally, for $f(x) = x^2$, we have $F(x) = \int_0^x u^2\,du = \frac{x^3}{3}$ and, therefore,

$$\left(\frac{x^3}{3}\right)' = x^2.$$

The next chapter will be almost exclusively devoted to a study of this new operation of differentiation which we introduced in this section, and there we will find an entirely different method for the derivation of the three differentiation formulas which we listed just now.

Problems II.88–II.92

II.88. Find $F(x) = \int_0^x f(u)\,du$ for the following functions:

(a) $f(x) = x^2 + 3x$ (b) $f(x) = -3x^2 + 4$
(c) $f(x) = 2x^2 + 3x - 1$ (d) $f(x) = x^2 + 13x + 7$
(e) $f(x) = -4x + 2$ (f) $f(x) = (x + 3)^2$

II.89. Using the three differentiation formulas which are listed at the end of this section and some imagination, find $F'(x)$ for the following functions:

(a) $F(x) = 2x$ (b) $F(x) = \dfrac{x^2}{4} + x$

(c) $F(x) = -2x^3 + 2x^2$ (d) $F(x) = x^3 + 3x^2 - 4x$

(e) $F(x) = 4x^3 - x$ (f) $F(x) = \dfrac{2x^3}{3} + \dfrac{5x^2}{2} - 7x$

II.90. The area of a right isosceles triangle of side length x is given by

$$A(x) = \int_0^x u\,du.$$

Justify this formula. Find the rate of change of this area as $x = 4$.

II.91. Same as in Problem II.90 for the area under the parabolic arc $y = x^2$ between 0 and x:

$$A(x) = \int_0^x u^2\,du.$$

II.92. $G(x) = \int_x^b g(u)\,du$ is a function of the variable *lower* limit x. Express $G(x)$ as a function of a variable upper limit x and find the rate of change of $G(x)$ with respect to x. (*Hint:* Note that a switch of integration limits means that the widths of the inscribed rectangles in the lower sum are now measured from left to right, i.e., the sign is changed.)

Supplementary Problems II

1.1. The circumference of a square of side length a is given by $C = 4a$. Express the area A of the square as a function $f(C)$ of the circumference. What is $f(x)$?

1.2. Express the circumference C of a square of side length a as a function $g(A)$ of its area. What is $g(x)$? What is $f[g(x)]$ where f is the function defined in Problem 1.1?

1.3. Assume that the area measure of a rectangle of dimensions a and b is given by

$$A[r(a, b)] = ab^2.$$

Demonstrate with the rectangles $r(2, 3)$ and $r(2, 5)$ that condition 4 (p. 76) is still satisfied. However, condition 3 is not satisfied any more.

1.4. Given a function $F(x)$ and a function $F(y)$ where x and y are independent variables that are in no relation to each other. Show that if $F(x) = F(y)$ is to hold for any pair of values (x, y), then $F(x) = F(y) =$ constant. (*Hint:* Assume the opposite to be true, i.e., $F(x)$ and $F(y)$ are not constant and show that this leads to a contradiction.)

2.1. Let a, b, c be the lengths of the three sides of a triangle. Show by inspection that $a + b > c$ and $a + c > b$ and $b + c > a$.

2.2. What happens if in Problem 2.1 $a + b = c$?

2.3. The perimeter of an equilateral triangle of side length a is given by $C = 3a$. Express the area A of the equilateral triangle as a function $f(C)$ of the perimeter. What is $f(x)$?

2.4. Express the perimeter C of an equilateral triangle of side length a as a function $g(A)$ of its area. What is $g(x)$? Find $g[f(x)]$ where f is the function defined in Problem 2.3.

2.5. Find the area of the quadrangle with vertices at $A(0, 0)$, $B(1, 0)$, $C(3, 5)$, and $D(1, 3)$ in two different ways by considering two different partitions of the quadrangle into triangles.

3.1. Write down the general term of the following sequences:

(*a*) $1, -2, 4, -9, 16, -25, \cdots$ (*b*) $1, \frac{1}{4}, \frac{1}{9}, \frac{1}{16}, \frac{1}{25}, \cdots$

(*c*) $1, -\frac{1}{2}, \frac{1}{3}, -\frac{1}{4}, \cdots$ (*d*) $1, -\frac{1}{4}, \frac{1}{16}, -\frac{1}{64}, \frac{1}{256}, \cdots$

3.2. Write the number $\frac{1}{6}$ as the limit of a sequence.

3.3. What is the limit of the sequence 0.9, 0.99, 0.999, 0.9999, $\cdots$?

3.4. Evaluate the sum $\sum_{k=0}^{\infty} \left(\frac{99}{100}\right)^k$.

3.5. Simplify $\sum_{k=1}^{n} k^2 - 2\sum_{k=1}^{n} k + \sum_{k=1}^{n} 1$.

3.6. Write $\frac{x}{1 - x^2}$ as an infinite series.

4.1. Evaluate the following limits

(*a*) $\lim_{n\to\infty} \frac{n^2 + 5n + 6}{n^2 - 2}$ (*b*) $\lim_{n\to\infty} \frac{2n^3 - 3n^2 + 1}{(n + 1)^3}$

(*c*) $\lim_{n\to\infty} \frac{n\sqrt{n}}{2n(\sqrt{n} - 1)}$ (*d*) $\lim_{n\to\infty} \frac{4n^3 - 1}{2n^4 + 4}$

4.2. Find

(*a*) $\lim_{n\to\infty} \left[n - \frac{n^2}{(n - 1)^2}\right]$ (*b*) $\lim_{n\to\infty} \left(\sqrt{n} - \frac{n}{\sqrt{n} + 1}\right)$

(*c*) $\lim_{n\to\infty} \left[4n^2 - \frac{16n^2}{(4n - 1)^2}\right]$ (*d*) $\lim_{n\to\infty} \left(12n - \frac{4n + 1}{\frac{1}{2}n - 3}\right)$

4.3. Find

(*a*) $\lim_{x\to 0} \frac{x^2 + x}{4x^2 - 1}$ (*b*) $\lim_{x\to 0} \frac{(x - 1)^2}{x^2 + 1}$

(*c*) $\lim_{x\to 0} \frac{x^3 + 3x^2 - 4x + 1}{(1 - x)^3}$ (*d*) $\lim_{x\to 0} \frac{(x + 1)(x - 1)}{x^2 - 4}$

4.4. Let $a_n = \frac{2n + 1}{n - 1}$ and assume that $\lim_{n\to\infty} \frac{a_n}{b_n} = 1$. Choose a sequence b_n ($b_n \neq a_n$ for *all* n) for which the stated limit relation holds.

4.5. Choose a sequence c_n ($c_i \neq c_k$ for $i \neq k$) so that $\lim_{n\to\infty} \frac{1}{6c_n} = 1$.

4.6. Let

$$f(x) = \begin{cases} \frac{1}{n} \text{ when } x = \frac{1}{n} \text{ for all integers } n \\ 0 \text{ for all other values of } x. \end{cases}$$

Does $\lim_{x\to 0} f(x)$ exist? If so, what is its value?

4.7. Evaluate

(*a*) $\lim_{x\to 0} \frac{(a + x)^2 - a^2}{x}$ (*b*) $\lim_{h\to 0} \frac{\frac{1}{x + h} - \frac{1}{x}}{h}$

(*c*) $\lim_{k\to 0} \frac{(z - k)^3 - z^3}{k}$ (*d*) $\lim_{h\to 0} \frac{\sqrt{x + h} - \sqrt{x}}{h}$

5.1. Show that if it is true that for all elements of a sequence a_n the following inequality holds $a \leq a_n \leq A$ for some numbers $a < A$, then there exists at least one number L in $a \leq L \leq A$ so that there are infinitely many elements of the sequence a_n in any neighborhood of L, no matter how small this neighborhood is. (*Hint:* There are infinitely many points representing the elements of the sequence in the interval $a \leq x \leq A$. If you cut this interval in half, then there are infinitely many points in $a \leq x \leq \frac{a + A}{2}$, or in $\frac{a + A}{2} < x \leq A$, or in both. Now, repeat this argument for the one of these two intervals that contains infinitely many points, etc. . . .)

5.2. Show that if $a_n < a_{n+1}$ for all n in the sequence in Problem 5.1, then there can be only one such point L with the property that infinitely many elements of the sequence are located in any neighborhood of L, no matter how small this neighborhood is.

5.3. Consider the inequality (II.25) on p. 101 for $n = 2$. Is it still valid?

5.4. Same as in Problem 5.3 for $n = 1$.

5.5. A circular ring is a region that is bounded by two concentric circles of different radii. Find the area of a circular ring of inner radius 1 and outer radius 2.

5.6. Consider a line segment of length 2 which is tangent to the circle of radius R and center at the origin at the point $(0, R)$ so that the point of tangency cuts the segment into two parts of equal length. Now consider a circular ring of inner radius R and an outer radius that is chosen so that the outer circle passes through the endpoints of the line segment. Make a sketch. Show that the area of the circular ring thus obtained is independent of R, i.e., no matter how large R is, this area is always the same.

6.1. Find the area of a regular heptagon in terms of the radius of the circumscribed circle.

6.2. Find the area of a regular octagon in terms of the radius of the circumscribed circle.

6.3. An unenlightened State Legislature once defined π as $\frac{22}{7}$. Express the error they committed in per cent of the true value to four significant figures.

6.4. The radius of the earth is approximately 4000 miles. Based on this approximation, find the length of the equator, assuming that the earth is a sphere.

7.1. Find $\sin\frac{\pi}{12}$. [*Hint:* Use half-angle formula, Appendix III, formula (AIII.8).]

7.2. Find $\sin\frac{7\pi}{12}$. $\left(\textit{Hint:}\text{ Note that } \frac{7\pi}{12} = \frac{\pi}{3} + \frac{\pi}{4}\right.$ and use the formula which was developed in Problem AIII.14.$\left.\right)$

7.3. Derive the relation (II.30) considering the area of the circular sector of radius 1 and curved boundary of length x, the triangle $0CB$ and the triangle $0CD$ (see Fig. II.17).

8.1. Find an approximation to the area under the curve $y = \frac{1}{1 + x^2}$ between $x = 0$ and $x = 1$ by taking $\underline{S}_8$.

8.2. Same as in Problem 8.1 taking $\bar{S}_8$.

8.3. Find a better approximation to the area in Problem 8.1 by taking the arithmetic mean of $\underline{S}_8$ and $\bar{S}_8$.

9.1. Given the function

$$f(x) = \begin{cases} x \text{ for } 0 \leq x < 1 \\ -x + 2 \text{ for } 1 \leq x \leq 2 \end{cases}$$

Find $\int_0^2 f(x)\, dx$ by geometric inspection.

9.2. Same as in Problem 9.1 for the function $f(x) = \sqrt{1 - x^2}$ between the limits $x = 0$ and $x = 1$.

9.3. Show by geometric inspection that $\int_0^4 f(x)\, dx = 0$ where $f(x)$ is the function represented in Fig. I.41.

9.4. Let

$$f(x) = \begin{cases} 0 \text{ for } 0 \leq x < 3 \\ \text{not defined for } 3 \leq x < 3.0000000000001 \\ 1 \text{ for } 3.0000000000001 \leq x \leq 5. \end{cases}$$

Does $\int_0^5 f(x)\, dx$ exist?

9.5. Let $0 < g(x) < f(x)$ in $a \leq x \leq b$. Interpret the formula

$$\int_a^b [f(x) - g(x)]\, dx = \int_a^b f(x)\, dx - \int_a^b g(x)\, dx$$

geometrically. Is this a true formula? Does it also hold if $f(x) = g(x)$ for all x?

10.1. Find an approximation to $\int_0^\pi \sin x\, dx$ by the trapezoidal rule, using $n = 6$ subintervals. (For values of $\sin x$, see Table AIII.2 in Appendix III, Section 2.)

10.2. Same as in Problem 10.1 for $\int_0^\pi \sin^2 x\,dx$.

10.3. Find an approximation to $\int_1^6 \sqrt{x^3 - 1}\,dx$ by the trapezoidal rule using $n = 5$ subintervals.

10.4. Find an approximation to $\int_{-5}^1 \frac{1}{2x^2 + 1}\,dx$ by the trapezoidal rule using $n = 6$ subintervals.

11.1. Given

$$f(x) = \begin{cases} x + 1 \text{ for } 0 \le x \le 1 \\ -x + 3 \text{ for } 1 \le x \le 2. \end{cases}$$

Find $\int_0^2 f(x)\,dx$ by a limit of a sum process.

11.2. Show that $\int_a^b dx = b - a$.

11.3. Find the area of a region which is bounded by $y = x$, $y = \frac{x}{2}$ and $x = 1$ by a limit of a sum process.

11.4. Find the area of the region bounded by $y = 1$, $y = -x$, $y = x$ by a limit of a sum process.

12.1. Show that

$$\sum_{k=1}^{3} k^2 = \sum_{k=1}^{5} k - 1$$

12.2. Show that

$$3\sum_{k=1}^{2} k^2 = \sum_{k=1}^{5} k.$$

12.3. Show that

$$\sum_{k=0}^{n} a_k = \sum_{k=\nu}^{n+\nu} a_{k-\nu}$$

12.4. Show that $\sum_{k=1}^{n-1} k^2 = \sum_{k=0}^{n-2} (k + 1)^2$. (*Hint:* Use the result of Problem 12.3.)

12.5. Simplify

$$\sum_{k=1}^{n-1} k^2 + n\sum_{k=1}^{n-1} k + 2n^2 \sum_{k=1}^{n-1} 1$$

and evaluate.

13.1. Evaluate

(*a*) $\int_1^2 (x^2 + x + 1)\,dx$ (*b*) $\int_{-1}^1 (3x^2 + 2x + 1)\,dx$

(*c*) $\int_{-5}^0 (4x^2 - 100)\,dx$ (*d*) $\int_1^{1000} 3x^2\,dx$

13.2. Find the area of the region between $y = f(x)$, the x-axis, $x = a$, and $x = b$:

(*a*) $f(x) = x^2 - 4, a = 2, b = 3$ (*b*) $f(x) = x^2 + 2x + 1, a = -1, b = 0$
(*c*) $f(x) = 2x^2 - 50, a = 5, b = 6$ (*d*) $f(x) = x^2 - 9, a = 2, b = 4.$

13.3. Find the area of the region bounded by $y = 4x^2 + 1$, the x-axis, $x = 0$, and $x = 4$ and compare the value with the approximative value obtained from the trapezoidal rule with 8 subintervals. Express the error in per cent of the true value.

13.4. Find the area of the region encompassed by

$$y = \tfrac{1}{2}x^2 \text{ and } y = \tfrac{1}{50}x.$$

13.5. Find the area of the region encompassed by

$$y = x^2 + 1 \text{ and } y = -x^2 + 2.$$

14.1. Show by inspection that

(*a*) $\displaystyle\int_{-h}^{h} x^3\,dx = 0$ (*b*) $\displaystyle\int_{-h}^{h} x^2\,dx = 2\int_0^h x^2\,dx$

(*c*) $\displaystyle\int_{-h}^{h} x\,dx = 0$ (*d*) $\displaystyle\int_{-h}^{h} dx = 2\int_0^h dx = 2h$

14.2. Show that

$$\int_{-h}^{h} (Ax^3 + Bx^2 + Cx + D)\,dx = \int_{-h}^{h} (Bx^2 + D)\,dx$$

(*Hint:* Use the results of Problem 14.1.)

14.3. Show that Simpson's rule yields the exact result for an integral of the type

$$\int_{-h}^{h} (Ax^3 + Bx^2 + Cx + D)\,dx$$

even though a curve of third order is approximated by a quadratic parabola in Simpson's rule. (*Hint*: Make use of the result in Problem 14.2.)

14.4. Use Simpson's rule to obtain an approximation for

$$\int_0^{\pi} \sin^2 x\,dx$$

using $n = 6$ subintervals. Compare your result with the approximation obtained in Problem 10.2 by using the trapezoidal rule and with the exact value which is found to be $\frac{\pi}{2}$. (Try to establish $\frac{\pi}{2}$ as the exact value of this integral by geometric inspection.)

14.5. Use Simpson's rule to find an approximation for the integral

$$\int_1^2 \frac{dx}{x}$$

for $n = 16$ subintervals.

15.1. Find $F(x) = \displaystyle\int_0^x f(u)\,du$ for the following functions

(*a*) $f(x) = x^2 - 2x + 1$ (*b*) $f(x) = (x - 1)(x + 1)$

(*c*) $f(x) = (2x - 3)^2$ (*d*) $f(x) = \dfrac{x - x^3}{x - 1}$

15.2. Find $F'(x)$ for the following functions

(*a*) $F(x) = x^3 + 4x + 1290$ (*b*) $F(x) = (x - 1)^2(x + 1)$

(*c*) $F(x) = \frac{x^3}{3} + \frac{x^2}{2} + x + 1$ (*d*) $F(x) = \frac{x^4 - 16}{x - 2}$

15.3. The area under $y = x^2 + 2x + 3$ above the x-axis between $x = 0$ and x is given by

$$A(x) = \int_0^x (x^2 + 2x + 3)\,dx.$$

Find the rate of change of $A(x)$ at $x = 1, 3, 7$.

15.4. Same as in Problem 15.3 for the area under the curve

$$y = x^2 - x + 10.$$

15.5. Show that

$$\int_a^x f(u)\,du + \int_x^a f(u)\,du = 0.$$

(*Hint:* See also Problem II.92.)

CHAPTER III

RATES

1. THE DERIVATIVE

In the preceding section, we accidentally came across the limit of the quotient

$$\text{(III.1)} \qquad \frac{F(x + h) - F(x)}{h}$$

as $h \to 0$. In this section we will attempt to attribute some geometric significance to this limit quite independently of its meaning in the context of the preceding section. We will henceforth refer to the quotient in (III.1) as the *difference quotient of the function* $F(x)$ because it is the quotient of differences: the numerator is the difference of two values of the function $F(x)$, namely, $F(x + h)$ and $F(x)$, and the denominator is the difference of two values of x, namely, $x + h$ and x itself.

Let us consider the function

$$y = F(x)$$

which is represented by its graph in Fig. III.1 (we assume that it has a graph), and let us try to give a geometric representation to the difference quotient (III.1) and, if possible, also to its limit as $h \to 0$. For this purpose, we consider a fixed point $(x, 0)$ on the x-axis and some other point at a distance h from x, with the abscissa $x + h$ (see Fig. III.1). Then we erect the corresponding ordinates which terminate in the points denoted by P and R. We can see now that the difference quotient (III.1) represents the ratio of the distances RQ to QP, i.e., the slope of the line segment from P to R. We call the segment PR a *chord* or a *secant* (Latin: *secare* = to cut) of the curve $y = F(x)$. We can thus state

$\dfrac{F(x + h) - F(x)}{h}$ *is the slope of the chord joining* $P[x, F(x)]$ *and* $R[x + h, F(x + h)]$.

Thus far everything has gone quite smoothly. Now let us proceed to the more complicated task of trying to interpret the meaning of the limit of

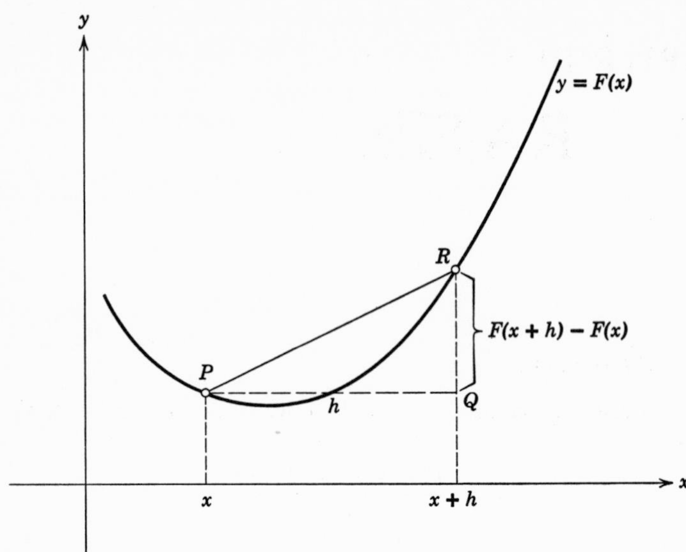

Fig. III.1

(III.1) as $h \to 0$. In Fig. III.2 we have drawn the chords for progressively smaller values of h, for positive as well as negative values of h. In all cases, we drew the continuation of the chord to both sides beyond the curve in dotted lines. We can see that the smaller h is, the closer the position of the chord is to what we would intuitively call the tangent line to the curve at the point $P[x, F(x)]$ and which is drawn in a bold line.

So far we have not defined what we mean by tangent line to a curve except for the case of a quadratic parabola (see Chapter I, Section 10). We remember that in case of a parabola, we considered first a line which intersects the parabola in two distinct points and then we let the one point slide into the other one and called the line which was thus obtained, the tangent line to the parabola. But this is exactly what we are doing now in a more general form. More general, insofar as we consider now any curve $y = F(x)$, and not necessarily a quadratic parabola. We give the definition: The *tangent line* to the curve $y = F(x)$ at the point $P[x, F(x)]$ is the line which passes through this point P and has a slope which is equal to the limit of the difference quotient (III.1) as $h \to 0$ (from either side), provided this limit exists. (If the limit does not exist, then the tangent line does not exist either.)

Thus:

(III.2) $\lim_{h \to 0} \frac{F(x + h) - F(x)}{h}$ *is the slope of the tangent line to* $y = F(x)$ *at the point* $P[x, F(x)]$, *by definition.*

In the preceding section, we introduced the term *derivative* for this limit and denoted it by $F'(x)$. Thus we can state in this terminology:

The slope of the tangent line to the curve $y = F(x)$ *at the point* $P[x, F(x)]$ *is given by its derivative* $F'(x)$.

To illustrate how the nonexistence of the derivative at a certain point has the nonexistence of the tangent line at this point as a consequence, and vice versa, let us consider the example

$$y = |x|.$$

We have seen in Chapter I, Section 12, that this function is represented by the graph in Fig. III.3. We see by inspection that this curve does not have a tangent line at $x = 0$ and, indeed, it can be demonstrated that the derivative fails to exist at this point. If we denote the derivative of $F(x) = |x|$ at the point $x = 0$ by $F'(0)$, we have

$$F'(0) = \lim_{h\to 0} \frac{|x + h| - |x|}{h}\bigg|_{\text{at } x=0} = \lim_{h\to 0} \frac{|h|}{h}.$$

Now, we have to distinguish between positive and negative values of h, i.e., we have to distinguish between an approach to the origin from the right and from the left:

If $h > 0$, then $|h| = h$ and

$$F'(0) = \lim_{h\to 0} \frac{h}{h} = \lim_{h\to 0} 1 = 1.$$

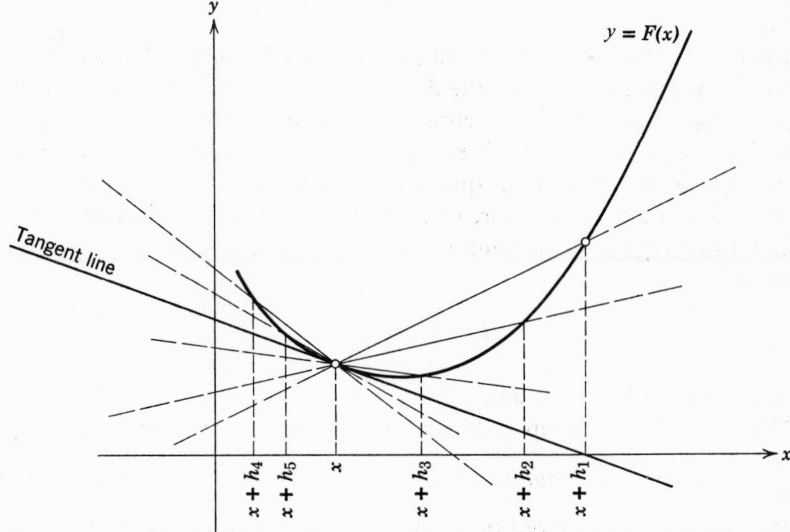

Fig. III.2

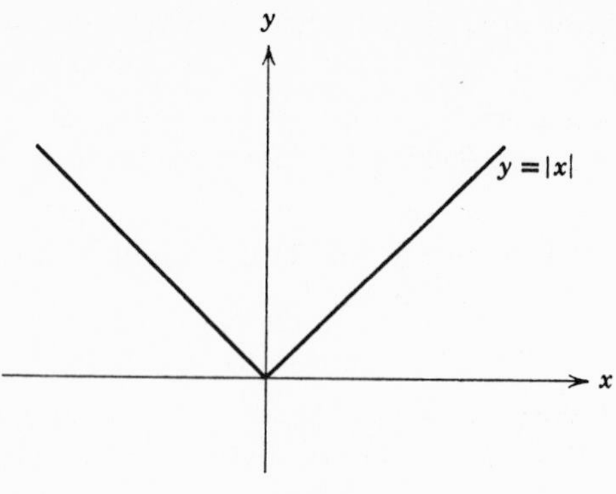

Fig. III.3

On the other hand, if $h < 0$, then $|h| = -h$ and

$$F'(0) = \lim_{h\to 0} \frac{-h}{h} = \lim_{h\to 0} (-1) = -1.$$

Thus we see that the limit does not exist because we obtain different values, depending on whether we approach the origin from the right or from the left. This is geometrically quite obvious. If we approach the origin from the right, all chords (which incidentally coincide with the curve itself) have the slope 1 and if we approach from the left, all chords have the slope -1. At the origin itself, there is no tangent line, as pointed out earlier.

Before we consider further examples, let us introduce some technical terms. The process by which the derivative of a function is found is called *differentiation process*, as we mentioned in the preceding section, the corresponding verb being "to differentiate." (The derivative is sometimes referred to as the *differential* quotient.) Specifically: we *differentiate the function* $F(x)$ *with respect to* x, meaning that we find the derivative $F'(x)$. This terminology finds its counterpart in the following, often very useful, notation:

$$F'(x) = \frac{dF(x)}{dx}.$$

(*Read:* "de ef of ex over de ex.")

However, this notation is to be handled with great care. The d's in $\frac{dF(x)}{dx}$ are symbols and *not* numbers. So, do not attempt to cancel the d's, unless you want to wipe out the harvest of many centuries of mathematical thought and effort.

Because the values of $F(x)$ are customarily denoted by $y{:}y = F(x)$, we also use $\frac{dy}{dx}$ to denote the derivative of the function $y = F(x)$ with respect to x. Summarizing, we list all the customary notations for the derivative

$$F'(x) = \frac{dF(x)}{dx} = \frac{d}{dx}F(x) = \frac{dy}{dx} = y'.$$

If we have, for example, the function $w = G(z)$, then the derivative of G with respect to z can be designated by either one of the following symbols:

$$G'(z) = \frac{dG(z)}{dz} = \frac{d}{dz}G(z) = \frac{dw}{dz} = w'.$$

Let us now consider a few simple examples. First, we take the function

$$y = C$$

where C is a constant number. This function is represented by a horizontal line C units away from the x-axis (see Fig. III.4). Clearly, the tangent line to this curve coincides with the curve itself and has the slope zero. This can also be seen from the formal standpoint by taking the derivative (or, as we may say, by differentiating C with respect to x):

$$\frac{dC}{dx} = \lim_{h\to 0}\frac{C - C}{h} = \lim_{h\to 0} 0 = 0,$$

i.e.,

$$\frac{dC}{dx} = 0. \tag{III.3}$$

In words: *The derivative of a constant is zero.*

Next, we take the function

$$y = x.$$

This function is a straight line with slope 1. The tangent line coincides with the graph and, hence, the derivative has to be 1. This is indeed the case

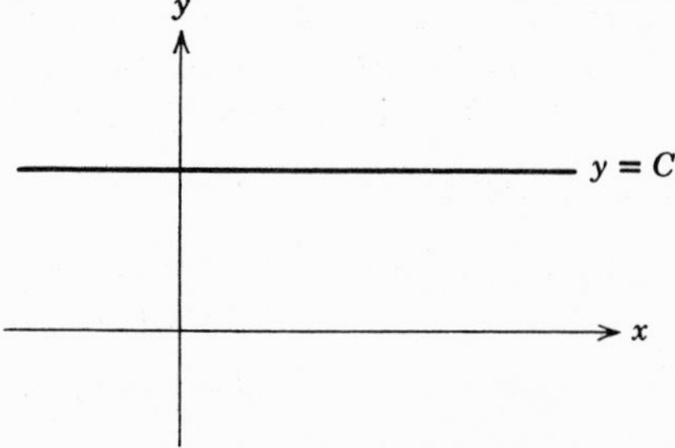

Fig. III.4

as we can verify directly:

$$\frac{dx}{dx} = \lim_{h\to 0} \frac{x + h - x}{h} = \lim_{h\to 0} \frac{h}{h} = \lim_{h\to 0} 1 = 1,$$

i.e.,

$$\frac{dx}{dx} = 1. \tag{III.4}$$

(Again, we wish to point out that this result cannot be obtained simply by cancellation of dx in numerator and denominator, even if it may look appealing. d is a symbol, hence dx is a symbol and *not* a number.)

Finally, we consider the quadratic parabola

$$y = x^2.$$

We find for its derivative

$$\frac{dx^2}{dx} = \lim_{h\to 0} \frac{(x + h)^2 - x^2}{h} = \lim_{h\to 0} \frac{x^2 + 2hx + h^2 - x^2}{h} = \lim_{h\to 0} \frac{2hx + h^2}{h}$$

$$= \lim_{h\to 0} (2x + h) = 2x,$$

i.e.,

$$\frac{dx^2}{dx} = 2x. \tag{III.5}$$

(Now, try to get this result by cancellations without any hokus-pokus!)

We remind the reader that the result in (III.5) is in agreement with the result which we obtained in Chapter I, Section 10, where we discussed the tangent to the parabola. We also point out that the formulas (III.4) and (III.5) seem to be in agreement with the differentiation formulas which we listed at the end of the preceding section.

Problems III.1–III.4

III.1. Given $F(x) = x^2$. Evaluate $\dfrac{F(x + h) - F(x)}{h}$ at the point $x = 1$ for the following values of h: $h = 1, 0.5, 0.2, 0.1, 0.01, 0.001$. Observe that the sequence of values thus obtained tends to the limit 2 in agreement with (III.5).

III.2. Do the same as in Problem III.1 with the function $F(x) = x^3$. Make a guess about the limit as $h \to 0$ and compare your result with the formula $\left(\dfrac{x^3}{3}\right)' = x^2$ from Chapter II, Section 15.

III.3. Simplify the difference quotients for the following functions $F(x)$ to a point where the factor h in numerator and denominator cancels out:

(*a*) $F(x) = x^3$ (*b*) $F(x) = \sqrt{x}$

(*c*) $F(x) = \dfrac{1}{x}$ (*d*) $F(x) = (1 - x)^2$

III.4. Consider the difference quotient of the function $y = \sin x$. By a skilful manipulation of the identity in Problem AIII.14 of Appendix III, Section 4, it can be shown that

$$\sin \alpha - \sin \beta = 2 \cos \frac{\alpha + \beta}{2} \sin \frac{\alpha - \beta}{2}.$$

Let $\alpha = x + h$, $\beta = x$ and simplify the difference quotient until you can write it as a product of $\frac{\sin h/2}{h/2}$ with some other function.

2. DIFFERENTIATION RULES

We will devote this section to a few basic rules which serve to facilitate to some extent the differentiation process of functions.

First, let us consider the function

$$y = 4x^2.$$

According to the definition of the derivative given in (III.2), we obtain

$$y' = \lim_{h \to 0} \frac{4(x + h)^2 - 4x^2}{h} = \lim_{h \to 0} \frac{4x^2 + 8hx + 4h^2 - 4x^2}{h}$$

$$= \lim_{h \to 0} \frac{8xh + 4h^2}{h} = \lim_{h \to 0} (8x + 4h) = 8x = 4 \cdot 2x.$$

In the preceding section we saw that

$$\frac{dx^2}{dx} = 2x$$

and we see now that

$$\frac{d(4x^2)}{dx} = 4 \cdot 2x$$

which appears to be simply $4 \dfrac{dx^2}{dx}$.

That it is true, in general, that a multiplicative constant remains unchanged upon differentiation, can be seen quite easily. Let us consider

$$y = cf(x)$$

where c is a constant and $f(x)$ is a *differentiable function*, i.e., a function whose derivative exists. We obtain from the definition of the derivative

$$y' = \lim_{h \to 0} \frac{cf(x + h) - cf(x)}{h} = \lim_{h \to 0} c \frac{f(x + h) - f(x)}{h}$$

$$= c \lim_{h \to 0} \frac{f(x + h) - f(x)}{h} = cf'(x).$$

Thus we can state

$$\frac{d[cf(x)]}{dx} = c\,\frac{df(x)}{dx} \tag{III.6}$$

or in words: *a multiplicative constant remains unchanged upon differentiation.*

Next, we consider the example

$$y = 3x^2 + 2x - 5.$$

This function is the sum of the three functions

$$y_1 = 3x^2,\ y_2 = 2x,\ y_3 = -5$$

and we know from the preceding section and (III.6) that

$$\begin{aligned} y_1' &= 6x, \\ y_2' &= 2 \\ y_3' &= 0 \end{aligned}$$

[see (III.3, 4, and 5)].

Now, if it were true that

$$\frac{d}{dx}(y_1 + y_2 + y_3) = y_1' + y_2' + y_3',$$

then we would have right away

$$y' = 6x + 2 + 0.$$

That this is, indeed, the case can be seen by a direct check:

$$\begin{aligned} y' = \frac{d}{dx}(y_1 + y_2 + y_3) &= \lim_{h\to 0} \frac{3(x+h)^2 + 2(x+h) - 5 - 3x^2 - 2x + 5}{h} \\ &= \lim_{h\to 0} \frac{3x^2 + 6xh + 3h^2 + 2x + 2h - 5 - 3x^2 - 2x + 5}{h} \\ &= \lim_{h\to 0} \frac{6xh + 3h^2 + 2h}{h} = \lim_{h\to 0}(6x + 3h + 2) = 6x + 2. \end{aligned}$$

(We wish to point out that this result also follows from the formula (I.38) which we developed for the slope of the tangent line to a quadratic parabola.)

Again, we can easily see that the derivative of a sum of functions can be obtained by differentiation of each term in the sum. Consider

$$y = f_1(x) + f_2(x)$$

where $f_1(x)$ and $f_2(x)$ shall be differentiable functions. Then

$$y' = \frac{d}{dx}[f_1(x) + f_2(x)] = \lim_{h\to 0} \frac{f_1(x+h) + f_2(x+h) - f_1(x) - f_2(x)}{h}$$

$$= \lim_{h\to 0} \left(\frac{f_1(x+h) - f_1(x)}{h} + \frac{f_2(x+h) - f_2(x)}{h} \right)$$

$$= \lim_{h\to 0} \frac{f_1(x+h) - f_1(x)}{h} + \lim_{h\to 0} \frac{f_2(x+h) - f_2(x)}{h} = f_1'(x) + f_2'(x),$$

or in words: *the derivative of a sum of two functions is the sum of the derivatives of the two functions, provided that the derivatives of the two functions exist.*

This latter qualification is quite necessary as we can see from a very simple example. Take

$$f_1(x) = \begin{cases} 1 \text{ for all irrational values of } x \\ 0 \text{ for all rational values of } x \end{cases}$$

$$f_2(x) = \begin{cases} 0 \text{ for all irrational values of } x \\ 1 \text{ for all rational values of } x. \end{cases}$$

Then,

$$f_1(x) + f_2(x) = 1$$

and, consequently,

$$\frac{d}{dx}[f_1(x) + f_2(x)] = \frac{d(1)}{dx} = 0.$$

However, neither the derivative of $f_1(x)$ nor the derivative of $f_2(x)$ exists. We can show this quite easily (even though it should be obvious): Let us try to find the derivative of $f_1(x)$ at a rational point x. Then, $f_1(x + h) = f_1(h)$ because if x is rational, then $x + h$ is rational if h is rational, and irrational if h is irrational. Then we have

$$f_1'(x) = \lim_{h\to 0} \frac{f_1(x+h) - f_1(x)}{h} = \lim_{h\to 0} \frac{f_1(h) - 0}{h} = \lim_{h\to 0} \frac{f_1(h)}{h}$$

and we see that, while the denominator approaches zero, the numerator oscillates between 0 and 1. Clearly, the limit cannot exist. A similar argument shows that the limit fails to exist at every irrational point and an analogous argument holds for $f_2(x)$.

The requirement that both limits

$$\text{(III.7)} \qquad \lim_{h\to 0} \frac{f_1(x+h) - f_1(x)}{h}, \lim_{h\to 0} \frac{f_2(x+h) - f_2(x)}{h}$$

have to exist enters our argument at the point where we break the limit

$$\lim_{h\to 0} \frac{f_1(x+h) + f_2(x+h) - f_1(x) - f_2(x)}{h}$$

into the sum of the two limits (III.7). Such a procedure is only permissible if both limits exist (as we pointed out when discussing limits of sequences, Chapter II, Section 4).

Again, we can illustrate this by a simple example. Take

$$\lim_{h\to 0} \left(\frac{1}{h} - \frac{1}{h}\right).$$

Clearly,

$$\lim_{h\to 0} \frac{1}{h}$$

does not exist, i.e., is not a finite number. Hence,

$$\lim_{h\to 0} \left(\frac{1}{h} - \frac{1}{h}\right) \neq \lim_{h\to 0} \frac{1}{h} - \lim_{h\to 0} \frac{1}{h},$$

because the limit on the left side does exist:

$$\lim_{h\to 0} \left(\frac{1}{h} - \frac{1}{h}\right) = \lim_{h\to 0} 0 = 0.$$

The student might claim that "of course, if we split this limit into two limits, then we obtain $\infty - \infty$ and this is 0 anyway, or isn't it?" No, it isn't. Just try it with

$$\lim_{h\to 0} \left(\frac{1}{h} - \frac{1}{h^2}\right) = \lim_{h\to 0} \frac{h-1}{h^2}$$

which clearly does not exist. Still, if you split this limit into a sum of two limits, you obtain $\infty - \infty$.

Let us return to our problem at hand. We have shown thus far that the derivative of a sum of two functions is the sum of the derivatives of the two functions. We can generalize this statement easily to a sum of three functions, and, as a matter of fact, to a sum of any finite number of functions. Take

$$y = f_1(x) + f_2(x) + f_3(x)$$

and assume that the derivatives $f_i'(x)$ $(i = 1, 2, 3)$ exist. Then, we combine the two functions $f_2(x) + f_3(x)$ to a function $F(x)$:

$$F(x) = f_2(x) + f_3(x)$$

and have

$$y = f_1(x) + F(x),$$

i.e., a sum of two functions to which we can apply the rule which we have already established:

$$y' = f_1'(x) + F'(x).$$

Now, what is $F'(x)$? Again, $F(x)$ is the sum of two functions and, hence, accessible to our rule and we obtain

$$F'(x) = f_2'(x) + f_3'(x).$$

Thus, combining our partial results, we have

$$y' = f_1'(x) + f_2'(x) + f_3'(x).$$

In general, one can show that the derivative of a sum of n functions is equal to the sum of the derivatives of the n functions, provided the derivatives of the n functions exist:

$$\frac{d}{dx}\sum_{k=1}^{n} f_k(x) = \sum_{k=1}^{n} f_k'(x).$$

(For the case of $n = 4$ and 5, see Problems III.5 and 6.)

Now, we can really live it up and find the derivative of

$$y = 25x^2 + 8x - 786935420$$

right away: We obtain, observing the differentiation formulas of the preceding section and the two rules of this section,

$$y' = 25 \cdot 2x + 8 \cdot 1 - 0 = 50x + 8.$$

(We remind the reader that we could have obtained this result as early as Chapter I, Section 10, when we discussed the slope of the tangent line to a quadratic parabola.)

Problems III.5–III.10

III.5. Suppose $f_i'(x)$ $(i = 1, 2, 3, 4)$ exist. Show that

$$\frac{d}{dx}[f_1(x) + f_2(x) + f_3(x) + f_4(x)] = f_1'(x) + f_2'(x) + f_3'(x) + f_4'(x).$$

III.6. Same as in Problem III.5 with $i = 1, 2, 3, 4, 5$. (For the sum of five functions.)

III.7. Differentiate:

(a) $y = 4x^2 - 3x + 4$ (b) $y = -x^2 + 3x + 1$

(c) $y = (x + 10)^2$ (d) $y = (x - 1)(x + 1)$

III.8. Find the equation of the tangent line to the parabola

$$y = 2x^2 - 3x + 12$$

at the point $P(2, 14)$.

III.9. At which point does the curve

$$y = 4x^2 - 3x + 2$$

have a tangent line with slope 6?

III.10. At which point does the curve

$$y = 4x^2 - 16x + 12$$

have a horizontal tangent line? (A horizontal line has the slope 0.)

3. DIFFERENTIATION OF SOME SIMPLE FUNCTIONS

We are now going to find the derivative of some simple functions by the limit process which serves as the definition of the derivative.

First, let us consider

$$y = x^3.$$

We obtain

$$\frac{d(x^3)}{dx} = \lim_{h\to 0} \frac{(x+h)^3 - x^3}{h} = \lim_{h\to 0} \frac{x^3 + 3x^2h + 3xh^2 + h^3 - x^3}{h}$$

$$= \lim_{h\to 0} \frac{3x^2h + 3xh^2 + h^3}{h} = \lim_{h\to 0} (3x^2 + 3xh + h^2) = 3x^2.$$

Hence,

(III.8) $$\frac{d(x^3)}{dx} = 3x^2.$$

Now, if we inspect the following table which is compiled from the results (III.3), (III.4), (III.5) of Section 1 and (III.8) of this section,

y	y'
1	0
x	1
x^2	$2x$
x^3	$3x^2$

we can make an intelligent guess as to the derivatives of other powers of x, such as

$$\frac{d(x^4)}{dx} = 4x^3, \qquad \frac{d(x^5)}{dx} = 5x^4, \text{ etc.}$$

(See Problems III.11 and 12.)

It would appear that in taking the derivative of

$$y = x^n$$

where n is a positive integer or zero, we multiply the function by the exponent and diminish the exponent by 1:

$$\frac{d(x^n)}{dx} = nx^{n-1}. \tag{III.9}$$

(For a proof of this formula, see Problem III.18.)

If this were true also for negative exponents, then we would obtain for $n = -1$:

$$\frac{d(x^{-1})}{dx} = \frac{d\left(\frac{1}{x}\right)}{dx} = -1 \cdot x^{-2} = -\frac{1}{x^2}.$$

We can check directly that this is indeed the case:

$$\frac{d\left(\frac{1}{x}\right)}{dx} = \lim_{h\to 0}\frac{\frac{1}{x+h} - \frac{1}{x}}{h} = \lim_{h\to 0}\frac{\frac{x-(x+h)}{x(x+h)}}{h} = \lim_{h\to 0}\frac{-h}{hx(x+h)}$$

$$= \lim_{h\to 0}\frac{-1}{x(x+h)} = \frac{-1}{x(x+0)} = -\frac{1}{x^2}.$$

Thus,

$$\frac{d\left(\frac{1}{x}\right)}{dx} = -\frac{1}{x^2}. \tag{III.10}$$

Let us now live dangerously and consider the exponent $n = \frac{1}{2}$. If (III.9) also happens to be true for rational exponents, then we could expect that

$$\frac{d(x^{1/2})}{dx} = \frac{d\sqrt{x}}{dx} = \frac{1}{2}x^{-(1/2)} = \frac{1}{2\sqrt{x}}.$$

Again, a direct check will show that this is indeed the case:

$$\frac{d\sqrt{x}}{dx} = \lim_{h\to 0}\frac{\sqrt{x+h}-\sqrt{x}}{h} = \lim_{h\to 0}\frac{\sqrt{x+h}-\sqrt{x}}{h}\cdot\frac{\sqrt{x+h}+\sqrt{x}}{\sqrt{x+h}+\sqrt{x}}$$

$$= \lim_{h\to 0}\frac{x+h-x}{h(\sqrt{x+h}+\sqrt{x})} = \lim_{h\to 0}\frac{h}{h(\sqrt{x+h}+\sqrt{x})} = \lim_{h\to 0}\frac{1}{\sqrt{x+h}+\sqrt{x}}$$

$$= \frac{1}{\sqrt{x+0}+\sqrt{x}} = \frac{1}{2\sqrt{x}}.$$

Thus,

$$\frac{d\sqrt{x}}{dx} = \frac{1}{2\sqrt{x}}. \tag{III.11}$$

Similarly, we compute

$$\frac{d(x^{-(1/2)})}{dx} = \lim_{h\to 0} \frac{\dfrac{1}{\sqrt{x+h}} - \dfrac{1}{\sqrt{x}}}{h} = \lim_{h\to 0} \frac{\dfrac{\sqrt{x} - \sqrt{x+h}}{\sqrt{x}\sqrt{x+h}}}{h} = \lim_{h\to 0} \frac{\sqrt{x} - \sqrt{x+h}}{h\sqrt{x}\sqrt{x+h}}$$

$$= \lim_{h\to 0} \frac{\sqrt{x} - \sqrt{x+h}}{h\sqrt{x}\sqrt{x+h}} \cdot \frac{\sqrt{x} + \sqrt{x+h}}{\sqrt{x} + \sqrt{x+h}}$$

$$= \lim_{h\to 0} \frac{x - (x+h)}{h\sqrt{x}\sqrt{x+h}(\sqrt{x} + \sqrt{x+h})}$$

$$= \lim_{h\to 0} \frac{-h}{h\sqrt{x}\sqrt{x+h}(\sqrt{x} + \sqrt{x+h})}$$

$$= \lim_{h\to 0} \frac{-1}{\sqrt{x}\sqrt{x+h}(\sqrt{x} + \sqrt{x+h})}$$

$$= \frac{-1}{\sqrt{x}\sqrt{x+0}(\sqrt{x} + \sqrt{x+0})} = \frac{-1}{2\sqrt{x^3}}.$$

Thus,

$$\text{(III.12)} \qquad \frac{d\dfrac{1}{\sqrt{x}}}{dx} = -\frac{1}{2\sqrt{x^3}},$$

which can also be obtained from a direct application of (III.9) as the reader can easily verify.

We wish to state without proof that (III.9) is universally true for any real exponent, i.e., for any positive or negative number, be it rational or irrational. The proof of (III.9) for positive integers is quite simple (see Problem III.18). It is not difficult for negative integers, either, and can be found in most introductory treatments of the Calculus. There are no real difficulties to establish it for positive or negative fractions, which is also done in most Calculus books. It is, however, quite difficult and requires some background knowledge to establish the validity of (III.9) for irrational numbers. This is usually accomplished in a course that is customarily called "Advanced Calculus."

Problems III.11–III.29

III.11. Find the derivative of $y = x^4$ by the limit process and compare the result with the result obtained by a direct application of (III.9).

III.12. Same as in Problem III.11 for $y = x^5$.

III.13. Find the derivative of $y = x^{1/3}$ by the limit process.

III.14. Find the derivative of $y = x + \dfrac{1}{x}$.

III.15. Find the derivative of

(*a*) $y = 7x^5 - 3x^4 + 5x^3 - x^2 + 2x + 7$ (*b*) $y = \dfrac{1 - x}{x^2}$

(*c*) $y = 4x^2 - 1 + \dfrac{1}{x}$ (*d*) $y = \dfrac{1 - x^2}{1 + x}$

III.16. Demonstrate that

$$\frac{a^n - b^n}{a - b} = a^{n-1} + a^{n-2}b + a^{n-3}b^2 + \cdots + ab^{n-2} + b^{n-1}.$$

(*Hint:* Multiply both sides by $(a - b)$ and show that all terms on the right side except a^n and $-b^n$ cancel out.)

III.17. Let $a = x + h$ and $b = x$ in Problem III.16 and write the formula in terms of x and h.

III.18. Show that

$$\frac{d(x^n)}{dx} = nx^{n-1}$$

for any positive integer n. (*Hint:* Transform the difference quotient according to the formula you obtained in Problem III.17.)

III.19. Find the derivative of

$$y = \sqrt{x^2 + y_1^2},$$

where y_1 is a constant, by the limit process.

III.20. Find the derivative of

$$y = \sqrt{(x - x_2)^2 + y_2^2}$$

where x_2, y_2 are constants, by the limit process.

III.21. Take $y = f(x)$. Then the derivative is denoted by $y' = f'(x)$. $f'(x)$ is, in general, a function of x. Now we differentiate $f'(x)$ again with respect to x and denote the result by

$$y'' = [f'(x)]' = f''(x)$$

and call it the second derivative of f with respect to x. Similarly, we define the third derivative as the derivative of the second derivative, etc.

(*a*) Find the 4th derivative of $y = x^4$.
(*b*) Find the 5th derivative of $y = x^4$.
(*c*) Find the nth derivative of $y = x^n$.

III.22. Find the equation of the tangent line to the parabola

$$y = x^2 + 2x + 4$$

at the point with the abscissa 3.

III.23. Find the equation of the tangent line to the curve

$$y = x + \frac{1}{x}$$

at the point with the abscissa $x = 1$.

III.24. Find the intersection point of the tangent lines to the curve $y = x^3 - 3x^2 + 5$ at the points with the abscissae $x = 1$ and $x = 3$.

III.25. At what points does the curve $y = x^3 - 5x + 3$ have horizontal tangent lines?

III.26. At what points does the curve $y = x + \frac{1}{x}$ have horizontal tangent lines?

III.27. In which interval(s) does the curve $y = x^3 + 4x^2 - 2x + 2$ have a positive slope? (The slope of a curve at a point is defined as the slope of the tangent line to the curve at this point.)

III.28. Find all points at which the curve $y = 3x^5 - 25x^3 + 60x + 3$ has a horizontal tangent line. (*Hint:* Note that an equation of the type $ax^4 + bx^2 + c = 0$ can be solved for x^2 by the quadratic formula. Subsequently, x can be found by extraction of a square root.)

III.29. Given $y = \sin x$. Find y'. (*Hint:* Use the result of Problem III.4.)

▶4. THE CHAIN-RULE

Suppose we wish to differentiate the function

(III.13) $$y = (1 + x^2)^{365}.$$

This can be done, in principle, by the rules which we derived in the preceding two sections for the differentiation of polynomials, because, if we expand the right side of (III.13) according to the binomial formula, we obtain a polynomial of the 730th degree which contains 366 terms.

Before we dismiss this problem as solved, however, let us stop and think for a moment. If we actually expand the right side of (III.13) we would have to—according to a rough estimate—process about 36000 digits. If we allow 10 seconds for the processing of every digit (computation, writing, etc.), we have to keep working for about 4 days. It will take at least another 4 days to differentiate this polynomial, because every one of the digits has to be processed again, so that we come up with the (conservative) estimate of 8 days of continuous and rather uninspiring work required for the differentiation of (III.13). Nobody could possibly want this result that badly.

We will develop in this section a method that will enable us to achieve this result, and similar ones, in a matter of seconds. Let us consider the auxiliary function

$$u = 1 + x^2.$$

Then (III.13) can be written as

$$y = u^{365}$$

and we see immediately, that, according to (III.9),

$$\frac{dy}{du} = 365u^{364}$$

while

$$\frac{du}{dx} = 2x.$$

Now, if dy, du, and dx could be handled like numbers, everything would be quite easy. We could cancel

$$\frac{dy}{\cancel{du}} \cdot \frac{\cancel{du}}{dx} = \frac{dy}{dx}$$

and obtain as result

$$\frac{dy}{dx} = 365u^{364}2x = 365(1 + x^2)^{364}2x = 730x(1 + x^2)^{364}.$$

This procedure is indeed permissible, even though it cannot be justified simply by cancellation of terms which, as we know, are *not* numbers, but rather mysterious symbols. In order to establish the permissibility of this process, we may argue as follows: We consider

$$y = f(u)$$

where we assume that $f'(u) = \dfrac{df(u)}{du}$ exists and

$$u = g(x)$$

where we assume that $g'(x) = \dfrac{dg(x)}{dx}$ exists.

Thus, y will ultimately appear as a function of x:

$$y = f(g(x)).$$

We speak in such a case of a *function of a function.*

Now, by the definition of the derivative, (III.2), we have

$$\frac{dy}{dx} = \lim_{h \to 0} \frac{f(g(x + h)) - f(g(x))}{h}.$$

What is $g(x + h)$? We have $g(x) = u$. Thus, if x changes by the small amount h, then the value of $g(x)$ will change by some amount k:

$$g(x + h) = u + k$$

and it is quite obvious that $k \to 0$ as $h \to 0$ [unless the function $g(x)$ has a discontinuity at this particular point, which we can exclude since we assumed that $g'(x)$ exists (and how could a function have a tangent line at a point where it is not even continuous?)].

Hence, we can write

$$\frac{dy}{dx} = \lim_{\substack{h\to 0\\(k\to 0)}} \frac{f(u+k)-f(u)}{h}.$$

The expression under the limit sign will not change its value if we multiply it by

$$1 = \frac{u+k-u}{k} = \frac{u(x+h)-u(x)}{k}.$$

Then

$$\frac{dy}{dx} = \lim_{\substack{h\to 0\\(k\to 0)}} \frac{f(u+k)-f(u)}{h} \cdot \frac{u(x+h)-u(x)}{k}$$
$$= \lim_{\substack{h\to 0\\(k\to 0)}} \frac{f(u+k)-f(u)}{k} \cdot \frac{u(x+h)-u(x)}{h}.$$

We assumed that $f'(u)$ as well as $g'(x)$ exist. Hence, both fractions under the limit sign approach a limit and we can use our rule according to which the limit of a product is equal to the product of the limit, provided that both limits exist and we obtain

$$\text{(III.14)} \qquad \frac{dy}{dx} = \lim_{k\to 0} \frac{f(u+k)-f(u)}{k} \lim_{h\to 0} \frac{g(x+h)-g(x)}{h}$$
$$= f'(u)g'(x) = \frac{dy}{du}\frac{du}{dx}.$$

In words: *The derivative of a function f of a function g of x with respect to x is obtained by differentiation of f with respect to the function g and then multiplication by the derivative of g with respect to x* (the so-called *inner derivative*).

This is called the *chain rule*.

Now we can return to our original time-consuming problem: We have, according to (III.14),

$$\frac{d(1+x^2)^{365}}{dx} = \frac{du^{365}}{du} \cdot \frac{d(1+x^2)}{dx} = 365u^{364}2x = 730(1+x^2)^{364}.$$

We see that (III.14) provides, indeed, for a substantial simplification over the process which we outlined in the beginning of this section.

In practice, we do not actually make a substitution by u at all. One differentiates $(1 + x^2)^{365}$ "with respect to $(1 + x^2)$" and then multiplies the result by the "inner derivative" of $(1 + x^2)$, namely $2x$, and that is that.

To demonstrate the wide range of applications of the chain rule, let us consider the following example. Take

$$y = \sqrt{x^3 - 3x^2 + 16}.$$

According to (III.11),

$$\frac{d\sqrt{u}}{du} = \frac{1}{2\sqrt{u}}.$$

Hence, we obtain with the chain rule

$$\frac{d\sqrt{x^3 - 3x^2 + 16}}{dx} = \frac{1}{2\sqrt{x^3 - 3x^2 + 16}}(3x^2 - 6x).$$

The reader will certainly appreciate this shortcut after he has tried to find the same derivative by going through the lengthy and awkward limit process, as we have done in some instances in Section 3 of this chapter.

Problems III.30–III.33

III.30. Write the following rule symbolically and justify it: The derivative of a square root of an expression is equal to one half the derivative of the expression, divided by the square root.

III.31. Differentiate by the chain rule:

(a) $y = \dfrac{1}{\sqrt{x^2 - 4}}$ [see (III.12)]

(b) $y = \sqrt[3]{x^4 - 3x^2 + 4x}$ (see Problem III.13)

(c) $y = \sqrt{x + 1}(x + 1)$ (Find first the derivative of $u^{3/2}$ by the limit process.)

(d) $y = x - 7 + \dfrac{1}{x - 7}$ (see Problem III.14.)

III.32. Differentiate by the chain rule

(a) $y = \sin(x^2)$ (b) $y = \sin(1 - 3x + x^3)$

(c) $y = \sqrt{\sin x}$ (d) $y = \sin^2 x$

(see Problem III.29.)

III.33. The chain rule can be generalized to functions of functions of functions of . . . . Specifically, if $y = f(u)$, $u = g(v)$, $v = h(x)$, then

$$\frac{dy}{dx} = \frac{dy}{du} \cdot \frac{du}{dv} \cdot \frac{dv}{dx}.$$

Using this rule, find the derivative of

$$y = \sqrt{1 + (x^2 - 2x + 4)^{12}}$$

(*Hint:* Let $y = \sqrt{u}$, $u = 1 + v^{12}$, $v = x^2 - 2x + 4$.) ◀

5. INTEGRATION BY ANTIDIFFERENTIATION

We have seen in Chapter II, Section 15, that if

$$\int_a^x f(u)\,du = F(x),$$

for some constant lower integration limit a, then

$$F'(x) = f(x).$$

For example, in Chapter II, Section 13, we found that with $f(x) = x^2$,

$$\int_a^b u^2\,du = \frac{b^3}{3} - \frac{a^3}{3}.$$

Now let $b = x$ and obtain

$$\int_a^x u^2 du = \frac{x^3}{3} - \frac{a^3}{3} = F(x)$$

and we know from the preceding section that

$$F'(x) = \frac{d}{dx}\left(\frac{x^3}{3} - \frac{a^3}{3}\right) = x^2.$$

We can see that with every function $f(x)$ for which the integral exists and every lower integration limit a within the domain in which the integral exists, there corresponds a function $F(x)$ such that

$$\int_a^x f(u)\,du = F(x)$$

where $F'(x) = f(x)$. However, if we do not specify the lower integration limit a, then there are clearly infinitely many functions $F(x)$ with the property that $F'(x) = f(x)$, and all these functions differ from each other only by an additive constant. Certainly, if we take $F(x)$ and $F(x) + C$, where C is an arbitrary constant, then

$$\frac{d}{dx}[F(x) + C] = \frac{dF(x)}{dx} + \frac{dC}{dx} = \frac{dF(x)}{dx}$$

and if $F'(x) = f(x)$, then it is also true that $\frac{d}{dx}[F(x) + C] = f(x)$.

Take, for example, the two functions

$$x^2 + 2x + 1 \text{ and } x^2 + 2x + 1896.$$

We obtain from both functions the same derivative, $2x + 2$.

If a function $F(x)$ is in relation

$$F'(x) = f(x) \tag{III.15}$$

to a function $f(x)$, then we call $F(x)$ the *antiderivative* of $f(x)$. The reason for this terminology is obvious: $f(x)$ is the derivative of $F(x)$, i.e., $f(x)$ is found from $F(x)$ by differentiation. So, in order to get back to $F(x)$ from $f(x)$ we have to do the opposite of what we have done in getting from $F(x)$ to $f(x)$, namely, *anti*differentiate.

Since there correspond with $f(x)$ infinitely many functions that differ from each other by an additive constant only, if we do not specify in

$$\int_a^x f(u)\,du = F(x)$$

the constant lower integration limit, we also call $F(x) + C$ the *indefinite integral of* $f(x)$ and write

$$\int f(x)\,dx = F(x) + C \tag{III.16}$$

where C is an arbitrary constant.

Here it is expressed explicitly that the antiderivative is determined except for an additive constant, which we call *integration constant*. Therefore, the relation (III.16) is to be preferred to (III.15), even though both statements express the same thing.

For example,

$$\int (x^2 - 4x + 3)\,dx = \frac{x^3}{3} - 2x^2 + 3x + C$$

is equivalent to

$$\frac{d}{dx}\left(\frac{x^3}{3} - 2x^2 + 3x + C\right) = x^2 - 4x + 3,$$

where C is an arbitrary constant.

If we consider the problem of finding the equation of a curve which has at any point with the abscissa x the slope $y' = 3x^2 - 2x + 1$ and passes through the point $P(0, 1)$, we proceed as follows.

First, we find the antiderivative (the indefinite integral) of y', namely, y:

$$y = \int (3x^2 - 2x + 1)\,dx = x^3 - x^2 + x + C$$

and then we determine the value of the integration constant C so that $y = 1$ when $x = 0$, obtaining $C = 1$. Thus,

$$y = x^3 - x^2 + x + 1$$

is the solution to our problem.

Now we can relate the antidifferentiation process to the process of evaluation of a definite integral as follows. Suppose we want to find

$$\int_a^b f(x)\,dx.$$

First, we find by antidifferentiation the indefinite integral of $f(x)$:

$$\int f(x)\,dx = F(x) + C.$$

We know that

$$\int_\alpha^a f(x)\,dx = F(a) + C$$

$$\int_\alpha^b f(x)\,dx = F(b) + C$$

for some suitable lower integration limit α and some constant C. Then,

$$\int_a^b f(x)\,dx = \int_\alpha^b f(x)\,dx - \int_\alpha^a f(x)\,dx = F(b) + C - F(a) - C$$
$$= F(b) - F(a)$$

as we have already seen in Chapter II, Section 15.

If $F(x)$ is the antiderivative of $f(x)$, it is also customary to write

$$\int_a^b f(x)\,dx = F(x)\Big|_a^b$$

meaning, that $F(x)$ is to be taken at the upper integration limit $x = a$ and from this $F(x)$ taken at the lower integration limit $x = b$ is to be subtracted. For example,

$$\int_1^2 (3x^2 - 2x + 1)\,dx = (x^3 - x^2 + x)\Big|_1^2 = 6 - 1 = 5.$$

We can state now all the differentiation formulas which we have developed thus far as antidifferentiation formulas, or *integration formulas*, as they are customarily called. We have seen in Section 1 that

$$\frac{dC}{dx} = 0,$$

i.e., C is the antiderivative of 0 (C is an arbitrary constant):

(III.17) $$\int 0\,dx = C.$$

From

$$\frac{dx}{dx} = 1$$

follows now

$$\int 1\,dx = \int dx = x + C$$

and from

$$\frac{dx^2}{dx} = 2x$$

it follows after division by 2 that

$$\int x\,dx = \frac{1}{2}x^2 + C, \text{ etc.}$$

In general, we obtain from (III.9), Section 3,

$$\frac{dx^n}{dx} = nx^{n-1}$$

after division by n and writing $m + 1$ instead of n (n is an integer, hence $m + 1$ is also an integer)

$$\text{(III.18)} \qquad \int x^m\,dx = \frac{x^{m+1}}{m+1} + C.$$

This formula is loaded with danger because, if $m = -1$, we obtain $\frac{x^0}{0} = \frac{1}{0}$ on the right side which is quite senseless. So we have to demand that in formula (III.18)

$$m \neq -1.$$

Otherwise we can say about (III.18) the same thing that we stated about the differentiation formula (III.9), namely, that it is valid for all real numbers m (except, of course, for $m = -1$).

This is funny in a way, because $m = -1$ corresponds to $n = 0$ and the differentiation formula (III.9) *is valid* for $n = 0$. On the other hand, we see from (III.9) that no matter what value of n we might choose, we cannot possibly obtain $\frac{1}{x}$ as the derivative of a power of x. Hence, $\frac{1}{x}$ does not appear to have an antiderivative among the powers of x.

It can be shown, however, that there is a function, call it $l(x)$, which has $\frac{1}{x}$ as its derivative or, as we may state, is such that

$$\int \frac{1}{x}\,dx = l(x) + C,\ x > 0.$$

We choose the constant C such that

$$\text{(III.19)} \qquad \int_1^x \frac{1}{u}\,du = l(x).$$

It can be shown that the function defined in (III.19) has the properties of a logarithm, namely,

$$l(xy) = l(x) + l(y),$$

$$l\left(\frac{x}{y}\right) = l(x) - l(y),$$

$$l(x^\alpha) = \alpha l(x).$$

$l(x)$ is called the *natural logarithm*. The numerical values of $l(x)$ can be found to any degree of accuracy from (III.19) by any one of the approximation formulas for the evaluation of definite integrals. We found, for example, in Problem II.50 that

$$l(2) = \int_1^2 \frac{1}{u}\, du = 0.6 \cdots$$

Problems III.34–III.41

III.34. Find the antiderivative of

(*a*) $y' = x^2 + 4x - 1$ (*b*) $y' = x^3 - 3x^2 + 2x + 1$

(*c*) $y' = x^4 + x^2 + 1$ (*d*) $y' = 7x^5 + 3x^3 - 2x^2 + 12x + 3$

(*e*) $y' = \dfrac{1}{\sqrt{x}}$ (*f*) $y' = -\dfrac{12}{x^2} + 3x$

III.35. Find

(*a*) $\int (x^3 - 4x^2 + 4x + 7)\, dx$ (*b*) $\int (x^4 + x^3 + x^2 + x + 1)\, dx$

(*c*) $\int (4x^3 - 3x^2 + 2x + 1)\, dx$

(*d*) $\int (6x^5 + 5x^4 + 4x^3 + 3x^2 + 2x + 1)\, dx$

(*e*) $\int \dfrac{dx}{\sqrt{x^3}}$ (*f*) $\int \dfrac{dx}{x^2}$

III.36. Find the equation for the curve which has for any x the slope

$$y' = x^2 + 3x + 4$$

and passes through the point $P(1, 3)$.

III.37. Utilizing the antidifferentiation process, evaluate the following definite integrals:

(*a*) $\int_1^2 (x^3 - 3x^2 + 1)\, dx$ (*b*) $\int_2^5 (x^2 - 4x + 5)\, dx$

(*c*) $\int_{-1}^2 (x^4 + x + 3)\, dx$ (*d*) $\int_{-1}^1 (x^3 - 4x)\, dx$

III.38. Find an approximation to $l(2)$ using Simpson's rule and 32 subintervals. ($l(2) = 0.6931 \cdots$)

III.39. Same as in Problem III.38 for $l(3)$. ($l(3) = 1.0986 \cdots$)

III.40. Find an approximation to $l(6)$. (*Hint:* $l(6) = l(2.3) = l(2) + l(3)$. For $l(2)$ and $l(3)$ use the approximations found in the two preceding problems. ($l(6) = 1.7917 \cdots$)

III.41. Take $F(x) = x^2 + 2$. Clearly, $F'(x) = 2x$. Show that it is impossible to find a real number a such that

$$\int_a^x 2x\,dx = x^2 + 2.$$

Why does this not contradict our statement preceding and including formula (III.16)?

▶6. THE INVERTED CHAIN-RULE (Substitution Method)

We have seen in Section 4 that if $y = f(u)$ and $u = g(x)$, then $y = f(g(x))$ and

$$\frac{dy}{dx} = \frac{dy}{du} \cdot \frac{du}{dx}$$

[see (III.14)].
Hence, if we have an integral like

$$\int \frac{x\,dx}{\sqrt{1 + x^2}}$$

we see that with $u = 1 + x^2$ and consequently $du/dx = 2x$, the integrand is of the form

$$\frac{1}{2\sqrt{u}}\frac{du}{dx}$$

where $\dfrac{1}{2\sqrt{u}} = \dfrac{d\sqrt{u}}{du}$ [see (III.11)]. Thus we can see that $\sqrt{u}$ with $u = g(x)$ is the function, which has, according to the chain rule, $\dfrac{1}{2\sqrt{u}}\dfrac{du}{dx}$ as its derivative:

$$\frac{d\sqrt{u(x)}}{dx} = \frac{1}{2\sqrt{u}}\frac{du}{dx},$$

or, as we may write in view of (III.15) and (III.16),

$$\int \frac{1}{2\sqrt{u}}\frac{du}{dx}\,dx = \sqrt{u(x)} + C$$

which becomes, in our example with $u = 1 + x^2$,

$$\int \frac{x\,dx}{\sqrt{1+x^2}} = \int \frac{1}{2\sqrt{u}}\, 2x\,dx = \sqrt{u(x)} + C = \sqrt{1+x^2} + C.$$

We see immediately that this integration method is applicable, whenever we have an integral of the form $\int f'(u)u'(x)\,dx$ and we obtain

$$\int f'(u)u'(x)\,dx = f[u(x)] + C. \tag{III.20}$$

In practice, we apply this rule (which is obviously an inversion of the chain rule) as follows.

We have the integral

$$\int f'(u)u'(x)\,dx$$

and carry out the substitution $u = u(x)$. Then $du/dx = u'(x)$ and we have

$$\int f'(u)u'(x)\,dx = \int f'(u)\frac{du}{dx}\,dx = \int f'(u)\,du = f(u) + C.$$

Then, we substitute $u = u(x)$ back again and obtain

$$\int f'(u)u'(x)\,dx = f[u(x)] + C.$$

Let us work some more problems. Consider

$$\int \frac{dx}{(1+x)^2}.$$

We substitute

$$u = 1 + x$$

and obtain

$$\frac{du}{dx} = 1 \text{ or, as we may write, } dx = du.$$

Hence,

$$\int \frac{dx}{(1+x)^2} = \int \frac{du}{u^2} = -\frac{1}{u} + C = -\frac{1}{1+x} + C$$

(in view of (III.10).

Next consider

$$\int \frac{x^2\,dx}{(1+x^3)^2}.$$

Let

$$u = 1 + x^3. \text{ Then } \frac{du}{dx} = 3x^2 \text{ and, consequently, } x^2\,dx = \tfrac{1}{3}\,du$$

and we obtain

$$\int \frac{x^2\,dx}{(1+x^3)^2} = \frac{1}{3}\int \frac{du}{u^2} = -\frac{1}{u} + C = -\frac{1}{1+x^3} + C.$$

Finally, let us consider

$$\int x(1+x^2)^{10}\,dx.$$

Let $u = 1 + x^2$, then $du/dx = 2x$ and $x\,dx = \frac{1}{2}\,du$.
Hence

$$\int x(1+x^2)^{10}\,dx = \frac{1}{2}\int u^{10}\,du = \frac{1}{2}\cdot\frac{u^{11}}{11} + C = \frac{1}{22}(1+x^2)^{11} + C.$$

Problems III.42–III.45

III.42. Integrate

(*a*) $\int \sqrt{1+x}\,dx$ (*b*) $\int (1-x)^{780}\,dx$

(*c*) $\int \frac{1}{(1+x)^2}\,dx$ (*d*) $\int [x^2 + (1-x)^{150}]\,dx$

III.43. Integrate

(*a*) $\int x^2\sqrt{1+4x^3}\,dx$ (*b*) $\int 4x(1-7x^2)^{12}\,dx$

(*c*) $\int (1-4x^3)\sqrt{x-x^4}\,dx$ (*d*) $\int \frac{1}{x^2}\left(1-\frac{1}{x}\right)^7 dx$

III.44. Integrate

$$\int \sin x \cos x\,dx$$

(*Hint:* Let $u = \sin x$).

III.45. Integrate

$$\int \sqrt{1-\cos^2 x}\cos x\,dx.$$

7. THE DIFFERENTIAL

Suppose we wish to evaluate

$$\sqrt{16.098},$$

at least approximately, without getting involved in too much numerical computation. Clearly, the value of this square root will be a value that is quite close to 4 since $4 = \sqrt{16}$ and 16.098 is very close to 16 (and this is really the intuitive meaning of the statement that $y = \sqrt{x}$ is continuous at $x = 16$).

Let us write this square root as follows

$$\sqrt{16.098} = \sqrt{16 + 0.098}.$$

We know the value of $\sqrt{16}$ and we want to know the value of the square root for a value very close to 16. We can state this problem in a more general form as follows.

Suppose we know the value of $\sqrt{x}$ for a certain value of x and we wish to find the value of

$$\sqrt{x + h}$$

where h is a small number. So the question arises: How much bigger is $\sqrt{x+h}$ than $\sqrt{x}$? The amount by which the square root increases as x increases by the amount h is given by

$$\sqrt{x+h} - \sqrt{x}.$$

Let us divide this difference by h:

$$\frac{\sqrt{x+h} - \sqrt{x}}{h}$$

and we see that we have here the difference quotient of the function $\sqrt{x}$. We know that the difference quotient approaches the derivative $y' = \dfrac{d\sqrt{x}}{dx}$ as $h \to 0$. So we expect that for small values of h, the difference quotient will be very close to the derivative:

$$\frac{\sqrt{x+h} - \sqrt{x}}{h} \cong \frac{d\sqrt{x}}{dx}.$$

Since

$$\frac{d\sqrt{x}}{dx} = \frac{1}{2\sqrt{x}}$$

[see (III.11)], we have

$$\frac{\sqrt{x+h} - \sqrt{x}}{h} \cong \frac{1}{2\sqrt{x}}$$

and hence

$$\sqrt{x+h} - \sqrt{x} \cong \frac{1}{2\sqrt{x}}\, h.$$

Substituting $x = 16$ and $h = 0.098$,

$$\sqrt{16.098} - \sqrt{16} \cong \frac{1}{2\sqrt{16}} \cdot 0.098$$

and hence

$$\sqrt{16.098} \cong 4 + \frac{1}{8}0.098 = 4.01225$$

while the exact value accurate to five decimal places is found to be

$$\sqrt{16.098} = 4.01223 \cdots$$

as we can find by cumbersome manipulations. We see that the approximation which we obtained is really quite good.

Now, in general, we have the problem of finding the value of a function in the neighborhood of a value for which the function is known (or can be found easily):

Given $y = f(x)$. Find an approximation to $f(x + h)$ for small values of h. We proceed as in the preceding example: We consider

$$\frac{f(x + h) - f(x)}{h}$$

and argue that for small values of h, this difference quotient will not differ much from the derivative $f'(x)$:

$$\frac{f(x + h) - f(x)}{h} \cong f'(x)$$

and we obtain the approximation formula

$$f(x + h) \cong f(x) + f'(x)h. \tag{III.21}$$

The correction term $f'(x)h$ is called the *differential* of the function $f(x)$. It furnishes an approximation of the amount by which the function increases as x increases by the small amount h.

Formula (III.21) is easily accessible to geometric interpretation. We refer to Fig. III.5: We have drawn the tangent line T to the curve $y = f(x)$ at the point $[x, f(x)]$. The slope of the tangent line at this point is $f'(x)$ (see (III.2)), which we can write as

$$f'(x) = \frac{hf'(x)}{h}.$$

Since the run between x and $x + h$ is h, we see that $hf'(x)$, the correction term, represents the rise of the tangent line at $x + h$ and we see that the bold segment denoted by E represents the error which we commit in using formula (III.21) for the approximation to the increase of the function. We can easily see from Fig. III.5 that the smaller h is, the better the approximation, i.e., the smaller is the error E.

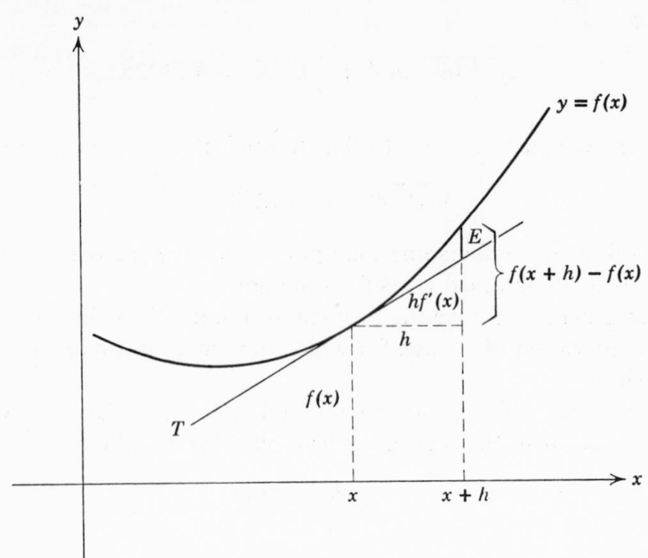

Fig. III.5

Problems III.46–III.53

III.46. Find approximations to

(*a*) $\sqrt{1.01}$ (*b*) $\sqrt{24.97}$

(*c*) $\sqrt{9.104}$ (*d*) $\sqrt{48}$

III.47. Find approximations to

(*a*) $(9.031)^2$ (*b*) $(10.0114)^2$

(*c*) $(100.236)^2$ (*d*) $(4.0029)^2$

III.48. Explain why values larger than the true values are obtained in Problem III.46 and values smaller than the true values are obtained in Problem III.47.

III.49. Find an approximation to $\sin\left(\frac{\pi}{3} + \frac{\pi}{240}\right)$. (According to the right answer to Problem III.29, $\frac{d \sin x}{dx} = \cos x$.)

III.50. A 5-ft square steel plate is subjected to heat, whereupon the edges expand by 0.0341 ft. Find an approximation to the area of the expanded plate.

III.51. The 36-sq-ft area of a square plate expands and reaches an area of 36.037 sq ft during the process. Find an approximation to the side of the expanded plate.

III.52. The radius of a circular disk of radius 1 ft expands by 0.0138 ft. Find an approximation to the area of the expanded disk.

III.53. A circular disk has initially the area of 9π sq in. The disk shrinks, when exposed to cold, to an area of 8.869π sq in. Find an approximation to the amount by which the radius became reduced.

8. NEWTON'S METHOD

In Chapter I, Section 9, we developed a formula which enables us to solve the quadratic equation

$$ax^2 + bx + c = 0.$$

We have not discussed the solution of *cubic* equations

$$ax^3 + bx^2 + cx + d = 0$$

or, for that matter, any other equation

$$f(x) = 0, \tag{III.22}$$

where $f(x)$ stands for some function of x, not necessarily a polynomial. Let us mention that there exists an algebraic formula for the solution of a *cubic* equation and there is also an algebraic formula for the solution of a *quartic* equation

$$ax^4 + bx^3 + cx^2 + dx + e = 0.$$

These formulas are so complicated that it is much better to stay away from them, no matter how badly one needs a solution. There are no algebraic formulas for the solutions of general algebraic equations of the 5th and higher order [equations of the type (III.22) with $f(x)$ representing a polynomial of the 5th or higher order with rational coefficients]. As a matter of fact, it can be shown that such formulas cannot exist. So it is not just a matter of not having found such formulas up to now. Nevertheless, there are methods which yield the solutions of special equations of higher order than the 4th and there are also various methods for solving equations of the type (III.22) for special functions $f(x)$ which are not polynomials. But there is no practical method which would allow us to deal with the general equation (III.22) without specifying what $f(x)$ is.

However, there are methods which allow us to solve approximately a general equation of the type (III.22) to any degree of desired accuracy, if we impose some restrictions on $f(x)$. The method which we will discuss here was designed by *Sir Isaac Newton* (1643–1727) and bears his name.

We will have to assume for the following that the derivative $f'(x)$ exists everywhere. Let us consider the graph of $y = f(x)$ (see Fig. III.6). Solving equation (III.22) is equivalent to the problem of finding the intersection point(s) of the graph of $y = f(x)$ with the x-axis $y = 0$. To find this intersection point, we proceed as follows: We pick just any point x_0 (see Fig. III.6), substitute it into $f(x)$ and obtain a value

$$y_0 = f(x_0).$$

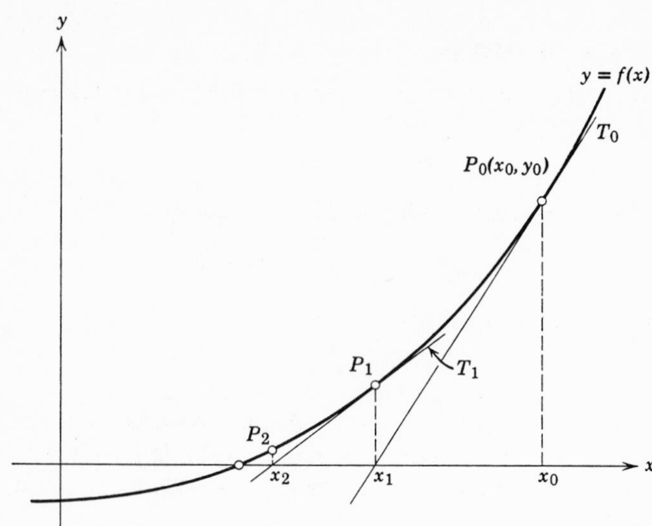

Fig. III.6

Now there are two possibilities: Either $y_0 = 0$, then we are through, because x_0 is then a solution of (III.22); or $y_0 \neq 0$. In the latter case, we locate the point $P_0(x_0, y_0)$ on the graph of $y = f(x)$ and determine the tangent line T_0 at this point by the point-slope formula [we know the coordinates of the point P_0 and the slope of T_0, namely, $f'(x_0)$]. Next, we intersect the tangent line T_0 with the x-axis and find the x-coordinate of the intersection point. We call it x_1. Again, we evaluate the function $f(x)$ for $x = x_1$ and obtain a value

$$y_1 = f(x_1).$$

If $y_1 = 0$, then $x = x_1$ is a solution of (III.22); or, more realistically, $y_1 \neq 0$. In the latter case, we locate the point $P_1(x_1, y_1)$ on the graph of $y = f(x)$ and determine the tangent line T_1 at P_1. This tangent line will intersect the x-axis at some point $x = x_2$ and we repeat the process, i.e., locate the point $P_2(x_2, y_2)$ and intersect the tangent line T_2 at P_2 with the x-axis to obtain the value $x = x_3$, etc.

In this manner we generate (we hope!) a sequence of values $x_0, x_1, x_2, x_3, \cdots$ which tends to the actual intersection point of $y = f(x)$ with $y = 0$ and which is the solution of (III.22).

Before we write down a general formula which condenses this process, let us work an example. We wish to solve

$$f(x) = x^2 - 2 = 0$$

approximately, which means that we want to find numerical approximations to $\sqrt{2}$ because $x = \sqrt{2}$ is a solution of this equation.

Let us start with just any value—for example, $x_0 = 2$ (see Fig. III.7). We obtain $P_0(2, 2)$. The slope of $y = x^2 - 2$ is given by $y' = 2x$. Hence the tangent line T_0 at P_0 has the slope 4 and, therefore, the equation of T_0 (by the point-slope formula) is

$$y - 2 = 4(x - 2)$$

or

$$y = 4x - 6.$$

We intersect T_0 with $y = 0$ by solving

$$4x - 6 = 0$$

with the solution

$$x_1 = \frac{3}{2} = 1.5.$$

Now we locate the point $P_1(\frac{3}{2}, \frac{1}{4})$. The slope of T_1 at P_1 is $2 \cdot \frac{3}{2} = 3$ and consequently

$$T_1\colon\quad y = 3x - \frac{17}{4}.$$

The intersection point of T_1 with $y = 0$ is found to be

$$x_2 = \frac{17}{12} = 1.41\dot{6}.$$

Next, we repeat the process. We obtain $P_2(\frac{17}{12}, \frac{1}{144})$ and

$$T_2\colon\quad y = \frac{17}{6}x - \frac{577}{144}$$

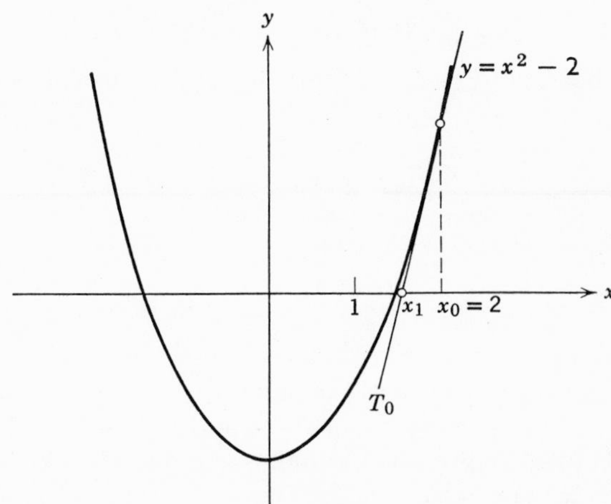

Fig. III.7

and, consequently,

$$x_3 = \frac{577}{408} = 1.4142156 \cdots \cong \sqrt{2}.$$

The value of $\sqrt{2}$ accurate to five decimal places with the sixth decimal place rounded off is found to be

$$\sqrt{2} = 1.414214.$$

So we see that our third approximation, x_3, is already very close to the true value.

In order to develop a general formula for this process, let us note that the procedure is the same at every step of our *iteration*. So we can pick out any step for our general discussion, say, the $(k + 1)$th step. After k steps, we obtain the approximation x_k:

$$y_k = f(x_k)$$

and determine the equation of the tangent line at the point $P_k(x_k, y_k)$. The slope of $y = f(x)$ at $x = x_k$ is given by

$$m_k = f'(x_k).$$

Thus we obtain from the point-slope formula

$$y - y_k = f'(x_k)(x - x_k)$$

or

$$T_k\colon\ y = f'(x_k)x - f'(x_k)x_k + y_k.$$

If we intersect this tangent line with the x-axis $y = 0$, we arrive at the equation

$$f'(x_k)x - f'(x_k)x_k + y_k = 0.$$

The solution of this equation yields the next approximation x_{k+1}:

$$x_{k+1} = \frac{f'(x_k)x_k - y_k}{f'(x_k)} = x_k - \frac{y_k}{f'(x_k)},$$

or, if we write again $f(x_k)$ instead of y_k, we have

$$\text{(III.23)} \qquad x_{k+1} = x_k - \frac{f(x_k)}{f'(x_k)}, \qquad k = 0, 1, 2, 3, \cdots$$

This method works most of the time quite well, inasmuch as the sequence $x_0, x_1, x_2, x_3, \cdots$ approaches the solution (or a solution) of $f(x) = 0$.

However, it could happen, for example, that we start out with a value x_0 such that after a number of steps a point at which the slope of $y = f(x)$ is zero is reached (see Fig. III.8), just to mention a simple case where the

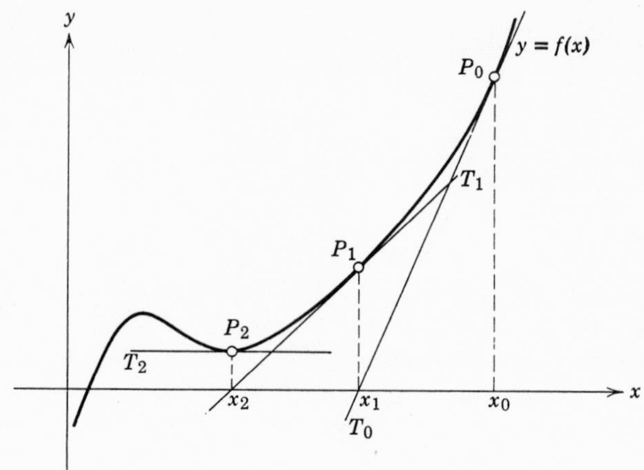

Fig. III.8

method does not work. In Fig. III.8, we unfortunately have $f'(x_2) = 0$ and, consequently, $x_3 = -\infty$ and the process falls apart.

Problems III.54–III.57

III.54. Find an approximation to $\sqrt{3}$ by Newton's method. Take $x_0 = 2$ and take three steps. (*Hint:* $\sqrt{3}$ is the solution of $x^2 - 3 = 0$.)

III.55. Find approximate solutions of

$$x^3 + 7x^2 - 5x - 35 = 0$$

by Newton's method.

(*a*) take $x_0 = 2$ (*b*) take $x_0 = -2$ (*c*) take $x_0 = 6$.

Take two steps in each case. If you are puzzled by the results, try to explain what puzzles you.

III.56. Find an approximation to $\sqrt[3]{7}$ by Newton's method. Take $x_0 = 2$ and use three steps. Compare your result with the value $\sqrt[3]{7} = 1.912931$ which is found in tables and with the approximation which you obtain for $\sqrt[3]{7} = \sqrt[3]{8 - 1}$ by the method of Section 7. (Remember: $\dfrac{d}{dx}x^{1/3} = \frac{1}{3}x^{-(2/3)}$).

III.57. Find an approximation to $\sqrt{6}$ by Newton's method. Start with $x_0 = \frac{5}{2}$ and go as far as you think is needed to obtain the result accurate to three decimal places.

9. MAXIMA AND MINIMA

Let us consider the function $y = f(x)$ and let us assume that the derivative $f'(x)$ exists for all values of x, i.e., the curve representing the function has a tangent line at every point.

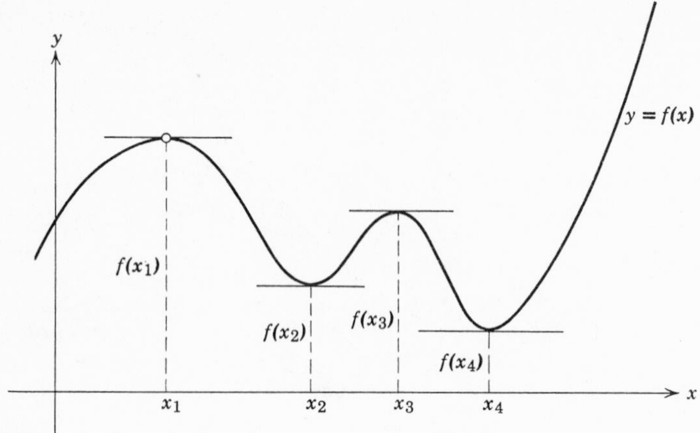

Fig. III.9

For the following discussion we refer to Fig. III.9. We observe that the value of the function at $x = x_1$ is greater than the values which the function assumes in a neighborhood of the point $x = x_1$. The same thing can be said about the point $x = x_3$. We call the value of the function at such a point a *relative maximum value*, and give the following definition.

$y = f(x)$ is said to assume a *relative maximum* at the point $x = x_1$, if there exists some neighborhood* of $x = x_1$, i.e., some intervals $x_1 - \delta_1 < x < x_1$ and $x_1 < x < x_1 + \delta_2$ such that the values of the function for all x in these intervals are smaller than the value of the function at $x = x_1$:

$f(x_1) = \text{rel. max.} f(x)$ if $f(x_1) > f(x)$ for all x in $x_1 - \delta_1 < x < x_1$ and $x_1 < x < x_1 + \delta_2$ for some δ_1, δ_2.

The reason for calling such a value a *relative* maximum is quite obvious. The function as represented in Fig. III.9 assumes much greater values than $f(x_1)$ for large values of x, but $f(x_1)$ is still a maximum, *relative to* (compared with) values in a neighborhood of x_1.

Similarly, the function $y = f(x)$ is said to assume a *relative minimum* at the point $x = x_2$, if there exists some neighborhood of $x = x_2$, i.e., some intervals $x_2 - \delta_1 < x < x_2$ and $x_2 < x < x_2 + \delta_2$ such that the values of the function for all x in these intervals are greater than the value of the function at $x = x_2$:

$f(x_2) = \text{rel. min.} f(x)$ if $f(x_2) < f(x)$ for all x in $x_2 - \delta_1 < x < x_2$ and $x_2 < x < x_2 + \delta_2$ for some δ_1, δ_2.

* The term *neighborhood* is used here in the naive sense. Technically, we are dealing here with what is called a *deleted* neighborhood.

We can see that the function depicted in Fig. III.9 has relative minimum values at x_2 and x_4 and relative maximum values at x_1 and x_3.

The question which now arises is this: If a function is not given by its graph, but rather by its mathematical representation, how do we find the values of x for which the function assumes a relative maximum or a relative minimum—or, if we lump the two together, a relative *extreme value*?

Recall that we assumed that the derivative (tangent line) exists everywhere. Again we consult Fig. III.9 and see that the tangent line to the curve at points which represent relative extreme values is *horizontal.* If it were not horizontal, then the slope of the tangent line would be either positive or negative, indicating that the function is either climbing from smaller to larger values or descending from larger to smaller values at this point.

Thus we can state: If $y = f(x)$ is a function which everywhere has a derivative, and if $y = f(x)$ has a relative extreme value at the point $x = x_0$, then it is necessary that the tangent line at this point be horizontal, i.e.,

$$f'(x_0) = 0. \tag{III.24}$$

First, let us point out that it is quite essential to assume that the tangent line exists everywhere. Consider the function

$$y = |x|$$

(see Fig. III.10) which has a minimum value at $x = 0$. Observe that the derivative at this point is not zero; as a matter of fact, it does not even exist, as we have seen in Section 1.

Second, we wish to point out that condition (III.24) is by no means sufficient, i.e., if the derivative at a certain point is zero, that does not guarantee that the function assumes at this point a relative extreme value. Consider

$$y = x^3.$$

Clearly, the derivative

$$y' = 3x^2$$

vanishes at the point $x = 0$; still, the function does not assume a relative extreme value at this point (see Fig. III.11).

Thus all we can say is: If an everywhere differentiable function has extreme values at all, then it assumes these extreme values at points for which the derivative of the function vanishes. Therefore, in order to find extreme values we have to find first the values for which the derivative vanishes, and then investigate each such point individually to see whether it really yields a relative maximum or a relative minimum.

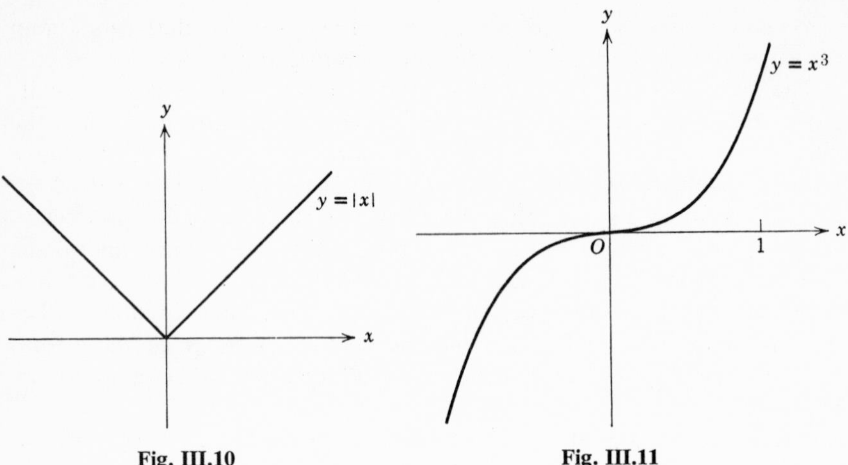

Fig. III.10

Fig. III.11

To illustrate the procedure, let us consider some problems. First, we consider the function

$$y = 2x^3 + 3x^2 - 12x - 6.$$

Its derivative is

$$y' = 6x^2 + 6x - 12.$$

In order to find all points for which the derivative vanishes, we have to solve the equation

$$6x^2 + 6x - 12 = 0.$$

The solutions of this equation are

$$x_1 = 1, x_2 = -2.$$

Hence, if there are extreme values at all (note that the derivative of our function exists everywhere), these extreme values can only be assumed for these values $x_1 = 1$, $x_2 = -2$.

Let us evaluate our function for these two values. We have

$$y\,\Big|_{x=1} = 2 + 3 - 12 - 6 = -13$$

$$y\,\Big|_{x=-2} = -16 + 12 + 24 - 6 = 14.$$

Offhand, we might say that 14 is the relative maximum and -13 is the relative minimum of our function because 14 is greater than -13. Even though this is true in this particular case, we warn the reader not to offer such faulty argumentation (see the next problem discussed in this section), because it could easily lead to wrong conclusions.

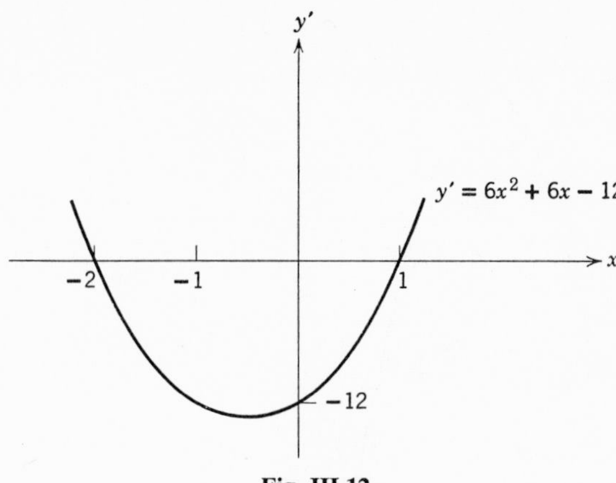

Fig. III.12

In order to graph our function, we first draw a graph representing the derivative y'. This is a quadratic parabola (see Fig. III.12). We see that the derivative is positive for all values $x < -2$ and all values $x > 1$ and it is negative for all x which are in the interval $-2 < x < 1$. We tabulate this information together with the fact that the derivative vanishes at $x = 1$, -2 in Fig. III.13, and draw underneath the table straight lines with slopes that are indicated by the table.

We then obtain a polygon which has a very rough resemblance to the graph we seek. It seems to indicate specifically that the value at $x = -2$ is indeed the relative maximum value, and the value at $x = 1$ is the relative minimum value of the function. The information we thus gained about our function, together with the construction of a few points, will yield its graphic representation as given in Fig. III.14.

Next we consider the following function

$$y = x + \frac{1}{x}.$$

x	$x < -2$	$x = -2$	$-2 < x < 1$	$x = 1$	$x > 1$
y'	+	0	−	0	+

Fig. III.13.

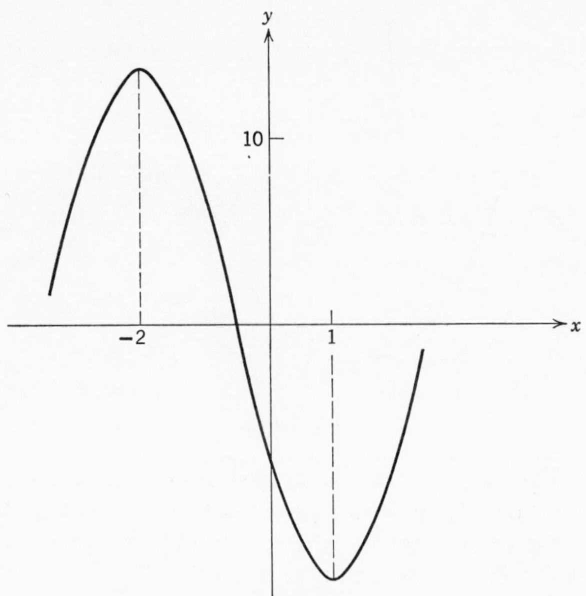

Fig. III.14

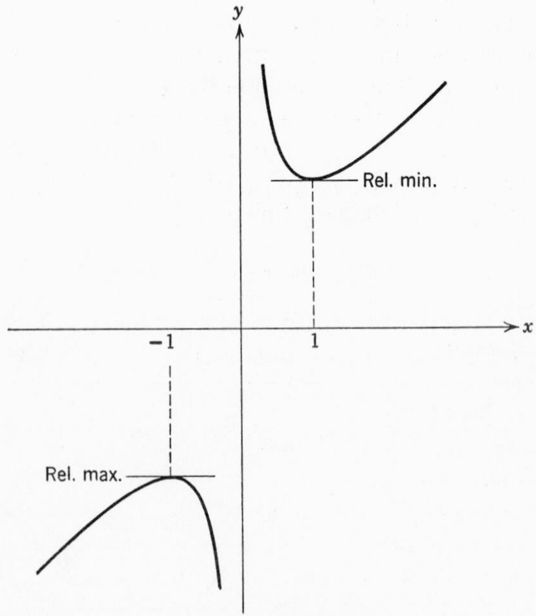

Fig. III.15

The derivative is

$$y' = 1 - \frac{1}{x^2}$$

(see Problem III.14). The values for which the derivative vanishes are the solutions of the equation

$$1 - \frac{1}{x^2} = 0$$

or, after multiplication by $x^2 \neq 0$,

$$x^2 - 1 = 0.$$

The solutions of this equation are $x_{1,2} = \pm 1$.
The corresponding values of the function at these points are:

$$y\,\big|_{x=1} = 1 + 1 = 2$$
$$y\,\big|_{x=-1} = -1 - 1 = -2.$$

So, offhand, we would state that 2 is the maximum and -2 is the minimum value. *Wrong*! From the graph, which is given in Fig. III.15, we see that it is exactly the other way around.

It may sound crazy to say that -2 is the maximum while 2 is the minimum value. But, remember, we are dealing with relative extreme values and we see that -2 is indeed larger than any value of the function in the neighborhood of $x = -1$, while 2 is smaller than any value of the function in the neighborhood of $x = 1$.

The graph of this function, by the way, can easily be obtained from the graph of $y = x$ and the graph of $y = 1/x$ by addition of corresponding ordinates, as indicated in Fig. III.16.

Finally, we wish to discuss the celebrated example of the *open square box with maximum volume* which is to be found in most Calculus books ever since the differential calculus was invented. The problem is: Given a square sheet of cardboard of sidelength 6. This sheet is to be folded into an open box with square bottom such that it contains the largest possible volume.

In order to formulate the problem mathematically, let us refer to Fig. III.17. We fold the cardboard along the dotted lines at a distance x from the edges. We thus obtain an open box with square bottom. The sidelength of the square bottom is $6 - 2x$ and the height of the box is x. Thus the volume is given by the following expression, which is a function of x:

$$V(x) = (6 - 2x)^2 x = 4x^3 - 24x^2 + 36x.$$

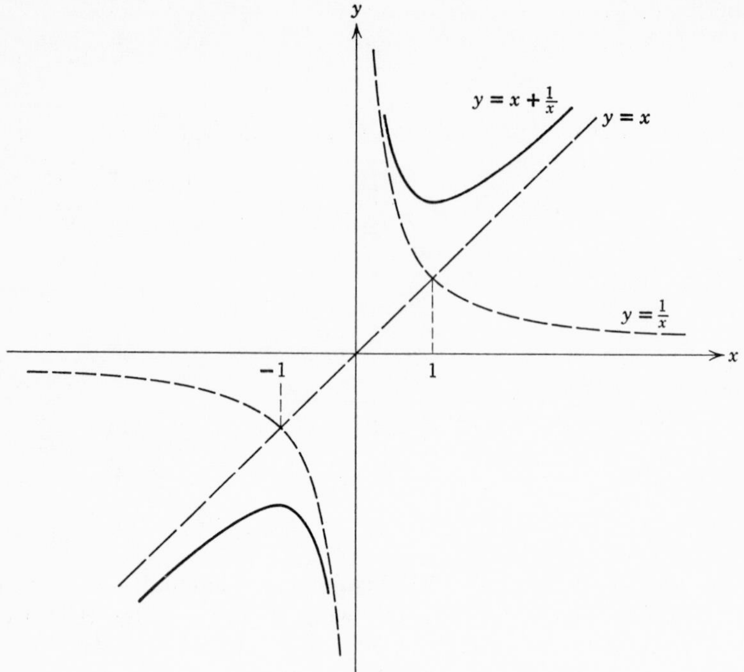

Fig. III.16

Now we have to choose the distance x of the fold from the edge such that the volume of the box becomes as large as possible. This means that we have to choose x such that $V(x)$ assumes a maximum. The derivative of $V(x)$ is given by

$$V'(x) = 12x^2 - 48x + 36.$$

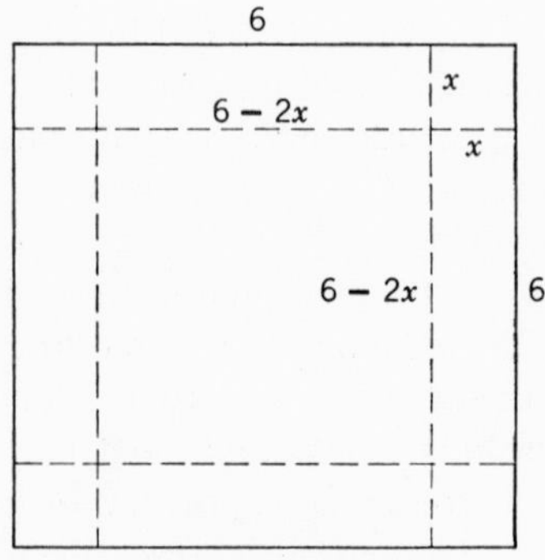

Fig. III.17

To find the values x for which this derivative vanishes, we have to solve the quadratic equation

$$12x^2 - 48x + 36 = 0$$

or, after division by 12,

$$x^2 - 4x + 3 = 0.$$

The solutions are

$$x_{1,2} = \frac{4 \pm \sqrt{16 - 12}}{2} = \frac{4 \pm 2}{2}.$$

Hence,

$$x_1 = 3, x_2 = 1.$$

If we choose $x_1 = 3$, then this means that we fold the square sheet in the middle and obtain thus a "box" of volume zero. This is certainly the smallest box we can possibly obtain. However, if we consider the other solution $x_2 = 1$, a simple argument will reveal that this leads to the largest box obtainable.

Problems III.58–III.68

III.58. Find all extreme values of the functions

(*a*) $y = x^3 - 3x^2 + 3x - 1$ (*b*) $y = x^3 - 3x + 2$

(*c*) $y = 2x^3 - 9x^2 + 12x - 4$ (*d*) $y = 2x^3 - 3x^2 - 36x + 12$

(*e*) $y = 3x^5 - 50x^3 + 135x + 27$ (*f*) $y = 3x^4 + 4x^3 - 12x^2 + 4$

and sketch the graphs of the functions.

III.59. Find all extreme values of the function

$$y = 2x + \frac{1}{x}$$

and sketch the function.

III.60. Find the extreme value of the function

$$y = \frac{1}{x^2 + 1}$$

(For differentiation, use limit process.)

III.61. Show that the extreme value of the function in Problem III.60 is an *absolute* extreme value; i.e., if it is a maximum, then it is the largest value that the function can possibly attain; and if it is a minimum value, then it is the smallest value that the function can possibly attain.

III.62. Find a necessary condition for the minimum of the function $y = \sqrt{x^2 + y_1^2} + \sqrt{(x - x_2)^2 + y_2^2}$, where x_2, y_1, y_2 are constants. (For differentiation, see Problems III.19 and III.20.)

III.63. Find the extreme values of the function

$$y = x^2 + \frac{1}{x^3}$$

and sketch the function. (For differentiation of $1/x^3$, use limit process.)

III.64. Given two numbers such that their sum is equal to a given number $2a$. Choose the two numbers such that their product is a maximum. [*Hint:* Given $x + y = 2a$. Choose x and y such that xy becomes a maximum. Since $y = 2a - x$, we have $xy = x(2a - x)$ which is to be maximized.]

III.65. A horsetrader wishes to encompass the largest possible rectangular corral with a fence 240 yards long. What are the dimensions of the corral?

III.66. A collection is taken up in a country club with the object of purchasing a fence. The money raised will buy a fence of a total length of 1.6 miles. What are the dimensions of the largest possible rectangular golf course, if it is to be fenced in on three sides with a straight river forming the supplementary boundary?

III.67. A right triangle with given perimeter c is to be made as large as possible. What are its dimensions?

III.68. Sketch and discuss the function $V(x)$ which represents the volume of the open rectangular box in the example which we worked at the end of this section.

10. MOTION

Suppose a point moves along a straight line starting from a position which is marked by $s = 0$, and reaches after t seconds the position

$$s = s(t) \tag{III.25}$$

units away from the origin $s = 0$. We will agree to use negative values of s to indicate a position on the left (or below) the starting point and positive values of s to indicate a position to the right (or above) the starting point. Formula (III.25) expresses the position of the moving point as a function of the time t. We call (III.25) the *law of motion* of this particular point. The structure of the function $s(t)$ will depend on the type of motion it is supposed to represent.

For example,

$$s = t$$

describes a motion which is such that during any time interval of unit length, the point will move through a distance of unit length. If we agree to measure time in seconds and the distance in feet, then, the moving point described by the above formula will move 1 foot per second. If we have a motion of the type where the point covers equal distances in equal time intervals (in our case, the point covers in time intervals of $\frac{1}{2}$ second, distances of $\frac{1}{2}$ foot, in intervals of 3 seconds distances of 3 feet, etc., no matter at what particular time relative to the starting time of the motion we may check), we say that the point proceeds with a constant velocity where we define velocity as the ratio of distance divided by the time interval during which the distance was covered:

$$\text{Velocity} = \frac{\text{Distance}}{\text{Time}}. \tag{III.26}$$

Thus, if a point travels through 7 feet every 12 seconds, then its velocity will be $\frac{7}{12}$ ft/sec. Clearly, it follows from (III.26) that the dimension of a velocity has to be ft/sec in order to make the dimensions on both sides of (III.26) agree.

Before we proceed to more general cases, let us discuss one more example. Let

$$s = at + b \text{ ft},$$

where a, b are constant numbers, be the formula describing the motion of a particular point. Then the distance covered after t_0 seconds is given by $s_0 = at_0 + b$ and the distance covered after t_1 seconds ($t_1 > t_0$) is given by $s_1 = at_1 + b$. Hence, the distance covered in the time interval from t_0 to t_1 is given by

$$s_1 - s_0 = at_1 + b - at_0 - b = a(t_1 - t_0)$$

and, according to (III.26), the velocity is

$$v = \frac{a(t_1 - t_0)}{t_1 - t_0} = a \text{ ft/sec.}$$

We see from this derivation that no matter what checkpoints t_0 and t_1 we may choose, we will always obtain a for the velocity. This shows that every motion that is described by a linear function in t is a motion with constant velocity. Later, we will also show the converse, i.e., that every motion with constant velocity is represented by a linear function in t.

Our definition (III.26) of a velocity breaks down, however, the moment we consider motions which are described by functions which are not linear in t. Let us consider the case

$$s = t^2 - 3.$$

Suppose we are interested in the velocity after 3 seconds. We have $s(3) = 6$. In order to apply (III.26) we have to know also the distance at a different time t_1, which is $s(t_1) = t_1^2 - 3$. On invoking (III.26), we have

$$v = \frac{t_1^2 - 3 - 6}{t_1 - 3} = \frac{t_1^2 - 9}{t_1 - 3} = t_1 + 3$$

which is a function of t_1, i.e., depends on the second checkpoint. This is clearly nonsense, because the velocity after 3 seconds cannot possibly depend on the behavior of the moving point $t_1 - 3$ seconds later, where t_1 is chosen quite arbitrarily.

We see from this example that we have to redefine velocity for motions which are not described by linear functions. Such a definition, in order to be senseful, has to be such that the definition (III.26) follows as a special case from this new, more general definition, or else we would be stuck with two different concepts of velocity which certainly is not a desirable situation.

Suppose we have a point P_0 moving according to

$$s = s(t)$$

where the function $s(t)$ may be any function that could conceivably describe a motion. (A function of the type

$$s(t) = \begin{cases} -t - 1 \text{ for } t < 0 \\ t \text{ for } t \geq 0 \end{cases}$$

would certainly have to be excluded since it is hard to imagine a moving point—in the framework of classical physics—which suddenly covers at $t = 0$ a distance of 1 foot in 0 seconds.)

It is our aim to give a definition of the velocity at a certain time t_0. In order to arrive at a reasonable definition, we will make use of (III.26) which is applicable to motions with constant velocity. For this purpose we substitute for the motion of P_0 as described in (III.25) another motion of a point P_1, which, although not the same, still comes very close to the motion of P_0. We subdivide the time interval in which the motion is considered ($0 \leq t \leq T$, where T could also be infinity) into subintervals $0 \leq t < t_1$, $t_1 \leq t < t_2$, $t_2 \leq t < t_3, \cdots, t_{k-1} \leq t < t_k, \cdots$, and replace our moving point P_0 with another point P_1 that moves as follows:

It covers the distance from $s(0)$ to $s(t_1)$ in t_1 seconds by moving with a constant velocity

$$\frac{s(t_1) - s(0)}{t_1},$$

the distance from $s(t_1)$ to $s(t_2)$ in $t_2 - t_1$ seconds by moving with a constant velocity

$$\frac{s(t_2) - s(t_1)}{t_2 - t_1}, \cdots,$$

the distance from $s(t_{k-1})$ to $s(t_k)$ in $t_k - t_{k-1}$ seconds with the constant velocity

$$\frac{s(t_k) - s(t_{k-1})}{t_k - t_{k-1}}, \text{ etc.}$$

The procedure which we followed here is interpreted graphically in Fig. III.18, where the solid line in the space-time-coordinate system represents the motion of the point P_0 and the broken line the motion of the point P_1.

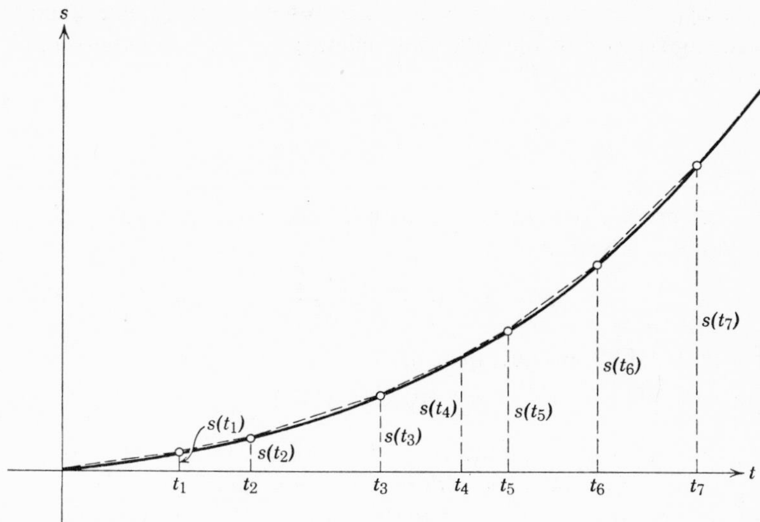

Fig. III.18

We now imagine both points (P_0 which moves according to $s = s(t)$ and P_1 moving as just defined) to start at $s = 0$ at the same time $t = 0$. Clearly, both points will arrive at $s(t_1)$ at the same time, they will both arrive at $s(t_2)$ at the same time, $\cdots$, they will both arrive at $s(t_k)$ at the same time, etc. The only difference between the two motions is that, in between any two checkpoints, the two moving points are not necessarily abreast. In general, one of them will lag behind the other.

However, it is intuitively quite clear, that the smaller we choose the time intervals $t_{k-1} \leq t < t_k$, the smaller is the difference in the distance between the two moving points in between checkpoints and we obtain a better and better approximation to the original motion as described by $s = s(t)$, the closer together we select the checkpoints. The velocity of P_0 at some time t_0 will then be very closely approximated by the velocity of the second point P_1 in the time interval $t_{k-1} \leq t < t_k$ which contains t_0. We can even simplify the situation by choosing t_0 as one of the division points, e.g.,

$$t_0 = t_k.$$

Then the velocity of P_0 at t_0 will be approximately equal to the velocity of the other point P_1 in the interval $t_{k-1} \leq t < t_k$ or the interval $t_k \leq t < t_{k+1}$, namely,

$$\frac{s(t_k) - s(t_{k-1})}{t_k - t_{k-1}} \quad \text{or} \quad \frac{s(t_{k+1}) - s(t_k)}{t_{k+1} - t_k},$$

and the approximation will be better, the closer t_{k-1} or t_{k+1} are taken to t_0. This idea gives rise to the following definition of the velocity of P_0 at the time t_0:

$$v(t_0) = \lim_{h \to 0} \frac{s(t_0 + h) - s(t_0)}{h} \tag{III.27}$$

where h is positive or negative.

If we compare (III.27) with the definition of the derivative of a function $F(x)$ as given in Section 1,

$$F'(x) = \lim_{h \to 0} \frac{F(x + h) - F(x)}{h},$$

we see that (III.27) is equivalent to

$$v(t) = s'(t), \tag{III.28}$$

where we again write t instead of t_0. In words: *The velocity is defined as the derivative of the distance with respect to the time.*

We can see immediately that the definition (III.26) is a special case of (III.28), since for $s = at + b$, we obtain $s' = a$. We wish to make quite clear that (III.28) does *not* follow from (III.26). The argument which we put forth leading us from (III.26) to (III.28) was *not* a derivation, but rather a heuristic argument which did show us the way in our search for a reasonable definition of velocity.

The *acceleration* of a motion is defined as the "*velocity of the velocity*," i.e., the rate with which the velocity changes as the time increases. Again, for a motion where the velocity increases at a constant rate (i.e., if the velocity is a linear function of the time), the acceleration is defined as

$$\text{Acceleration} = \frac{\text{Velocity increase}}{\text{Time increase}}.$$

If the quotient on the right is not independent of t, then we run into the same difficulties as before and we have to search for a more general definition which will apply to any motion. If we go through the same argument as before for velocity and time instead of distance and time, we finally arrive at the definition

$$a(t) = v'(t) = [s'(t)]' = s''(t). \tag{III.29}$$

Since the acceleration as derivative of the velocity thus appears as the derivative of the derivative of the distance, we call it the second derivative of the distance and denote it as in (III.29) by $s''(t)$.

We have seen in Section 5 that $F'(x) = f(x)$ is equivalent to

$$\int f(x)\,dx = F(x) + C$$

where C is an arbitrary constant. Hence, we can write (III.28) and (III.29) in the form

$$\int v(t)\,dt = s(t) + C$$

and

$$\int a(t)\,dt = v(t) + C.$$

Hence,

$$\int_0^t v(u)\,du = s(t) - s(0)$$

and

$$\int_0^t a(u)\,du = v(t) - v(0).$$

From this it follows that

$$s(t) = \int_0^t v(u)\,du + s(0) \tag{III.30}$$

and

$$v(t) = \int_0^t a(u)\,du + v(0). \tag{III.31}$$

Therefore, if we want to establish the formula of a motion uniquely, knowing the velocity, we have to prescribe the initial position (*initial distance*) $s(0)$, i.e., the distance from $s = 0$ which the point occupies when the motion starts. Similarly, if we want to establish the formula for the velocity uniquely if the acceleration of the motion is known, we have to prescribe the *initial velocity* $v(0)$, i.e., the velocity with which the motion starts out. [If $v(0) = 0$, we say that the motion starts from *rest*.] Thus, if we know the acceleration of a motion and wish to obtain the distance formula, we have to know the initial velocity and the initial distance in order to arrive at a unique result.

Mathematically this means that, if we know the second derivative of a function (acceleration) and we want to find the function itself (distance), we have to prescribe a point through which the function is to pass and also the slope with which it is to pass through this point.

It follows readily from (III.30): if

$$v = c \text{ (constant)},$$

then

$$s = \int_0^t c\,du + s(0) = ct + s(0),$$

i.e., s is a linear function of the time.

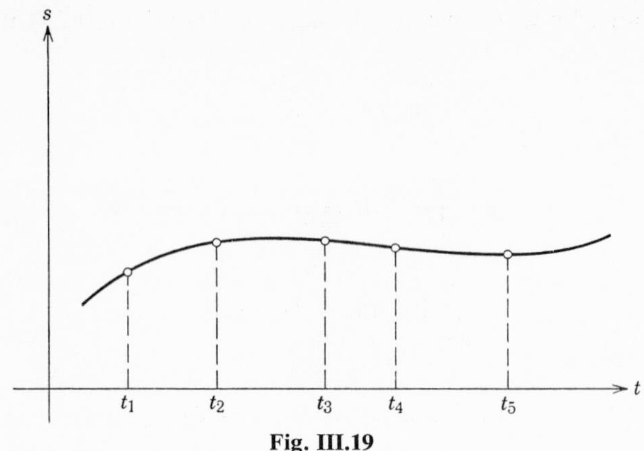

Fig. III.19

Formulas (III.30) and (III.31) are very important in the analysis of physical motion, while the formulas (III.28) and (III.29) are merely of academic value, inasmuch as they enable us to establish the notion of a velocity and acceleration conceptually. The reason for the practical unimportance of formulas (III.28) and (III.29) in the analysis of motion shall be discussed now.

In order to make use of (III.28), we have to know the distance as a function of the time:

$$s = s(t).$$

How do we acquire knowledge of this function? Clearly, we know it from experiments, if this function is to describe a motion which is actually taking place. Now, what do we really do when we establish such a formula experimentally, i.e., by carrying out measurements? We observe a certain motion (e.g., freely-falling body) and measure either the distance after the lapse of certain time intervals terminating in $t_1, t_2, t_3, \cdots$, or the elapsed time when the moving point reaches certain distances $s_1, s_2, s_3, \cdots$.

In either case, we will obtain a discrete and finite number of data which can be plotted in an s, t-diagram, as illustrated in Fig. III.19. In order to compress this information (which may consist of 1 million points) into a practical and compact mathematical form, we join the points which represent the measured data by a "smooth" curve, preferably one which can be represented by a simple mathematical function [e.g., the data (0, 0), (1, 1), (2, 4), where the first coordinate represents the time and the second coordinate represents the distance, can be represented by $s = t^2$.] In this way we arrive at a representation $s = s(t)$.

First, let us mention that this representation is certainly not unique. (In the example which we just mentioned in the brackets, $s = \frac{1}{2}t^3 - \frac{1}{2}t^2 + t$

seems to serve the purpose just as well, inasmuch as it assumes the required values at $t = 0, 1, 2$.) Of course, we can arrive at unique results by mathematical trickery, i.e., by making additional hypotheses about the curve which is to join the given points, or by prescribing a certain method by which this function is to be secured. This means, however, that an element is brought into the picture which does not rightly belong here, namely, mathematical assumptions and hypotheses. Mathematics has *nothing* to do with motion nor has motion anything to do with mathematics. Mathematics is very useful in describing physical phenomena; however, one has to distinguish very clearly between mathematical assumptions that have physical motivation and mathematical ad hoc assumptions which lack motivation entirely but serve only to make everything come out nicely.

Now, in order to find the velocity of a motion for which the mathematical formula $s = s(t)$ was found, we have to differentiate this function. All we really know about this function are its values at certain discrete points $t_1, t_2, t_3, \cdots, t_k$. We do not know anything about the values of the function in between. Of course, the formula $s = s(t)$ will yield values for s for every value of t, but we have no right whatever to expect the point really to be there. Even if, in order to obtain more complete information, we increase the number of checkpoints and decrease at the same time the lengths of the time intervals between checkpoints, we cannot resolve our problem. What was said before about the behavior of the function $s(t)$ between consecutive checkpoints can now be said in regard to the smaller intervals between the new checkpoints, and we face basically the same problem.

Figure III.20 illustrates the unreliability of the information which we obtain by taking the derivative of such an experimentally established function. The same data are joined in three different ways by curves in solid, broken, and dotted lines. In all three cases the derivative at the point t_0 is represented by the tangent line. We can see that the derivative can really have any value between $-\infty$ and ∞, but we have no way of deciding which one it ought to be.

The situation may become still clearer if we consider an example taken from "life" itself. Suppose a little green man from outer space comes to Earth and observes a pig standing behind a picket fence. All he really sees are a number of sections of the pig's body and, having had no previous experience with Earth pigs, he will be unable to complete the picture of the pig mentally, provided he has a mind, because "almost anything" could be in between, for all the little green man knows.

This brings out another point we wish to make. We, in the same position, would have no difficulties whatever in imagining the hidden parts of the pig's body, because we have previous experience in this matter. The same point holds true for the physicist who has had previous experience

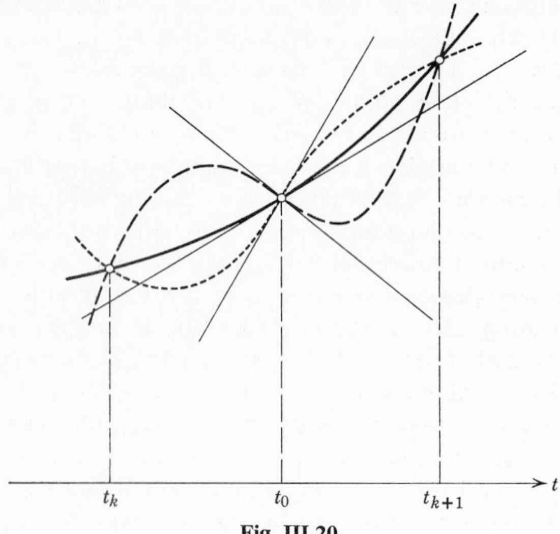

Fig. III.20

with motions. He is in a position to make additional hypotheses in regard to what can happen in between checkpoints and thus arrive at a satisfactory representation of the motion by a mathematical function that will stand up to differentiation and may yield useful results. However, in both cases—the pig as well as the motion—we have to be prepared for surprises, because something could be in between after all which surpasses both our imagination and previous experience.

So much about the unreliability of any results that are obtained from formulas (III.28) and (III.29). The situation is quite different in regard to the integral formulas (III.30) and (III.31). Here it does not matter so much how the function behaves in between checkpoints. The reader can see for himself that all the areas under the three different curves in Fig. III.20 are almost the same.

Before closing this section, let us work two examples. Suppose we know that a certain motion follows the law

$$s = 3t^2 + t + 5 \text{ ft.}$$

Then the initial distance is found for $t = 0$, $s(0) = 5$ ft, the velocity is found according to (III.28) as

$$v = 6t + 1 \text{ ft/sec}$$

where the initial velocity, obtained for $t = 0$ is given by $v(0) = 1$ ft/sec and, finally, the acceleration is found from (III.29) to be

$$a = 6 \text{ ft/sec·sec}$$

Now, suppose we have a motion of which we know that it has the acceleration

$$a = 3 \text{ ft/sec·sec}$$

We know in addition that the initial velocity is $v(0) = 12$ ft/sec and the initial distance is given by $s(0) = 14$ ft. Then we obtain from (III.31)

$$v = 3t + 12 \text{ ft/sec}$$

and from (III.30)

$$s = \frac{3t^2}{2} + 12t + 14 \text{ ft.}$$

Problems III.69–III.76

III.69. $s = t^2 + 3t + 4$. Find v and a as functions of t.

III.70. $s = 4t^2 - 12t + 3$. Find v at $t = 3$.

III.71. What are $v(0)$ and $s(0)$ in Problem III.69?

III.72. $s = 12t^2 + 4t + 1$. Find $v(0)$.

III.73. $a = -2$, find v and s if $v(0) = 12$, $s(0) = 3$. At what time t is $v = 0$?

III.74. Given $v = 12t + 3$. Find a and s, if $s(0) = 12$.

III.75. The functions $s = t^2$ and $s = \frac{1}{2}t^3 - \frac{1}{2}t^2 + t$ both join the same three points (0, 0), (1, 1) and (2, 4). Compare the values of the derivatives of these two functions at $t = 0, \frac{1}{2}, 1$, and 2.

III.76. $a = -32$ ft/sec·sec, $v(0) = v_0$, $s(0) = s_0$. Find the equation of motion.

11. FREELY FALLING BODIES

It is our experience that whenever we release an object (e.g., pencil, ball, typewriter) which has been suspended in some reasonable neighborhood of the surface of the earth, it embarks on a straight motion directed downwards and only comes to rest when it hits an obstacle in its path (e.g., table, gymnasium floor, surface of the earth). Although this phenomenon has not been observed on all the bodies that exist, it is nevertheless a fact that all the bodies which have been subjected to such treatment have never behaved otherwise, i.e., none ever fell upwards, or sideways, or stayed unsupported in free space.

Although there is no logical reason whatever that all droppable but not yet dropped objects shall behave in the same way, men, even in primitive and unsophisticated environments will—and as a matter of fact did—conclude, on the basis of the available evidence, that it is a general physical phenomenon that all bodies relatively near the earth's surface have the tendency to fall down if unsupported. We wish to point out that we never will be able to prove a law of such general character because a proof (physical proof, that is) would involve the verification of this law for all—and we really mean *all*—bodies, which is of course quite impossible. It would be very easy (logically, that is), on the other hand, to disprove this law simply by demonstrating that it does not hold in one particular instance. So, until somebody finds a body that falls sideways or upwards or does anything but fall downwards along a straight line, we are compelled to accept this law as a reasonable working hypothesis.

Once we have accepted the working hypothesis that bodies, if unsupported, fall down, our inquiring mind pushes us further to investigate the nature of the descent. It is a widely spread custom in the entire civilized and scientific minded world among children who dwell in city quarters to engage in a pastime which really should not be encouraged, however, does have merit in molding the innocent little minds of the perpetrators of the game. We are speaking of a game which involves the dropping of a paper bag filled with water (the bigger the bag, the more gratifying the result!) from a window onto the street, preferably onto a bald, bare-headed passer-by. Everybody with a scientific mind whoever engaged in this game will know that the higher the point of release, the more gratifying the effect, because the *impact velocity* (velocity at the moment of the hit) increases with the height through which the paper bag has fallen after being released, and therein lies a definite advantage of the twelfth floor dwellers over the third floor dwellers.

While we can be reasonably sure that the Italian scientist, *Galilei Galileo* (1564–1642), did not engage in throwing or dropping water-filled paper bags (paper bags being a product of our present highly overdeveloped civilization), he nevertheless recognized in carrying out a great number of experiments that the velocity increases as the distance through which the object falls increases. He went further than that and determined experimentally the law of freely falling bodies, according to which the distance t seconds after the release is proportional to the square of the elapsed time interval t, the proportionality factor having approximately the value 16 in a foot-second measure system.

Thus we write

$$h = 16t^2 \text{ ft.} \quad (t \text{ in seconds}). \tag{III.32}$$

Ever since this formula was established, it has been subjected to a great number of tests ranging from simple high school experiments with the falling machine to very sophisticated and complicated scientific scrutinization.

According to the formulas which we developed in the preceding section, disregarding for the moment what we said in connection with the differentiation of experimentally established functions, we obtain for the velocity of the freely falling body

$$v = \frac{dh}{dt} = 32t \text{ ft/sec} \tag{III.33}$$

and for the acceleration

$$a = \frac{dv}{dt} = 32 \text{ ft/sec·sec.} \tag{III.34}$$

Now, if we could establish by an independent argument the fact that the acceleration of the freely falling body is 32 ft/sec·sec, then we could arrive at (III.32) via a logically satisfactory method by successive integrations of (III.34), using the formulas (III.30) and (III.31) of the preceding section.

This question—why an acceleration of 32 ft/sec·sec, or why an acceleration at all—leads us to a very deep problem, one which the physicist always faces after having investigated a physical phenomenon from a quantitative standpoint: *the problem of searching for the cause.*

What causes an object to embark on an accelerated downward motion towards the earth? Nowadays, every high school student will smugly supply the answer: *gravity.* This answer, however, is really no answer at all as long as it is not embedded in a more general system and explainable in more general terms. *Sir Isaac Newton*, the English physicist (1643–1727) asked himself this question many times, together with many other—not obviously related—questions such as why does the moon orbit around the earth and why do the planets orbit around the sun, and why specifically, along elliptical orbits as quantitatively described by *Johannes Kepler*?

After a great deal of thought and experimental work, Newton came up with a new working hypothesis, namely: Between any two masses there exists a force of attraction which causes the two masses to move towards each other.

The first new and important concept that enters our discussion here is the concept of a *force.* What is a force? It is something which is not directly accessible to measurements. It can only be explained and measured in terms of its effects. We all have an intuitive notion of force. For the sake of the following argument, let us use this intuitive notion and set it in quotes. To set a mass motion, we have to exert a certain amount of "force." If the mass increases and we wish to cause the same effect as before, we have to exert a greater "force." If the mass remains the same and we wish to impart a greater acceleration, we also have to exert a greater "force." Thus, Newton was led to define force as jointly proportional to the mass m and the acceleration a of the motion on which the mass embarks upon being subjected to the force in question:

$$f = ma \text{ lb.ft/sec·sec.} \tag{III.35}$$

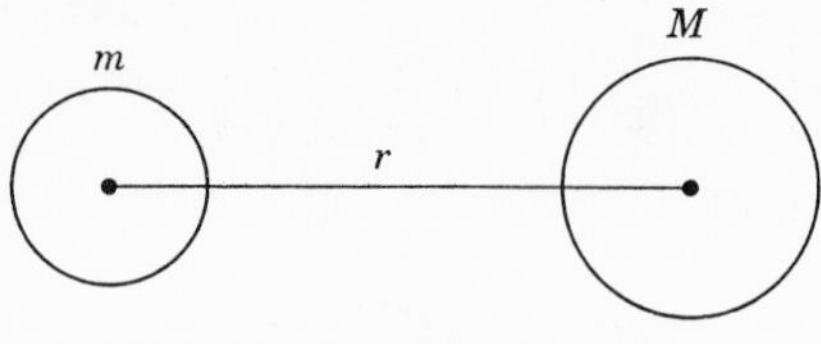

Fig. III.21

Now that the concept of force is clarified, we can go along with Newton in setting up a hypothesis about the magnitude of the force of attraction between two masses.

Newton conjectured (see also Fig. III.21)

$$f = G\frac{mM}{r^2} \tag{III.36}$$

where M and m are the masses of the two objects involved, r is their central distance (distance from the center of gravity of the one mass to the center of gravity of the other mass*), and where G represents the force of attraction between two unit masses at a distance 1 unit apart. (This is a physical constant which has to be established experimentally. Its value depends, of course, on the measure units which are chosen.)

We wish to point out that this law enables us to explain a great number of physical phenomena, in the mechanics of heavenly bodies as well as in simple phenomena such as the freely falling body in a neighborhood of the surface of the earth. It explains (in terms of this new and mysterious force of attraction) why objects fall downwards and why planets move the way they do. It does not explain why bodies attract each other. The answer, "because they like each other" is just as good as any other answer. (III.36) can never be verified (established as the "ultimate truth"—whatever that might be—) just as we can never verify that it is true for all bodies that they fall down. All we can do in regard to its truth is to show that it is *false* by finding a phenomenon which is not consistent with this law. (See some remarks towards the end of this section about *Einstein's* gravitational theory.)

We will not go into a general philosophical discussion here because that would lead us far afield and go definitely beyond the scope of this treatment. All we wish to do here is to explain Galilei's law for freely falling bodies (III.32) in terms of Newton's gravitational law (III.36) and thereby demonstrate how physical theories with a limited scope are embedded in

* The center of gravity is explained in Chapter IV, Section 5. For the time being, however, let us assume that the masses m and M are homogeneous spheres. Then their center of gravity is simply their geometric center.

theories of much wider scope and how, in turn, many simple physical phenomena are explained in terms of general hypotheses.

We have an object of mass m at a perpendicular distance d from the surface of the earth and release it from this initial position. According to Newton's law, the object of mass m and the earth of mass M attract each other (disregarding the air resistance) with a force

$$f = G\frac{mM}{(R+d)^2} \tag{III.37}$$

where R is the radius of the earth (see Fig. III.22). On the other hand we have, from (III.35),

$$f = am$$

where a is the acceleration of the downward motion of the object of mass m. Hence it follows, from (III.35) and (III.37) after division by m, that

$$a = G\frac{M}{(R+d)^2}. \tag{III.38}$$

We see from this formula that the acceleration a depends on the distance d of the falling object from the surface of the earth, and since this distance changes as the object proceeds in its motion, the acceleration appears ultimately as a function of the time t and cannot possibly be constant, as we assumed in the beginning. However, if d is small in comparison with R (e.g., 23 feet as compared to 4000 miles), which is the case for all practical purposes, the change in d from its initial value to its terminating value 0

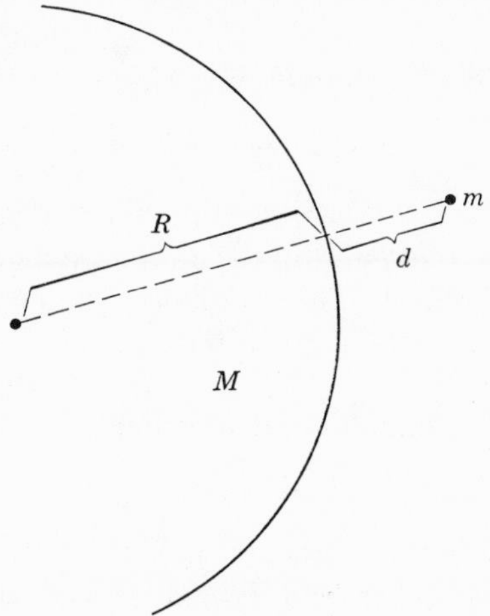

Fig. III.22

will be so insignificant that its effect on a will not be detectible by the usual measuring procedures. Therefore, we neglect d entirely and use

$$a = G\frac{M}{R^2} \tag{III.39}$$

for the acceleration of freely falling bodies which are released in a reasonable neighborhood of the surface of the earth. This formula will now be subjected to numerical evaluation. We find in tables*

$$G = 6.670 \times 10^{-8} \text{ dyne (dimension of force in } c\text{-}g\text{-}s\text{-system)}\dagger$$

$$\text{Mass density of earth} = 5.522 \text{ g/cm}^3$$

$$\text{Mean radius of earth} = 6371 \text{ km} = 6371 \times 10^5 \text{ cm}$$

Thus we obtain for the mass of the earth

$$\begin{aligned}\text{mass} &= \text{mass density} \times \text{volume}\\ &= \frac{5.522 \times 4\pi R^3}{3}\\ &= \frac{4 \times 5.522\pi(6371 \times 10^5)^3}{3}\end{aligned}$$

and consequently

$$a = \frac{6.670 \times 10^{-8} \times 4 \times 5.522\pi(6371 \times 10^5)^3}{3(6371 \times 10^5)^2} = 982.7 \text{ cm/sec·sec}$$

($\pi \cong 3.142$).

Since 1 cm = 0.03281 ft, we obtain

$$a = 32.24 \text{ ft/sec·sec}$$

to four significant figures. We point out that this value is arrived at by using a mean value for the radius of the earth. At a geographic latitude of 45° we obtain 32.17 ft/sec·sec. We see that the value of 32 as obtained by experiments is, indeed, explainable in terms of Newton's general gravitational theory.

Now we can reverse our steps and start with

$$a = 32 \text{ ft/sec·sec},$$

* Standard Mathematical Tables, 12th ed. CRC, 1959, p. 16.

† Note that the value of G can be determined without reference to freely falling bodies. *Cavendish* (1731–1810) was the first to determine G by measuring the force of attraction between two masses of known magnitude.

use formulas (III.30) and (III.31) with the understanding that the object is released from rest, i.e., initial velocity $v(0) = 0$, and the distance is measured from the point of release downwards, i.e., $s(0) = 0$, and we arrive at

$$v = \int_0^t 32\,du + v(0) = 32t,$$

$$s = \int_0^t 32u\,du + s(0) = 16t^2,$$

which is identical with (III.32).

We also wish to point out the fact that the velocity of a falling body is *independent* of its mass, a fact which may puzzle the layman and seem to contradict sound reasoning, whatever that may be, yet finds a beautiful explanation through this derivation.

That Newton's law explains the motion of a freely falling body in a sufficiently small neighborhood of the earth (d very small compared to R) is, of course, not sufficient evidence to establish the validity of this law, and nothing really is, as we already know. However, that Newton could also explain in terms of his law the planetary orbits around the sun along elliptical paths with the sun in one of the foci and even verify by computation the experimentally established dimensions of these ellipses is quite impressive and made us accept Newton's law as a very successful working hypothesis.

It should be mentioned, however, that *Leverrier* observed in 1845 that the major axis of the elliptical orbit of the planet Mercury turns in the direction of the motion of the Mercury by 43″ per century. This fact is not explainable in terms of Newton's theory. Here we have, so to speak, the object that falls sideways. The gravitational theory that was developed by *Albert Einstein* at the beginning of this century explains this phenomenon. Inasmuch as it also explains all the other phenomena which thus far have been explained in terms of Newton's theory, it is to be substituted for Newton's theory.

▶ Specifically, it follows from Einstein's theory that the angle of rotation of the major axis of the elliptical orbit of a planet amounts to

$$\frac{6\pi\alpha}{a(1 - \varepsilon)}$$

where α is the gravitational radius of the sun, a the semi-major axis of the ellipse, and ε the eccentricity of the ellipse. Indeed, this formula yields 43″ per century for the planet Mercury. ◀

Einstein's theory, which is now generally accepted, has stood up to tests this far. Our past experience, however, indicates that someday something may come up which will make the revision of our gravitational concept necessary and put a new theory in place of Einstein's theory.

Now let us return from our philosophical excursion into space back to earth and some practical problems.

In order to utilize the fact concerning the acceleration that a free body attains in the neighborhood of the earth's surface, we will introduce a coordinate system with a horizontal t-axis and a vertical h-axis, where $h = 0$ shall represent the position on the surface of the earth and the height is measured vertically upward. Then a downward motion as enforced by gravity will decrease the height and we will have to attach a minus sign to the acceleration:

$$a = -32 \text{ ft/sec}\cdot\text{sec}.$$

Suppose an object is thrown vertically upward with an initial velocity of $v(0) = 64$ ft/sec (if we were to throw it downward, the initial velocity would have to be assumed negative) from an initial height (cliff, steeple, etc.) of $h(0) = 80$ ft. Then, according to formulas (III.30) and (III.31) in the preceding section,

$$v = -\int_0^t 32\, du + v(0) = -32t + 64$$

and

$$h = \int_0^t (-32u + 64)\, du + h(0) = -16t^2 + 64t + 80.$$

This formula represents the height t seconds after the motion is started.

If we wish to know at what time the object will strike the ground, we have to solve $h = 0$ for t. This yields the quadratic equation

$$-16t^2 + 64t + 80 = 0$$

with the two solutions

$$t_{1,2} = -1, 5.$$

Clearly, the solution $t_1 = -1$ has to be disregarded, because this value refers to a time before the motion was started* and we obtain $t = 5$ for the duration of the motion (time the object was in the air). If we want to find the impact velocity, i.e., the velocity with which the object strikes the ground, we have to substitute this value we found for t into the formula for the velocity and obtain

$$v(5) = -32.5 + 64 = -96 \text{ ft/sec}.$$

* The negative solution $t = -1$ has the following significance: if the motion had been started 1 second earlier from the ground with an initial velocity the magnitude of which is equal to the impact velocity, then it would have reached after 1 second (at $t = 0$) the height $h = 80$ and would have at this instance the velocity 64 ft/sec.

If we, finally, want to know how high the object climbed, we have to find out first at what time the object turned, i.e., reversed its motion. Clearly, at this point the velocity changes from a positive (upward) velocity to a negative (downward) velocity, and since the function representing the velocity is continuous, it has to be zero at the time at which the object turns back. Therefore, we have to solve the equation $v = 0$, i.e.,

$$-32t + 64 = 0$$

and obtain $t = 2$, i.e., after 2 seconds in the air, the object reached the highest point. If we substitute this value into the formula for h, we have

$$h_{\text{max}} = -16.4 + 64.2 + 80 = 144 \text{ ft.}$$

The same result can be obtained by a purely mathematical argument, utilizing the theory of maxima and minima. We wish to find the maximum value of the function

$$h(t) = -16t^2 + 64t + 80.$$

We know from Section 9 that, if $h(t)$ has a maximum at a certain point, it is necessary that

$$h'(t) = 0.$$

Now,

$$h'(t) = v(t) = -32t + 64 = 0$$

and here we are again.

In general, the formula for the vertical motion of an object in the gravitational field of the earth is

$$h = -16t^2 + v(0)t + h(0),$$

as the reader can easily verify by application of (III.30) and (III.31) to $a = -32$ ft/sec·sec.

Problems III.77–III.83

III.77. Evaluate formula (III.38) for

(*a*) $d = 20$ feet (*b*) $d = 1$ mile (*c*) $d = 200$ miles

and compare your results with the value for a which is obtained in the text. Use the same values for mass density and radius of the earth as in the text and observe that only four significant digits are given.

III.78. The *neutral point* between earth and moon is the point where an object is not subject to any gravitational forces, i.e., where the force of attraction exerted by the moon is equal to the force of attraction exerted by the earth. Mean central distance between earth and moon = 60.3 radius of earth. Mass of moon $= \frac{1}{80}$ mass of earth. Find the distance of the neutral point from the surface of the earth.

III.79. An object is thrown upward with an initial velocity of 32 ft/sec from an initial height of 64 feet. How high does it go?

III.80. An object is thrown downward with an initial velocity of 64 ft/sec. from an initial height of 160 feet. Find the impact velocity.

III.81. We wish to throw an object vertically upward from the surface level of the earth so that it reaches a height of 320 feet. What initial velocity do we have to impart?

III.82. A projectile is to be shot to the moon. In order for it to reach the moon, it has to pass the neutral point. Therefore, its initial velocity has to be greater than the one which will make it reach the neutral point. Find the smallest possible initial velocity that will accomplish the purpose. (Note that we assume here that there is no air resistance, that a does not change its value during the entire process, and that earth as well as moon are throughout the entire trip of the projectile considered to be at rest relatively to each other.)

III.83. Suppose you are lurking in a window on the twenty-first floor (189 feet above the street) with a paper bag full of water and you see the university president (who is 6 feet tall) approach at a rate of two yard-steps per second. (*a*) How far from the vertical projection of the posed paperbag onto the street has the victim to be when you let go in order to achieve a perfect hit? (*b*) What is the impact velocity? (*c*) Verify your results by carrying out the experiment. (*d*) Apologize to the victim.

12. SNELL'S LAW OF REFRACTION

We will study in this section a very important application of the theory of maximum and minimum values to the propagation of light. Our investigation is based on a hypothesis originated by Pierre Fermat (1608–1665). Known now as *Fermat's principle*, it states that light, in traveling from one point P to another point Q, chooses a path along which it can cover the distance in the shortest possible time. This law is subject to certain modifications which we will skip for the moment, but which we will discuss briefly at the end of this section.

In addition to this principle, we make use of the experimental fact that the velocity of light in a homogeneous isotropic medium* is constant and is different in media of different density. The velocity of light depends on the density of the medium, just as the velocity of a boat depends on the density of the water through which it travels. For example, a boat which is capable of traveling at 30 knots in clear water cannot come near this velocity in the Salt Lake in Utah.

If both points P and Q, which are to be joined by a light ray, are located in the same medium and there is no obstacle between them, there is no problem because the velocity of light is constant within the same medium,

* *Homogeneous* means that the physical properties of the medium are independent of the point selected, and *isotropic* means that the physical properties are independent of the direction selected.

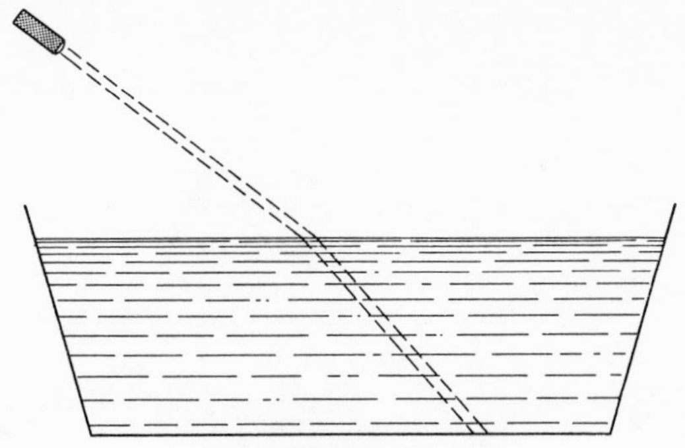

Fig. III.23

and light will choose the shortest geometric path, joining these two points, namely, the straight line. (Observe that as far as Fermat's principle is concerned, it makes no difference whatever whether we consider light as a corpuscular motion or a wave motion or both.)

Suppose, however, that P is located in a medium in which the light velocity is u ft/sec and Q is located in a medium in which the light velocity is v ft/sec. Let us assume further that the two media are separated by a plane surface. The following experiment will demonstrate what will happen in this case.

We fill a tank with water which is dyed green (or any other convenient color) and place a thin-beamed light source (e.g., a focused flashlight) somewhere above the water surface so that the beam of light hits the water surface at an acute angle (see Fig. III.23). Then we black out all light except that coming from our light source and generate smoke or dust in the vicinity of the water surface. We will observe that the lightbeam, which under the stated conditions should be clearly visible, will travel along a straight line from the source to the water surface and along a straight line from the water surface to the bottom of the tank. Upon entering the water, however, the beam will experience what is called a *refraction*, i.e., it will show a break as indicated in Fig. III.23.

Let us now analyze this situation mathematically in terms of Fermat's principle. We choose our coordinate system so that the x-axis lies in the water surface and x- and y-axes lie in the same plane as the light beam. Let us place the point P (light source) on the y-axis, at a distance y_1 from the water surface (see Fig. III.24). The point Q lies in the plane determined by P and x-axis and has coordinates (x_2, y_2) where $y_2 < 0$.

The beam of light as represented by the broken line PRQ will enter the water at a point $R(x, 0)$ where x is such that the time required to reach Q is a minimum. The angle between the incoming ray and the perpendicular to the water surface is denoted by α and the angle between the outgoing

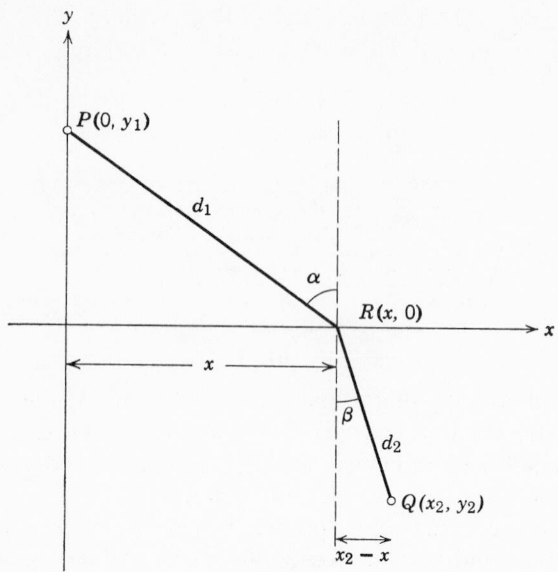

Fig. III.24

ray and the perpendicular is β. Let u be the velocity of light above the water surface and let v be the velocity of light in the water. If we call the distance $PR = d_1$ and the distance $RQ = d_2$, then the time required to go from P to Q is given by

$$T = \frac{d_1}{u} + \frac{d_2}{v},$$

because it follows from (III.26) that

$$\text{Time} = \frac{\text{Distance}}{\text{Velocity}}$$

for motions with constant velocity.

From the distance formula we obtain

$$d_1 = \sqrt{x^2 + y_1^2}$$

and

$$d_2 = \sqrt{(x - x_2)^2 + y_2^2}.$$

Hence, our problem is to find x such that

$$T(x) = \frac{\sqrt{x^2 + y_1^2}}{u} + \frac{\sqrt{(x - x_2)^2 + y_2^2}}{v} \to \text{minimum.}$$

A necessary condition for x to make $T(x)$ a minimum is that its first derivative vanish:

$$T'(x) = 0 \tag{III.40}$$

We have, according to Problems III.19 and III.20,

$$\frac{d}{dx}\sqrt{x^2 + y_1^2} = \frac{x}{\sqrt{x^2 + y_1^2}} = \frac{x}{d_1},$$

and

$$\frac{d}{dx}\sqrt{(x - x_2)^2 + y_2^2} = \frac{x - x_2}{\sqrt{(x - x_2)^2 + y_2^2}} = -\frac{x_2 - x}{d_2}.$$

Since

$$\frac{x}{d_1} = \sin \alpha$$

and

$$\frac{x_2 - x}{d_2} = \sin \beta,$$

we obtain for (III.40)

$$\frac{\sin \alpha}{u} - \frac{\sin \beta}{v} = 0$$

and from this

$$\frac{\sin \alpha}{\sin \beta} = \frac{u}{v}, \tag{III.41}$$

i.e., the ratio of the velocities is equal to the ratio of the sines of the angles of incoming and outgoing ray with the perpendicular. This is *Snell's law*. The ratio in (III.41) is called the *index of refraction*.

Formula (III.41) yields an indirect method of testing Fermat's principle. For example, if the light velocities u and v in two media are determined experimentally, then the ratio u/v can be computed and an experiment, such as that outlined in the beginning of this section where the angles α and β are measured, will substantiate the predicted result. If we are reasonably satisfied with the validity of this law, we can use it to find the light velocity in a certain medium if we know the light velocity in air by carrying out the tank experiment and measuring the refraction angles α and β. For example, we know that the velocity of light in air is

$$u(\text{air}) = 2.998 \times 10^{10} \text{ cm/sec.}$$

We wish to determine the velocity of light in water by carrying out the tank experiment. We measure the angles as

$$\alpha = 40°48', \beta = 30°.$$

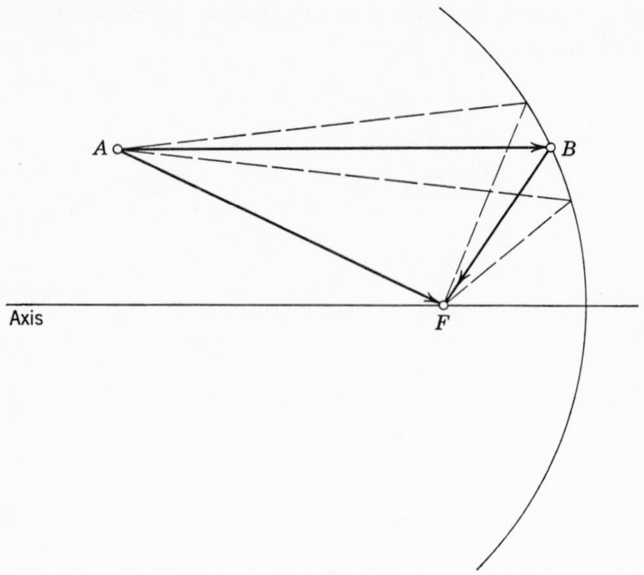

Fig. III.25

Hence, $\sin\alpha = 0.665 \cong \frac{2}{3}$ and $\sin\beta = \frac{1}{2}$. Thus, the refraction index turns out to be

$$\frac{\sin\alpha}{\sin\beta} = \frac{4}{3}.$$

With $u = 2.998 \times 10^{10}$ cm/sec, it follows that v (velocity in water) is

$$v = \frac{3 \times 2.998 \times 10^{10}}{4} = 2.248 \times 10^{10} \text{ cm/sec.}$$

In order to be in a better position to judge this difference in velocities, we assume the velocity of air as approximately 186,000 miles per second. Then we obtain for the velocity of light in water 139,000 miles per second, a marked difference.

We will conclude this section with a short discussion of an experiment which, upon superficial examination, seems to contradict Fermat's minimum principle. We place a lightsource at a point A and a parabolic mirror opposite A as indicated in Fig. III.25. We assume the light source is capable of emitting light in all possible directions. By inserting a mirror probe at the focus F of the parabolic mirror, we will observe that light arrives at this point.

It can be further established, by blacking out all other light, that it arrives there along a straight line directly from A, as we expect in view of Fermat's principle. However, if we black out this particular ray, we will observe, by turning the mirror in F, that light still arrives at F and we can trace this light by skilful experimentation to the parabolic mirror and from there along a line parallel to the axis of the mirror to the source A. The velocity of the light along both paths is the same. So it would follow that here light chooses the path ABF which does not yield a minimum for the time required to reach F from A, since the minimum clearly is rendered by the direct path from A to F. However, it can be shown that the path ABF does yield a minimum as compared to other paths which reach F via reflection in the mirror (see Problems III.85 and 86). We see that we have here the same situation as we encountered earlier in dealing with ordinary extreme value problems where the value of x that satisfies the vanishing condition for the first derivative does not necessarily yield a minimum; and if it does yield a minimum, then it is usually a relative minimum, i.e., it is a smallest value compared to values obtained in a neighborhood, as indicated by the broken lines in Fig. III.25.

Problems III.84–III.87

III.84. Find the derivatives of

$$y = \sqrt{(x-1)^2 + (x^2 - a)^2}$$

and

$$y = \sqrt{x^2 + (x^2 - \tfrac{1}{4})^2}$$

by the limit process.

III.85. Given a parabola $y = x^2$ which has its focus at $(0, \frac{1}{4})$. Join the point $(1, a)$ where $a > 1$, with a point (x, y) on the right branch of the parabola and this point, in turn, with the focus. Observe that $y = x^2$ holds for points on the parabola, and express the length of this path as a function of x.

III.86. Show that $x = 1$ makes the derivative of the function in Problem III.85 vanish. Interpret your result and make a sketch. (For differentiation, use the results in Problem III.84.)

III.87. Assume the velocity of light in air as 186,000 miles/sec. Find the velocity of light in ethyl ether, glycerin, and bromine. The refraction indices are 1.351, 1.474, 1.654, respectively.

▶13. THE CYCLOID

We will devote this section to the discussion of a remarkable curve which is quite simple in nature, but which possesses rather startling properties. Even though it would be far beyond the scope of this book to support by mathematical arguments all the statements which we are about to make, we still think that a narrative account should be of interest to the reader and prove quite stimulating.

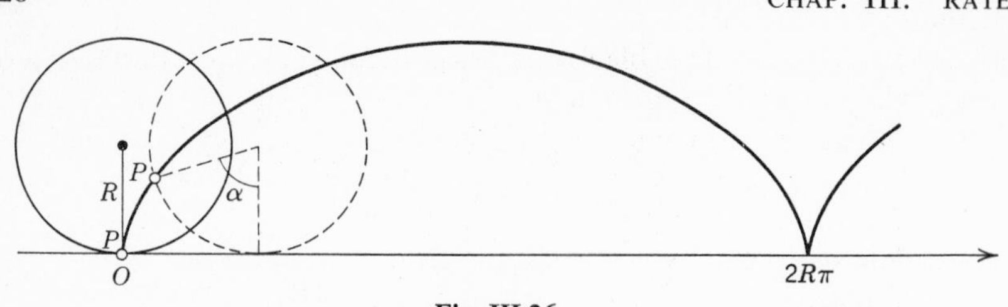

Fig. III.26

The curve which we are about to discuss is the so-called *cycloid*. This curve can be generated by a simple process, namely, by rolling a circle along a line and observing a fixed point on the circumference of the circle throughout this process. The curve which is traced by this point when the circle rolls along is the cycloid. It is represented in Fig. III.26. We will not indulge in trying to establish a mathematical representation of this curve for this is not quite simple. Instead we enter right away a discussion of the "startling" properties of this curve.

John Bernoulli, a famous Swiss mathematician who lived and worked in the late 17th and early 18th centuries, posed the following problem "to the mathematicians of the world to give their consideration": Given two points P_1 and P_2 in a vertical plane but not so that the one is vertically below the other. These two points are to be joined by a curve $y = f(x)$ which is such that the time required for a mass point under the influence of gravity to slide from P_1 to P_2 (without friction) along this curve shall be a minimum (see Fig. III.27). If we assume that the motion along the curve $y = f(x)$ is frictionless, the only force exerted upon the sliding masspoint is the gravitational force which will impart the constant acceleration $a = 32$ ft/sec·sec in the vertical downward direction upon the masspoint. (We neglect air resistance, of course.) Hence, we can apply our law of freely falling bodies

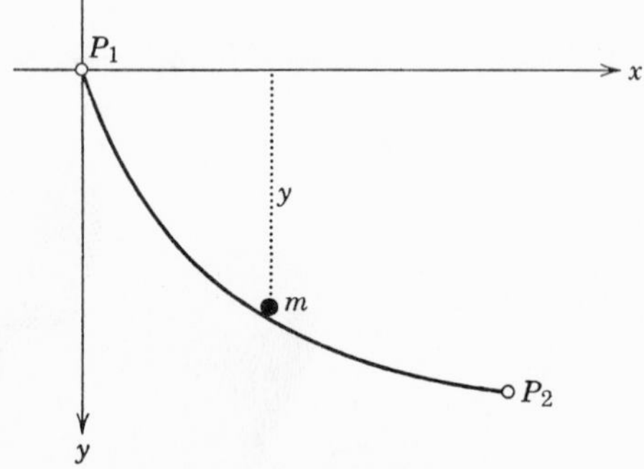

Fig. III.27

and we obtain, with the understanding that the y-axis points downward as indicated in Fig. III.27,

$$y = 16t^2$$

and for the velocity

$$v = \frac{dy}{dt} = 32t.$$

These two formulas allow us to compute the velocity v in terms of the vertical distance y and we obtain

$$v = 8\sqrt{y}, \tag{III.42}$$

i.e., the velocity of the vertical projection of the motion is directly proportional to the square root of the vertical distance through which the masspoint has moved.

We will now outline how Bernoulli obtained a solution to this problem. The means which he employed are not quite legitimate; however, the solution he arrived at is correct and can now be verified by more modern mathematical methods.

Instead of considering the gravitational "medium" as one that changes continuously as the height changes, Bernoulli considered it as consisting of a number of layers in each of which the velocity v is considered as constant (see Fig. III.28) and replaced the curve along which the masspoint is supposed to slide by a polygon with vertices in the boundary planes between two adjacent layers.

Let us investigate now the boundary plane between the kth and the $(k + 1)$th layer. This plane goes through the point $x = 0$, $y = y_k$ on the y-axis and is perpendicular to the y-axis. Throughout the kth layer we denote the velocity which is assumed to be constant by v_k, and throughout the $(k + 1)$th layer by v_{k+1}.

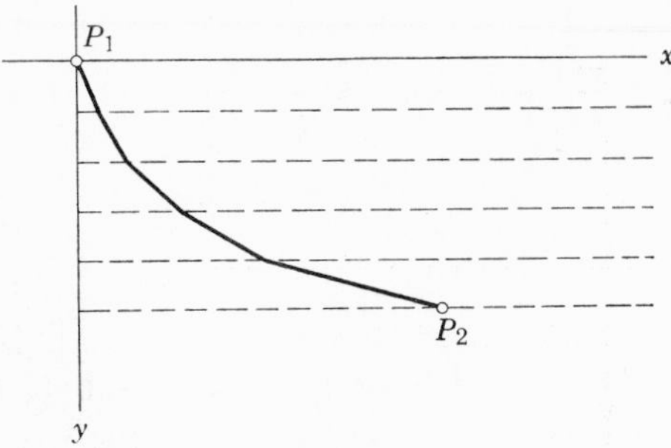

Fig. III.28

In view of (III.42), we have

$$v_k = 8\sqrt{y_k}$$

and

$$v_{k+1} = 8\sqrt{y_{k+1}}.$$

Now Bernoulli makes the ingenious, but hardly justifyable, hypothesis that the sliding masspoint will behave when entering a new layer like a lightray when penetrating through the border plane between two media, i.e., he invokes Snell's law (III.41)

$$\frac{\sin \alpha}{\sin \beta} = \frac{u}{v},$$

where u is the velocity of light in one medium and v is the velocity of light in the other medium. α is the angle of the incoming lightray with the perpendicular and β is the angle of the outgoing lightray with the perpendicular to the border plane.

Let us apply this law to the situation at hand: we denote the angle of the incoming path by α_k and the angle of the outgoing path by β_{k+1} (see Fig. III.29). We note that

$$\beta_{k+1} = \alpha_{k+1}$$

i.e., the angle of the outgoing path is the same as the angle of the incoming path at the next following border plane at $y = y_{k+1}$.

According to Snell's law

$$\text{(III.43)} \qquad \frac{\sin \alpha_k}{\sin \beta_k} = \frac{\sin \alpha_k}{\sin \alpha_{k+1}} = \frac{8\sqrt{y_k}}{8\sqrt{y_{k+1}}} = \frac{\sqrt{y_k}}{\sqrt{y_{k+1}}}.$$

Hence, we can conclude that the sine of the angle of the incoming path with the perpendicular is proportional to the square root of the vertical distance from the level of departure:

$$\sin \alpha_k = C\sqrt{y_k}$$

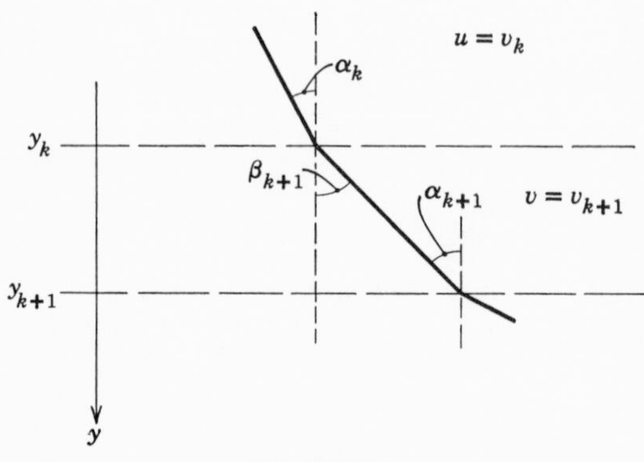

Fig. III.29

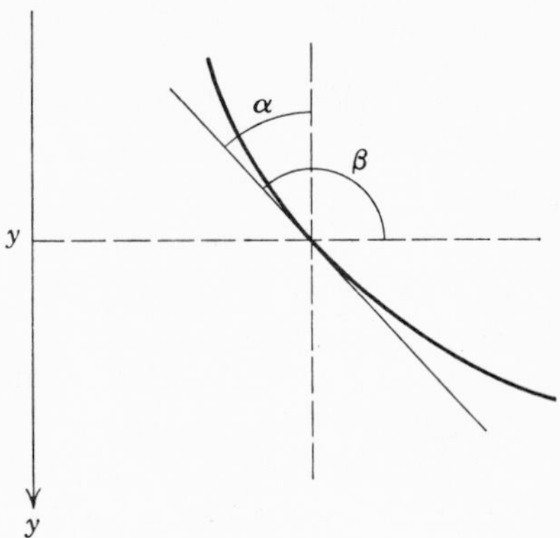

Fig. III.30

where C is a proportionality constant, the value of which depends on the coordinates of the endpoint P_2.

Now we put forth the traditional argument of the integral and differential calculus: we let the number of gravitational layers between the level of departure and the level of arrival increase and, at the same time, we let their thickness decrease to zero. This leads to the conclusion that the curve $y = f(x)$ which is the solution of our problem, has to intersect the perpendicular at any point at an angle α which satisfies the relation

$$\sin \alpha = C\sqrt{y}. \tag{III.44}$$

(see Fig. III.30). The angle between a curve and a line is defined as the angle between the tangent line to the curve and the line at the intersection point. On the other hand, if β is the angle of the tangent line with the horizontal, then the tangent of this angle is equal to the derivative at this point (rise/run).

Since

$$\beta = \alpha + 90$$

we obtain

$$y' = \tan(\alpha + 90) = \frac{\sin(\alpha + 90)}{\cos(\alpha + 90)}.$$

Since sine and cosine are complementary functions (see Appendix III, Section 3) and since the sine is odd and the cosine even, it follows that

$$\cos(\alpha + 90) = \cos(90 - (-\alpha)) = \sin(-\alpha) = -\sin \alpha,$$

$$\sin(\alpha + 90) = \sin(90 - (-\alpha)) = \cos(-\alpha) = \cos \alpha.$$

Hence, if we also observe that $\sin^2 \alpha + \cos^2 \alpha = 1$, we have

$$y' = -\frac{\cos \alpha}{\sin \alpha} = -\frac{\sqrt{1 - \sin^2 \alpha}}{\sin \alpha}.$$

From (III.44) we obtain now

$$y' = -\frac{\sqrt{1 - C^2 y}}{C\sqrt{y}}, \tag{III.45}$$

i.e., the curve $y = f(x)$ which provides the path of shortest descent is to be such that its derivative is related to the function itself according to (III.45). Such a relation is called a *differential equation*, because it is an equation for an unknown function that also contains the derivative (*differential* quotient) of the unknown function.

With our present knowledge it would be impossible to solve this equation for $y = f(x)$. However, with the background usually provided by an introductory course in differential equations it is merely a routine matter to show that the *cycloid* is the solution of this problem.

Since the cycloid emerges as the curve of shortest descent, it also is called the *brachistochrone*, which is a combination of the two Greek words *βράχιστος* for shortest and *χρόνος* for time.

But the cycloid has another property which makes it a remarkable curve indeed. In order to discuss this other property, let us build a model: We draw a cycloid on a board ($\frac{1}{2}$ inch or $\frac{3}{4}$ inch thick) by letting a circle roll on a ruler and tracing the path of a fixed point on its circumference. Then we cut the board along the cycloid and mount it on another board as indicated in Fig. III.31. This board is supported in the back so that it assumes an inclined position as indicated in Fig. III.31. Now we take two steelballs, place one in the position marked by A in Fig. III.31 and the other in a position marked by B and hold them in these positions with two electromagnets

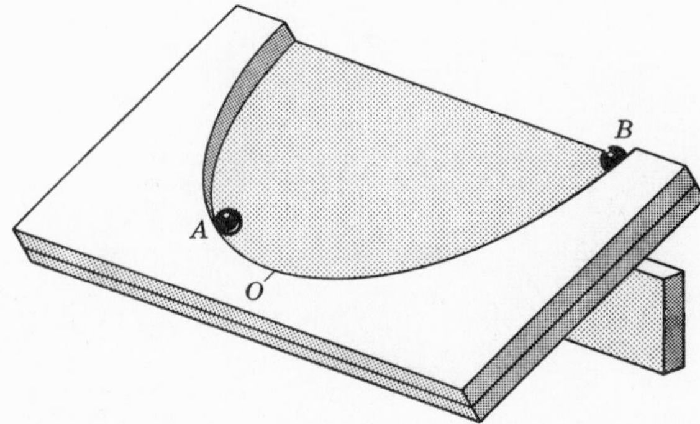

Fig. III.31

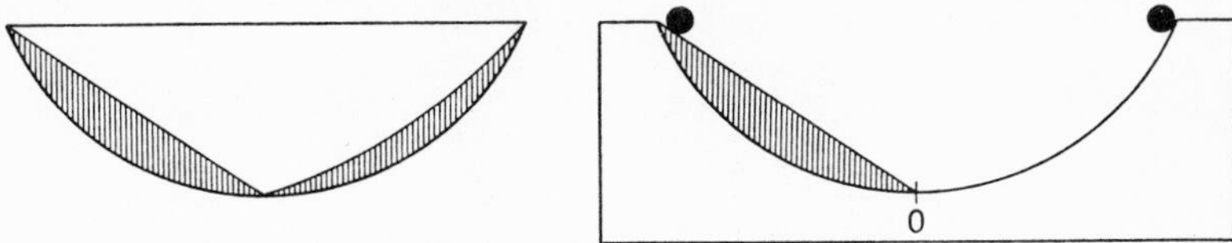

Fig. III.32

which are operated by the same switch. Now we are ready to take bets on a handicap race: which one will arrive first at the bottom 0? You may not believe it, unless you really carry out the experiment: both will arrive at 0 *simultaneously*—so, the house cannot possibly loose! No matter from which position we release a masspoint on a cycloid, the time required for the descent is always the same. So the cycloid not only is the curve of shortest descent (brachistochrone), it is also the curve of *equal descent* (*tautochrone*) as was first discovered by the Dutch physicist Ch. Huygens (1629–1695).

The model which we built can now also be used to illustrate the brachistochrone property. The portion which we cut out initially can be used to simulate two curves which are not cycloids and fitted into one-half of the model, as indicated in Fig. III.32. Then it will appear that whenever we start two steelballs at the same vertical distance from the bottom, the one on the cycloid will always arrive at 0 first. The students are urged to really build such a model. This is one of the simplest and still most impressive mathematical models there is. ◀

▶14. THE METHOD OF LEAST SQUARES

Suppose a physicist or engineer carries out an experiment that involves two variables: an independent variable x (e.g., the time) and a dependent variable y (e.g., temperature, velocity, etc.) Suppose he knows that within the framework of the theory that applies to this particular experiment, the relation between x and y is a linear one:

$$y = ax + b,$$

but he does not know the values of the constants a and b which are to be determined from the experiment. No experimental setup is ideal and no measurement is perfectly accurate. So, eventually, he will come up with a number of data which he tabulates. This table may look somewhat like Table III.1.

If we plot the pairs of corresponding numbers (x, y) from Table III.1 in a Cartesian coordinate system, we obtain the points in Fig. III.33. Due

Table III.1

x	y
0	−4
1	−3
2	−3
3	−1
4	0
5	1
6	2
7	2

to the imperfection of the experiment and the inaccuracies of measurements, these points do not lie on a straight line, but with some good will we can state that they cluster about a straight line.

The question which arises now is: How do we fit a straight line through these points which will fit the points best and represent the "true" relationship between x and y as closely as possible? One possibility is to pick out those points which do lie on a straight line and join them by this line (see solid line in Fig. III.33). This means, of course, that we accept those points that happen to lie on a straight line as accurate data and reject all the other points as inaccurate.

The reader can easily see that there is no justification whatever for such a procedure because the data selected are probably just as inaccurate as the ones which we rejected. For example, consider the case where 4 of the 8

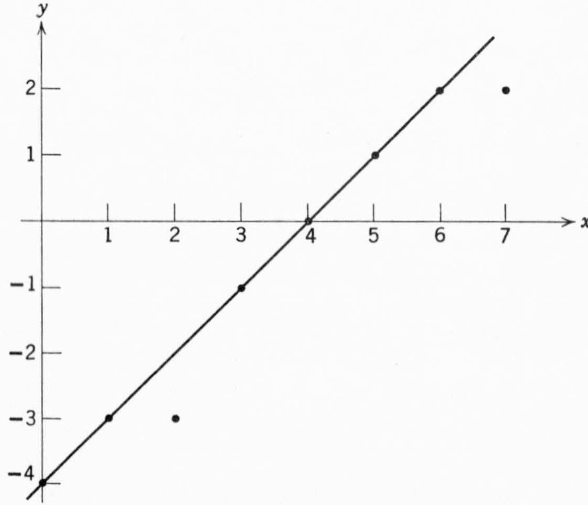

Fig. III.33

points lie on one line and the remaining 4 points lie on another line. Which one do we accept? Flip a coin? Most likely the true data, which we would obtain only under ideal circumstances making accurate measurements possible, will lie somewhere in between the ones which we actually obtained. Now we are back to our question: How do we choose a line such that the points representing the data cluster about the line as "closely" as possible?

Let us magnify Fig. III.33 somewhat and consider the line L which passes between the given points as indicated (see Fig. III.34). As a measure of the deviation of the measured data from the line L we may consider the differences between the measured y-value y_k that corresponds to x_k and the y-value that is obtained if we substitute x_k into the line equation

$$y = ax + b. \tag{III.46}$$

We obtain with $x_1 = 0$, $x_2 = 1$, $x_3 = 2$, etc.

$$\begin{aligned} d_1 &= y_1 - ax_1 - b = -4 - b \\ d_2 &= y_2 - ax_2 - b = -3 - a - b \\ &\cdot \\ &\cdot \\ &\cdot \\ d_8 &= y_8 - ax_8 - b = 2 - 7a - b. \end{aligned}$$

In general, we write

$$d_k = y_k - ax_k - b.$$

Clearly, these quantities d_k are positive or negative, depending on whether the kth measure point lies above or below the line L, and it is also clear that $|d_k|$ represents the vertical distance of the kth measure point from the line L. We may think naively that we can obtain the best fit if we choose the coefficients a and b such that the sum of all the d_k's is zero. That this is really a very poor procedure of obtaining a fitting line can be seen from Fig. III.35, where the sum of the d_k's is zero, but the line L does not fit the points at all.

However, if we consider the sum of the distances $|d_k|$ instead of the sum of the d_k's, we will certainly obtain a good fit when we try to make this sum as small as possible through proper choice of a and b. Thus our problem can be formulated as follows.

Choose a and b in $y = ax + b$ such that

$$|d_1| + |d_2| + |d_3| + \cdots + |d_8|$$

becomes a minimum. This procedure would yield a quite satisfactory result. It has, however, the disadvantage that absolute values are difficult to handle in computational processes. So we do the next best thing and require that the sum of the squares of the distances shall become a minimum:

$$d_1^2 + d_2^2 + d_3^2 + \cdots + d_8^2 \to \text{minimum}$$

(observe that $|d_k|^2 = d_k^2$) through proper choice of a and b. Now, in order to formulate our problem mathematically in greater generality, let us get away from our example for the time being, and assume that we have measured n values $y_1, y_2, y_3, \cdots, y_n$ which correspond to the n values $x_1, x_2, x_3, \cdots, x_n$ of the independent variable. Then, we have to choose a and b so that

$$d_1^2 + d_2^2 + d_3^2 + \cdots + d_n^2 = \sum_{k=1}^{n} d_k^2 \qquad \text{(III.47)}$$

becomes a minimum. Since

$$d_k = y_k - ax_k - b,$$

we obtain for (III.47)

$$\text{(III.48)} \quad (y_1 - ax_1 - b)^2 + (y_2 - ax_2 - b)^2 + (y_3 - ax_3 - b)^2 + \cdots + (y_n - ax_n - b)^2$$

and our problem is, if we also use the more sophisticated sum notation, the following one.

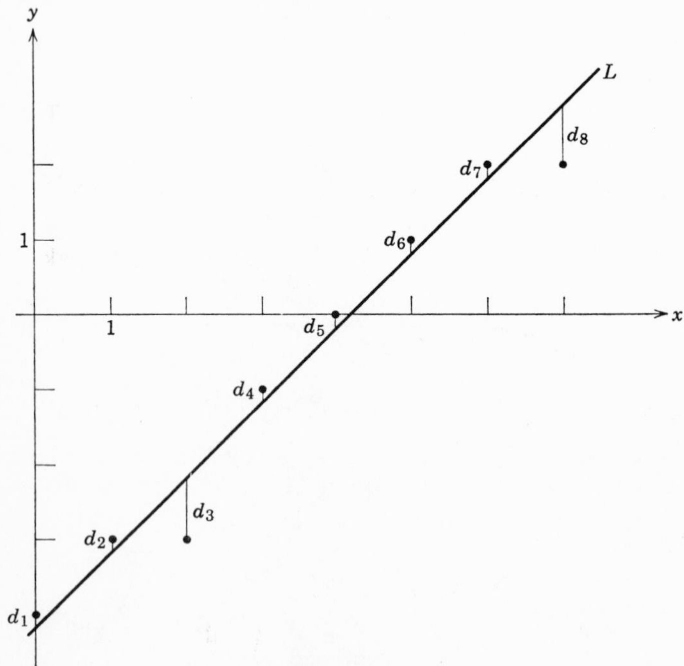

Fig. III.34

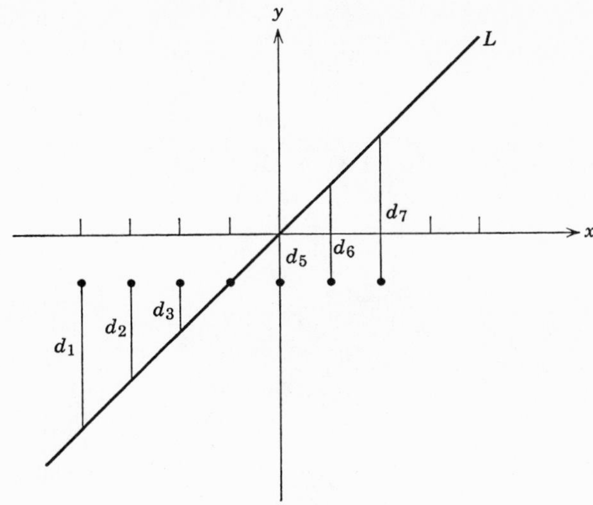

Fig. III.35

Choose the coefficients a and b such that

$$\sum_{k=1}^{n} (y_k - ax_k - b)^2 \tag{III.49}$$

becomes a minimum. Clearly, (III.49) is a function of two variables: a and b.

So far we have dealt only with functions of one variable and also only with the minimum of functions of one variable. We will see in the next section, however, that it is quite easy to find a necessary condition for the minimum of a function of two variables in terms of the theory which we developed for the minima (and maxima) of a function of one variable.

Problems III.88–III.92

III.88. Expand the expression in (III.49) for the following data: (0, 1), (1, 1), (2, 3), (3, 4), (4, 4), (5, 5), (6, 7), (7, 9).

III.89. Find b in $y = x + b$ such that (III.49) for the data in Problem III.88 becomes a minimum. Observe that this is a minimum problem for a function of one variable, b, only.

III.90. Given the data (0, 1), (4, 3), (8, 5). Find the equation of all lines for which $d_1 + d_2 + d_3 = 0$.

III.91. Evaluate the expression in (III.49) for the data in Table III.1 with

(*a*) $a = 1, b = -4$ (*b*) $a = \frac{20}{21}, b = -\frac{49}{12}$.

Which pair of coefficients yields the better fit?

III.92. Given the function of two variables $z = x^2 + y^2 + 1$. Assume that the minimum is attained for $y = 0$ and some x. For what x does the function attain the minimum under this assumption on y? What is the value of the function for the x which you found? Is it the minimum of the function? ◀

▶15. MINIMUM OF FUNCTIONS OF TWO VARIABLES

We consider the function

$$z = f(x, y) \tag{III.50}$$

where x and y are independent variables and z is a dependent variable. (III.50) is to be understood in the following sense: For every pair of values (x, y) which may be restricted to a region or may range over the entire x, y-plane, there corresponds a value z. As an example you may consider a thin rectangular plate which is heated at the edges. The coordinates x and y determine a point on the plate and the corresponding dependent variable z may stand for the temperature at this point.

Let us assume that the function $f(x, y)$ assumes its smallest value at the point $P_0(x_0, y_0)$:

$$\min f(x, y) = f(x_0, y_0).$$

Now: What condition(s) has (have) to hold at this point?

Suppose we substitute for y the value y_0 in (III.50). Then we obtain a function of one variable, namely x, $z = f(x, y_0) = F(x)$, which, according to our assumption, assumes its minimum value at $x = x_0$.

If the function $z = F(x)$ has everywhere a derivative, then it is necessary according to the theory which we developed in section 9 that

$$F'(x_0) = 0. \tag{III.51}$$

So we see that the derivative of $f(x, y)$ with respect to x has to vanish at $P_0(x_0, y_0)$ if $f(x, y)$ assumes its minimum value at this point.

If we would denote the derivative of $f(x, y)$ with respect to x by a prime, as we used to in dealing with functions of one variable, we would run into difficulties in case we should forget how this derivative is to be understood. To avoid any ambiguity in notation, we therefore denote the derivative of a function of two variables with respect to one of the variables by a subscript as follows:

$$\frac{d}{dx} f(x, y) = f_x(x, y),$$

$$\frac{d}{dy} f(x, y) = f_y(x, y).$$

Thus, we can write the condition (III.51) in the form

$$f_x(x_0, y_0) = 0. \tag{III.52}$$

Now we substitute for x the value x_0 in (III.50) and repeat our argument: We obtain thus a function of one variable only, namely, y

$$z = f(x_0, y) = G(y)$$

of which we know that it assumes its minimum for $y = y_0$. Hence, we obtain the necessary condition that

$$G'(y_0) = 0, \tag{III.53}$$

or, written in terms of f and the new notation which we introduced:

$$f_y(x_0, y_0) = 0. \tag{III.54}$$

Thus we can state: If $f(x, y)$ assumes its minimum value at the point $P_0(x_0, y_0)$, and if its derivatives with respect to x and with respect to y exist everywhere, then it is necessary that

$$f_x(x_0, y_0) = 0, \qquad f_y(x_0, y_0) = 0. \tag{III.55}$$

So, in order to find a point where the function $f(x, y)$ could have a minimum, we write down equations (III.55), solve for x and y (which is simple in case these equations turn out to be linear), and try to establish afterwards, by an independent argument, whether the function has indeed a minimum at this point. We will not enter such a discussion here because this is somewhat involved and quite unnecessary for our purpose. The functions we are going to deal with will be such that we can see by inspection that they can only have one minimum and it will turn out that the equations (III.55) will have only one solution. It then seems reasonable to assume that this solution will yield the minimum value.

As a first application, let us consider the simple example

$$z = x^2 + y^2.$$

We know that the smallest value this function can possibly assume is the value 0, and we can also see that the value 0 is obtained for $x = 0$, $y = 0$. This is indeed the solution of the equations (III.55) which read in this case

$$2x = 0$$
$$2y = 0.$$

As another application, let us consider a problem of the nature discussed in the preceding section, but let us simplify it to three data:

x_k	y_k
0	1
1	2
2	2

We try to fit the line $y = ax + b$ through these points such that (III.49) becomes a minimum. (III.49) turns out to be the following function of the variables a and b:

$$\begin{aligned} f(a, b) &= (y_1 - ax_1 - b)^2 + (y_2 - ax_2 - b)^2 + (y_3 - ax_3 - b)^2 \\ &= (1 - b)^2 + (2 - a - b)^2 + (2 - 2a - b)^2 \\ &= 3b^2 + 6ab + 5a^2 - 12a - 10b + 9. \end{aligned}$$

Hence

$$\begin{aligned} f_a(a, b) &= 6b + 10a - 12 = 0 \\ f_b(a, b) &= 6b + 6a - 10 = 0. \end{aligned}$$

The solution of this system of two linear equations in two unknowns is

$$a = \frac{1}{2}, \quad b = \frac{7}{6}.$$

Thus it appears that the line

$$y = \frac{1}{2}x + \frac{7}{6}$$

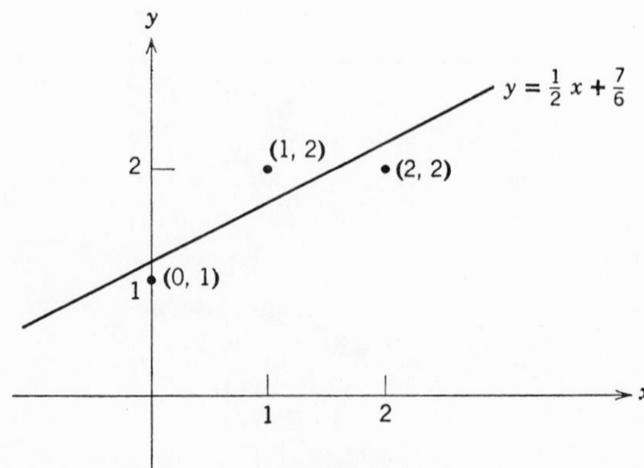

Fig. III.36

is the one which fits best the points representing the given empirical data in the sense that the sum of the squares of the deviations d_k assumes a minimum. We therefore call this method the "method of least squares" and say that the line is fitted best "*in the sense of the least square principle*".

In Fig. III.36 we have drawn the line which we obtained as solution to our problem and have indicated also the points representing the given data.

Problems III.93–III.96

III.93. Determine the points where the function $z = 16x^2 + 4xy + y^2 + 1$ could possibly have a minimum.

III.94. Suppose we know that $z = f(x, y)$ has a maximum at the point $P_1(x_1, y_1)$. Derive a necessary condition.

III.95. Suppose we know that the function $z = f(s, t, u, v, w)$ has a minimum at the point $(s_0, t_0, u_0, v_0, w_0)$. Derive necessary conditions.

III.96. Fit a line $y = ax + b$ through the points (1, 2), (3, 3), (5, 3), (7, 4) in the sense of the least square principle. ◀

▶16. THE METHOD OF LEAST SQUARES (*continued*)

We are now fully prepared to deal with and solve the problem which we posed in section 14, namely, to find two constants a and b such that the function

(III.56)
$$f(a, b) = \sum_{k=1}^{n} (y_k - ax_k - b)^2$$

assumes a minimum value, where the x_k and y_k $(k = 1, 2, 3, \cdots, n)$ are given numbers.

We know from the discussion in the preceding section that if $f(a, b)$ has a minimum value for a certain pair (a, b), then it is necessary that the derivatives of f with respect to a and with respect to b vanish for these values a, b:

(III.57a)
$$f_a(a, b) = 0$$

(III.57b)
$$f_b(a, b) = 0.$$

In computing f_a and f_b we remember that the derivative of a sum is equal to the sum of the derivatives (see Section 2). We note also that every term of the sum (III.56) is of the form

(III.58)
$$(y_k - ax_k - b)^2 = y_k^2 + a^2x_k^2 + b^2 - 2ax_ky_k - 2by_k + 2abx_k, \qquad k = 1, 2, 3, \cdots, n.$$

So all we have to do is differentiate the general term (III.58) and then take the sum of these derivatives from $k = 1$ to $k = n$. We obtain for the derivative of (III.58) with respect to a:

$$\frac{d}{da}(y_k - ax_k - b)^2 = 2ax_k^2 - 2x_ky_k + 2bx_k = 2(ax_k^2 - x_ky_k + bx_k).$$

Thus (III.57a) now reads

$$2\sum_{k=1}^{n}(ax_k^2 - x_ky_k + bx_k) = 0.$$

If we divide by 2 and split up the sum into its components, we obtain

$$\text{(III.59)} \qquad a\sum_{k=1}^{n}x_k^2 + b\sum_{k=1}^{n}x_k - \sum_{k=1}^{n}x_ky_k = 0.$$

Similarly, we obtain

$$\frac{d}{db}(y_k - ax_k - b)^2 = 2b - 2y_k + 2ax_k$$

and, consequently, we have for (III.57b)

$$2\sum_{k=1}^{n}(ax_k - y_k + b) = 0$$

or

$$\text{(III.60)} \qquad a\sum_{k=1}^{n}x_k - \sum_{k=1}^{n}y_k + b\sum_{k=1}^{n}1 = 0.$$

(III.59) and (III.60) constitute a system of two linear equations in two unknowns, a and b, which has, in general, a unique solution (see Chapter I, Section 6).

If we want to solve this system, we have to evaluate first the coefficients $\sum_{k=1}^{n}x_k$, $\sum_{k=1}^{n}y_k$, $\sum_{k=1}^{n}x_ky_k$ and $\sum_{k=1}^{n}x_k^2$. This can most efficiently be done by the following scheme, where we use again the data from Table III.1 in Section 14:

	x_k	y_k	x_k^2	x_ky_k
	0	−4	*0*	*0*
	1	−3	*1*	*−3*
	2	−3	*4*	*−6*
	3	−1	*9*	*−3*
	4	0	*16*	*0*
	5	1	*25*	*5*
	6	2	*36*	*12*
	7	2	*49*	*14*
$\sum_{k=1}^{n}$:	*28*	*−6*	*140*	*19*

Here the numerals set in roman type represent the given data and are inserted in the table first; the numerals set in italics are then computed in terms of the given data.

Thus, in our example, (III.59) and (III.60) become:

$$\left.\begin{aligned} 140a + 28b - 19 &= 0 \,\Big|\, .2 \\ 28a + 8b + 6 &= 0 \,\Big|\, .(-7) \end{aligned}\right\} +$$

If we multiply and combine these equations as indicated, we find that

$$a = \frac{20}{21}$$

and, consequently,

$$b = -\frac{49}{12}.$$

Thus the line

$$y = \frac{20}{21}x - \frac{49}{12}$$

will fit the given data best in the sense of the least square principle (see Fig. III.37).

The computation that was involved in solving this problem was quite simple and straightforward. Still, if we could accomplish some further simplifications, it would certainly help in case a great many data are given and/or the data involve large numbers or numbers with a great many decimal places.

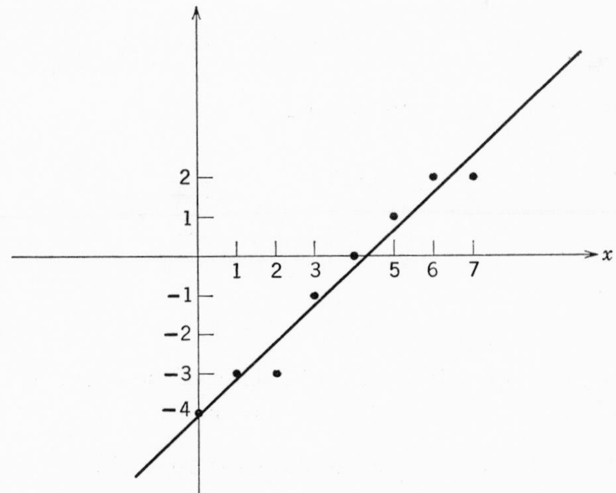

Fig. III.37

Looking at (III.59) and (III.60), we see that the solution could be found very easily if the terms which are multiplied by $\sum_{k=1}^{n} x_k$ were not present. Now, what would that entail? If $\sum_{k=1}^{n} x_k = 0$, then that means that the x-values are arranged symmetrically with respect to the origin, if they are equidistant to begin with. If this is not the case, then it can easily be arranged simply by shifting the y-axis until the new x-values $\bar{x}_k$ are such that $\sum_{k=1}^{n} \bar{x}_k = 0$. We take the arithmetic mean of all the x_k

$$x = \frac{x_1 + x_2 + x_3 + \cdots + x_n}{n}$$

and introduce the new coordinates

$$\bar{x}_k = x_k - \bar{x}.$$

Then, we obtain

$$\begin{aligned} \sum_{k=1}^{n} \bar{x}_k &= \sum_{k=1}^{n} (x_k - \bar{x}) = \sum_{k=1}^{n} x_k - \bar{x} \sum_{k=1}^{n} 1 \\ &= x_1 + x_2 + x_3 + \cdots + x_n - \frac{x_1 + x_2 + x_3 + \cdots + x_n}{n} n = 0. \end{aligned}$$

Hence, the equations (III.59) and (III.60) written in terms of the $\bar{x}_k$ appear in the form

$$a \sum_{k=1}^{n} \bar{x}_k^{\,2} - \sum_{k=1}^{n} \bar{x}_k y_k = 0$$

$$nb - \sum_{k=1}^{n} y_k = 0$$

and we obtain immediately the solution

$$\text{(III.61)} \qquad a = \frac{\sum_{k=1}^{n} \bar{x}_k y_k}{\sum_{k=1}^{n} \bar{x}_k^{\,2}}, \qquad b = \frac{1}{n} \sum_{k=1}^{n} y_k.$$

Hence,

$$y = a\bar{x} + b$$

is the line that fits the data best in the sense of the least square principle in the new $\bar{x}$, y-coordinate system and, consequently,

$$y = a(x - \bar{x}) + b = ax + (b - a\bar{x})$$

is the solution of our original problem.

To illustrate the superiority of this procedure over the previous one, let us solve the same problem again by the new method. We use the following scheme:

x_k	y_k	$\bar{x}_k = x_k - \bar{x}$	$\bar{x}_k^2$	$\bar{x}_k y_k$
0	-4	$-\frac{7}{2}$	$\frac{49}{4}$	$\frac{28}{2}$
1	-3	$-\frac{5}{2}$	$\frac{25}{4}$	$\frac{15}{2}$
2	-3	$-\frac{3}{2}$	$\frac{9}{4}$	$\frac{9}{2}$
3	-1	$-\frac{1}{2}$	$\frac{1}{4}$	$\frac{1}{2}$
4	0	$\frac{1}{2}$	$\frac{1}{4}$	0
5	1	$\frac{3}{2}$	$\frac{9}{4}$	$\frac{3}{2}$
6	2	$\frac{5}{2}$	$\frac{25}{4}$	$\frac{10}{2}$
7	2	$\frac{7}{2}$	$\frac{49}{4}$	$\frac{14}{2}$
28	-6	0	$\frac{168}{4}$	$\frac{80}{2}$

$$\bar{x} = \frac{28}{8} = \frac{7}{2}.$$

Thus, in accordance with (III.61),

$$a = \frac{20}{21}, \qquad b = -\frac{3}{4}$$

and, consequently,

$$y = \frac{20}{21}\bar{x} - \frac{3}{4} = \frac{20}{21}\left(x - \frac{7}{2}\right) - \frac{3}{4} = \frac{20}{21}x - \frac{49}{12}.$$

We wish to point out one additional advantage of this method. In computing the numbers in the column headed by x_k^2 in the previous procedure, we had to carry out 8 squaring processes. Now, because of the symmetry of the $\bar{x}_k$ data, we only have to carry out 4 squaring processes in column 4 and then copy these values in reverse order. (Of course this is not true anymore if the x_k are not equidistant to begin with.)

Problems III.97–III.102

III.97. Fit a line through the points (0, 1), (1, 0), (2, 0), (3, $-\frac{1}{2}$), (4, $-\frac{3}{2}$), (5, -1), (6, -2), (7, -3) in the sense of the least square principle.

III.98. Same as in Problem III.97 with the points (-2, 0), (-1, 0), (0, 0), (1, 1), (2, 1), (3, 2), (4, 1.5), (5, 2), (6, 4), (7, 4), (8, 4).

III.99. Fit a parabola $y = ax^2 + bx + c$ through the points (0, 0), (1, 1), (2, 3), (3, 8), (4, 17) in the sense of the least square principle. Note that $f(a, b, c) = \sum_{k=1}^{n} (y_k - ax_k^2 - bx_k - c)^2$ is now a function of three variables.

III.100. Fit a curve $y = a \cos x + b \sin x$ through the points (0, 0.7), ($\pi/6$, 0.6), ($\pi/4$, 1.1), ($\pi/3$, 0.8), ($\pi/2$, 0.6), ($2\pi/3$, 0.6), ($3\pi/4$, 0.1), ($5\pi/6$, -0.4), (π, -0.8) in the sense of the least square principle. (For the true values of sine and cosine for the listed arguments see the tables in Sections 2 and 3 of Appendix III.)

III.101. Prove that the line $y = ax + b$ which fits the points (x_k, y_k) ($k = 1, 2, 3, \cdots, n$) in the sense of the least square principle passes through the origin if $\sum_{k=1}^{n} x_k = 0$ and the y_k are symmetrical with respect to the x-axis.

III.102. The population of the United States is listed as follows

year	population in millions
1810	7
1840	17
1870	39
1900	76
1930	122
1960	160

Assume that the population increases quadratically and fit a parabola $y = ax^2 + bx + c$ through these data in the sense of the least square principle. Under this assumption, (*a*) find the rate of increase in 1945; (*b*) estimate the population in 1970. ◀

Supplementary Problems III

1.1. Given $F(x) = 1/x$. Evaluate $\dfrac{F(x + h) - F(x)}{h}$ at the point $x = 1$ for the following values of h: $h = 1, 0.5, 0.2, 0.1, 0.01, 0.001$. Can you guess what the limit will be as $h \to 0$?

1.2. Consider the difference quotient for the function $y = \cos x$. By a skilful manipulation of the identity in Problem AIII.13 of Appendix III, Section 4, it can be shown that

$$\cos \alpha - \cos \beta = -2 \sin\left(\frac{\alpha + \beta}{2}\right) \sin\left(\frac{\alpha - \beta}{2}\right).$$

Let $\alpha = x + h$, $\beta = x$ and simplify the difference quotient until it appears as a product, one factor of which is $\dfrac{\sin (h/2)}{h/2}$.

1.3. Let $F(x) = |x|$. Sketch the function $y = F'(x)$.

1.4. Simplify the difference quotients of the following functions to a point at which the factors h in numerator and denominator cancel out:

$$(a)\ F(x) = x^3 - x \qquad (b)\ F(x) = \frac{1 - x}{x}$$

1.5. Given the function

$$F(x) = \begin{cases} x^2 \text{ for } x \geq 0 \\ x^3 \text{ for } x < 0. \end{cases}$$

Find $\dfrac{F(x + h) - F(x)}{h}$ and $-\dfrac{F(x - h) - F(x)}{h}$ and evaluate these quotients at $x = 0$ for $h = 1, 0.5, 0.1, 0.01, 0.001, 0.0001$. Do both tend to the same limit?

2.1. Differentiate

$$(a)\ y = \frac{(1 + x)^3(1 - x)}{1 - x^2} \qquad (b)\ y = \frac{x^3 - 64}{x - 4}$$

2.2. Find the equation of the tangent line to the parabola

$$y = x^2 - 3x + 1$$

at the point (4, 5).

2.3. Given the functions

$$f_1(x) = \begin{cases} 2 \text{ for rational } x \\ 0 \text{ for irrational } x \end{cases}$$

$$f_2(x) = \begin{cases} 0 \text{ for rational } x \\ 2 \text{ for irrational } x \end{cases}$$

$$f_3(x) = -2x \text{ for all } x.$$

Find the derivative of $F(x) = f_1(x) + f_2(x) + f_3(x)$.

2.4. At which point does the curve

$$y = x^2 - 2x + 5$$

have a horizontal tangent line?

2.5. The general term a_n of the sequence $a_1, a_2, a_3, \cdots$ is defined as follows: a_n is the slope of the tangent line to the parabola $y = x^2 + x + 4$ at the point $x = \dfrac{1 + n^2}{n^2}$. Give an explicit representation of a_n. Find $\lim_{n\to\infty} a_n$. Can you check your result by an independent method?

3.1. Differentiate

$$(a)\ F(x) = x^7 + \frac{1}{x} \qquad (b)\ F(x) = \frac{x^6}{6} + \frac{x^5}{5} + \frac{x^4}{4} + \frac{x^3}{3} + \frac{x^2}{2} + x + 1$$

3.2. Given

$$F(x) = \begin{cases} x^3 + 1 \text{ for } x \leq 0 \\ x^4 + 1 \text{ for } x > 0. \end{cases}$$

Find $F'(x)$ and $F''(x)$ at $x = 0$. What about $F'''(x)$ at $x = 0$?

3.3. Find the equations of the tangent lines to the curve $y = x + \dfrac{1}{x}$ at those points at which the slope of the tangent lines is 1.

3.4. Given the parabola $y = x^2 - 4x + 2$. Find the equations of the tangent lines to the parabola which pass through the point $(1, -1)$.

3.5. Given $y = x^3 - 3x + 4$. Find those values of x for which $y' = 0$. Denote these values by x_k ($k = 1, 2, \cdots ?$) and evaluate y'' at $x = x_k$ for all k.

3.6. Given $y = \cos x$. Find y'. (*Hint:* See Problem 1.2.)

4.1. Differentiate:

(*a*) $y = (4x^2 - 6x + 7)^{1008}$ (*b*) $y = 9x^3 - \sqrt{x + 1}$

(*c*) $y = \dfrac{1}{x} + \dfrac{1}{\sqrt{x^2 + 4}}$ (*d*) $y = x\sqrt{x + 3}$

4.2. Differentiate:

(*a*) $y = \cos(x^3)$ (*b*) $y = \cos^4 x$

(*c*) $y = \sin^3(x^5)$ (*d*) $y = \sqrt{\sin^3 x}$

4.3. Show that

$$\frac{dx^{(p/q)}}{dx} = \frac{p}{q}x^{\frac{p}{q}-1}$$

where p and q are positive or negative integers. (*Hint:* Consider $y^q = x^p$ instead of $y = x^{p/q}$. Then $\dfrac{dy^q}{dx} = \dfrac{dy^q}{dy}\cdot\dfrac{dy}{dx} = qy^{q-1}\dfrac{dy}{dx}$. On the other hand, $\dfrac{dx^p}{dx} = px^{p-1}$. Since $y^q = x^p$, we have $\dfrac{dy^q}{dx} = \dfrac{dx^p}{dx}$, i.e., $qy^{q-1}\dfrac{dy}{dx} = px^{p-1}$.)

5.1. Find the antiderivative of

(*a*) $y' = 3x^2 - 4x + 5$ (*b*) $y' = 4x^3 + 12x^2$

(*c*) $y' = -12x^4 + 23x + 7$ (*d*) $y' = \dfrac{12}{x} - \dfrac{1}{x^2}$

5.2. Find

(*a*) $\displaystyle\int \frac{dx}{\sqrt{x}}$ (*b*) $\displaystyle\int \left(x^2 - \frac{2}{x^2}\right) dx$

(*c*) $\displaystyle\int x^{-3/2}\,dx$ (*d*) $\displaystyle\int (1 + x^2)(1 - x^2)\,dx$

5.3. Utilizing the antidifferentiation process, evaluate the following definite integrals.

(*a*) $\displaystyle\int_{-1}^{1} (1 - x^2)\,dx$ (*b*) $\displaystyle\int_0^{\pi} \cos x\,dx$

(*c*) $\displaystyle\int_{1000}^{1000.001} (4x + 1)\,dx$ (*d*) $\displaystyle\int_{-\pi}^{0} \sin x\,dx$

5.4. Take

$$\int_a^x x^2\,dx = \frac{x^3}{3} + C.$$

Show that for *any* value C (between $-\infty$ and ∞) there exists a value a which satisfies this relation. Compare this result with that of Problem III.41. Try to explain the difference between the two problems.

5.5. Is $\int_{-1}^{3} (\sqrt{x} + 3)\, dx$ meaningful? Explain.

6.1. Show that

$$\int f(u)u'(x)\, dx = F(u(x)) + C$$

if $\dfrac{dF}{du} = f(u)$.

6.2. Integrate

(*a*) $\int (1 + \sqrt[3]{3 + 4^7})\, dx$ (*b*) $\int \left(\frac{1}{x} + \frac{x^3}{\sqrt{x^4 - 1}}\right) dx$

(*c*) $\int \frac{\sin x\, dx}{\cos^2 x}$ (*d*) $\int (3x - x^2\sqrt{x^3 + 4})\, dx$

6.3. If $y = f(u)$, $u = g(v)$, $v = h(x)$, then $\dfrac{dy}{dx} = \dfrac{dy}{du} \cdot \dfrac{du}{dv} \cdot \dfrac{dv}{dx}$.

Show that

$$\int f'(u)u'(v)v'(x)\, dx = f(u(v(x))) + C.$$

6.4. Evaluate:

(*a*) $\int_0^{\pi/2} \sin x \cos x\, dx$ (*b*) $\int_0^{\pi/4} \frac{\sin x\, dx}{\cos^2 x}$

(*c*) $\int_0^{3} \frac{dx}{\sqrt{1 + x}}$ (*d*) $\int_0^{4} x\sqrt{x^2 + 9}\, dx$

7.1. Given $y = x^{3/2}$. Find an approximation to y' at $x = 4.01$. (Find the derivative y' of $x^{3/2}$ by the limit process.)

7.2. Find approximations for

(*a*) $(2.98)^4$ (*b*) $\sqrt{120.87}$

(*c*) $(1.0001)^7$ (*d*) $\sqrt{63.991}$

7.3. Height and base of an isosceles triangle both increase from a length of 2 ft to a length of 2.023 ft. Find an approximation for the increased area.

7.4. The area of a square decreases from $4m^2$ to $3.976m^2$. Find an approximation for the length of the perimeter of the shrunken square, assuming that all sides shrink at the same rate.

7.5. Find an approximation for the increase of the function $y = x^2$ between $x = 0.5$ and $x = 0.52$ and between $x = 4$ and $x = 4.02$. Find also the exact increase and express the errors in both cases in per cent of the exact increase.

8.1. Find an approximate solution of

$$x^3 + 7x^2 - 5x - 35 = 0$$

by Newton's method. Start with $x_0 = -6$ and take three steps. (See also Problem III.55.)

8.2. Specialize Formula (III.23) for the function $f(x) = x^2 - a$.

8.3. Apply the formula found in Problem 8.2 to $a = 5$; start with $x_0 = 2$, and take three steps. You thus obtain an approximation for what?

8.4. Find approximate solutions of

$$x^2 - 3x + 1 = 0$$

by Newton's method. Start with $x_0 = \frac{5}{2}$ and with $x_0 = \frac{1}{2}$. Take three steps in each case. Solve the equation by the quadratic formula, isolate the approximations for the square root involved, and compare the two approximations with each other.

8.5. Find an approximation for the solution x of the equation

$$\int_0^x u\,du - 3 = 0$$

by Newton's method.

9.1. Find all extreme values of the functions

$$(a)\ y = x^3 + 3x^2 - 105x + 1 \qquad (b)\ y = 4x^3 + 6x^2 - 9x - 4$$

9.2. A rectangle with the largest possible area is to be inscribed in a circle of radius 1. What are its dimensions?

9.3. Find all extreme values of the function

$$y = \sin x + \cos x$$

and sketch the function. (For differentiation of sine and cosine, see Problem III.29 and supplementary Problem 3.6.)

9.4. Given the function

$$f(x) = \begin{cases} x^2 - 2x + 2 \text{ for } x \geq 1 \\ x^3 - 3x^2 + 3x \text{ for } x < 1. \end{cases}$$

Find the minimum value of this function.

9.5. Sketch the function

$$y = \frac{1}{x} \sin x.$$

(*Hint:* The extreme values of $\sin x$ are 1 and -1. Wherever $\sin x = 1$, we have $y = 1/x$; and wherever $\sin x = -1$, we have $y = -1/x$.)

10.1. An object slides down an inclined plane, starting from rest at the top, with an acceleration of 12 ft/sec². The length of the inclined plane is 18 ft. When does it hit the bottom?

10.2. An object moves back and forth along a straight line according to the formula

$$s = 3 \cos t + \sin t$$

(*Harmonic Motion*). For what values of t does it pass through the point $s = 0$? How far does it go beyond the point $s = 0$?

10.3. A car starts from rest with an acceleration of 20 ft/sec². As soon as it reaches a velocity of 60 mi/h it will travel with this velocity for 3 min and then slow down to a velocity of 45 mi/h within $\frac{1}{2}$ minute. It will then travel at the velocity of 45 mi/h for 5 minutes and then slow down to a stop within 1 minute. (*a*) Find $a = a(t)$. (*b*) Find $v = v(t)$. (*c*) Find $s = s(t)$, assuming that the car starts from $s = 0$.

10.4. How far did the car in Problem 10.3 travel?

10.5. Sketch the functions $a = a(t)$, $v = v(t)$ and $s = s(t)$ from Problem 10.3.

11.1. A stone is thrown vertically upward from a window 24 ft above the ground with an initial velocity of 16 ft/sec. (*a*) How high did it go? (*b*) When did it pass the window on its way down? (*c*) When did it hit the ground? (*d*) What was the impact velocity?

11.2. What initial velocity do we have to impart to an object if we want to throw it 82 ft vertically upward?

11.3. The weight of an object on the surface of a heavenly body is defined as the force of attraction between the heavenly body and the object. Suppose, an object weighs 1 lb on the surface of the earth. How much does it weigh on the surface of the moon? (Mass of moon $\simeq \frac{1}{80}$ of mass of earth, radius of moon $\simeq$ 2200 mi.)

11.4. Find the acceleration of a freely falling body in a reasonable neighborhood of the surface of the moon. (For dimensions of moon, see Problem 11.3.)

11.5. A projectile is to be shot from the moon to the earth. Find the necessary initial velocity to shoot it beyond the neutral point. (See also Problem III.82 and Supplementary Problem 11.4.)

12.1. A light ray is emitted from the point $P(0, 1 \text{ in.})$ and proceeds within the x, y-plane through air until it hits a water surface $y = 0$ at an angle of 60° with the perpendicular. It then proceeds through water until it hits the surface of a layer of glycerin at $y = -1$ in. If the layer of glycerin is 1 inch thick, at what point does the light ray leave the glycerin layer? (Velocity of light in air = 186,000 mi/sec, in water = 139,000 mi/sec, in glycerin = 126,000 mi/sec.)

12.2. If a light ray penetrates the boundary of a medium, part of it is refracted into the new medium and part of it is reflected such that the angle of the reflected ray with the perpendicular is equal to the angle of the incoming ray with the perpendicular. Consider that part of the light ray that is reflected on the lower boundary of the glycerin layer in Problem 12.1. At what point does it emerge from the water layer into the air?

13.1. Consider the cycloid in Fig. III.26 (p. 228). After the circle of radius R rolled from its initial position through a distance d, the line joining P with the center of the circle will have turned through an angle of $\alpha = d/R$ radians. Express the coordinates x and y of the point P for any position of the generating circle as functions of the angle α.

13.2. Same as in Problem 13.1 for the case where the point P does not lie on the periphery of the circle but at a distance $a < R$ from the center of the circle. Sketch the curve.

13.3. Same as in Problem 13.2 for the case $a > R$. Make a sketch.

14.1. Find a in $y = ax$ so that the expression (II.49) becomes a minimum for the data in Problem III.88 (p. 237).

14.2. Given the data (0, 2), (3, 3), (6, 5), (9, 5). Find the equation of the line(s) for which $d_1 + d_2 + d_3 + d_4 = 0$. (For definition of the d_i's see p. 235).

15.1. At what point(s) could the function of three variables

$$w = x^2 + y^2 + 10z^2$$

possibly have an extreme value? (See also problem III.95.)

16.1. Find a line which fits the points (0, −4), (1, −2), (2, 1), (3, 2), (4, 5) according to the least square principle.

16.2. Same as in Problem III.102 (p. 246) with an assumed population of 170 millions in 1960. Compare the results with those of Problem III.102.

CHAPTER IV

VOLUMES

1. VOLUME OF A PRISM

We consider a right parallelepiped. A *right parallelepiped* is a box (see Fig. IV.1). Suppose the dimensions of the box are a, b, and c as indicated in Fig. IV.1. Our aim is to establish a measure of the volume of this solid, or in simple words: How much pink paint does the box hold? Again, we proceed in a way very similar to the one which we took in establishing the area measure of a plane rectangle.

Clearly, among many boxes with the same base (the shaded rectangle in Fig. IV.1 is called the *base*), i.e., with the same dimensions a and b, the one with the largest height c will hold the greatest amount of paint, i.e., has to be assigned the largest volume measure. On the other hand, if we have many boxes with the same height c but different bases (with different area measures), then it is clear that the one with the largest base will have the greatest volume. This leads us to define the volume of a rectangular box (right parallelepiped) as jointly proportional to the area of its base and the length of its height.

Since

$$\text{Area of base} = ab,$$

we are led to the definition

$$\text{(IV.1)} \qquad \text{Volume of right parallelepiped} = abc$$

if we agree to choose a box of the dimensions $a = 1, b = 1, c = 1$ as the unit of volume measurement, thereby making the proportionality constant equal to one. (If the sides are measured in inches, then the volume is accordingly measured in cubic inches—cu in.; if the sides are measured in feet, then the volume is measured in cubic feet—cu ft; and if the sides are measured in meters, then the volume is measured in cubic meters—m^3.)

We can see easily that the volume measure of a rectangular box, as defined in (IV.1), has analogous properties to the area measure, namely: it is always positive unless at least one of the sides has the length zero—in

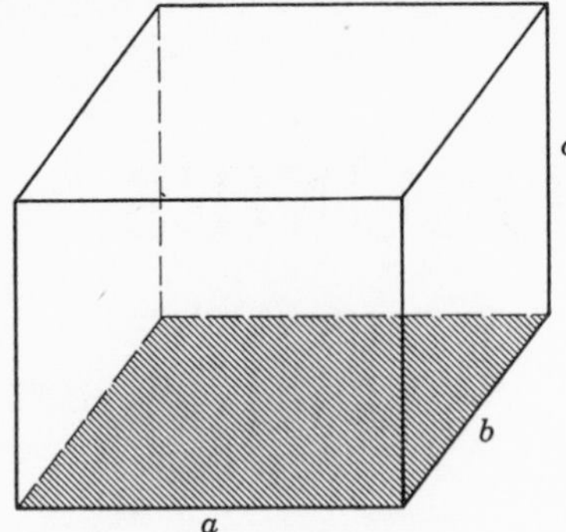

Fig. IV.1

which case we don't have a box at all; the volume measure is additive, i.e., if we fit two boxes together to make one box, then the volume of the newly created box equals the sum of the volumes of the two components. From this property we can again deduce that whenever one box is contained in another box, the volume measure of the submerged box is smaller than the volume measure of the containing box.

We proceed now to a generalization of this concept to a solid, as depicted in Fig. IV.2. The base of this solid is a planar region encompassed by a polygon and the lateral surface consists of a number of rectangles perpendicular to the base which are all of the same height h. Such a solid is called a *prism*.

Before we attempt to deal with this general case, let us first consider the case where the base is a right triangle. Such a prism can be obtained from

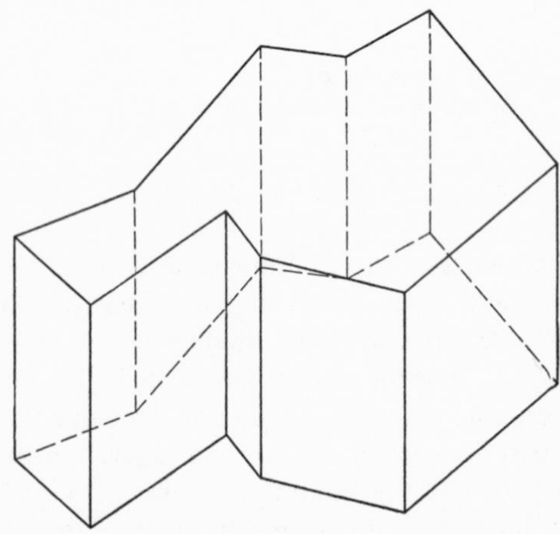
Fig. IV.2

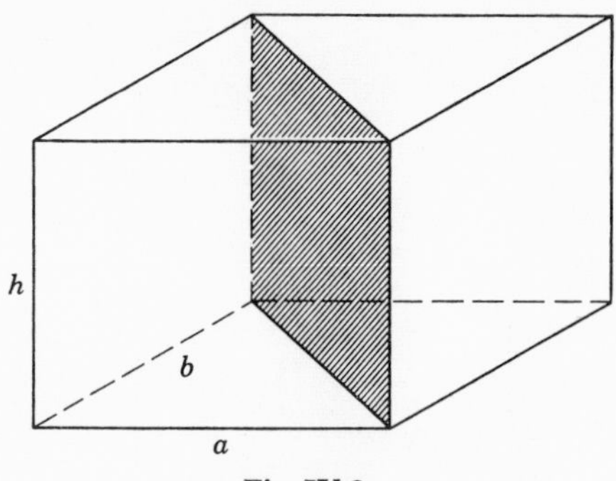

Fig. IV.3

a right parallelepiped simply by cutting the latter in two, as indicated in Fig. IV.3. Hence, we obtain for its volume

$$V = \tfrac{1}{2}abh.$$

Now, to obtain a prism which has a general triangle as its base, we go through essentially the same argument as in Chapter II, Section 2, p. 79 and obtain the following formula for the triangular prism:

$$\text{Volume of triangular prism} = \tfrac{1}{2}abh$$

where a is one side and b the corresponding height in the base triangle.

Dissecting the base of a general prism into triangles, we are led to the following formula for the volume measure of a prism:

$$\text{Volume of prism} = \text{Area of base} \times \text{height},$$

where the area of the base can be computed in terms of areas of triangles.

Problems IV.1–IV.4

IV.1. The base of a prism of height 12 is a right triangle with the sides 3 and 7. Find the volume.

IV.2. The base of a prism of height 10 is a regular octagon which is inscribed into a circle of radius 6. Find the volume.

IV.3. The base of a prism of height h is a regular hexagon which is inscribed into a circle of radius r. Express r as a function of the volume V.

IV.4. The base of a prism of height h is a regular polygon with n vertices inscribed into a circle of radius r. Find the volume.

2. VOLUME OF A RIGHT CIRCULAR CYLINDER

What is commonly referred to as a cylinder is what mathematicians more precisely call a *right circular cylinder* (see Fig. IV.4). Top and bottom are circles of radius r which lie in parallel planes and are joined together by a

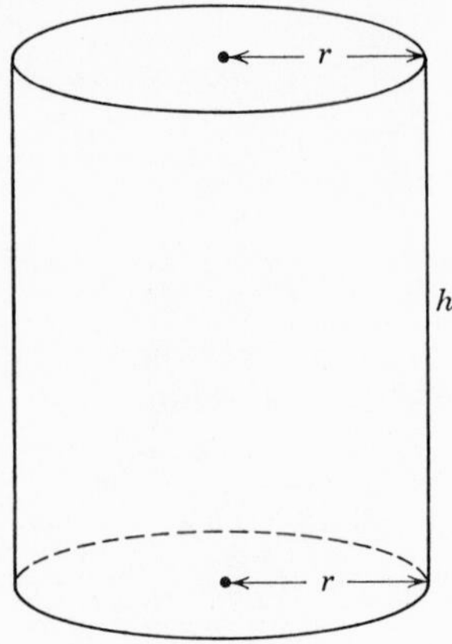

Fig. IV.4

sheet of height h which is perpendicular to the planes in which top and bottom lie.

How do we define the volume of such a right circular cylinder in order to be consistent with the volume definitions which we have given so far? Now the volume is to be greater than the volume of any solid which lies entirely within the cylinder. If we inscribe a regular polygon into the circular base, we obtain a prism which is contained in the cylinder (see Fig. IV.5). The volume of this prism, according to the formula which we developed in the preceding section, is given by

$$V(\text{prism}) = hB_n$$

where B_n represents the area of the regular polygon with n vertices inscribed

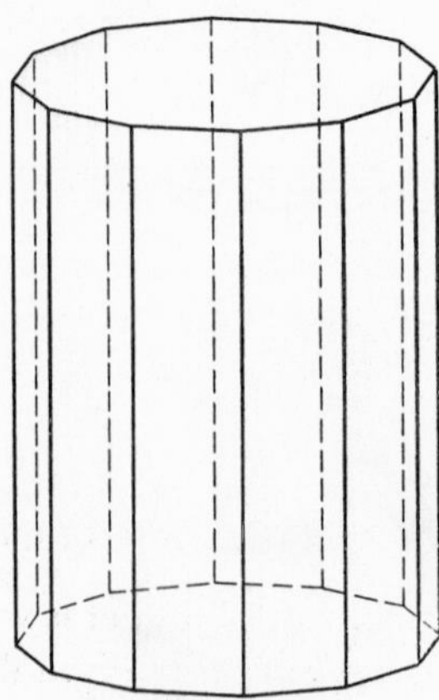

Fig. IV.5

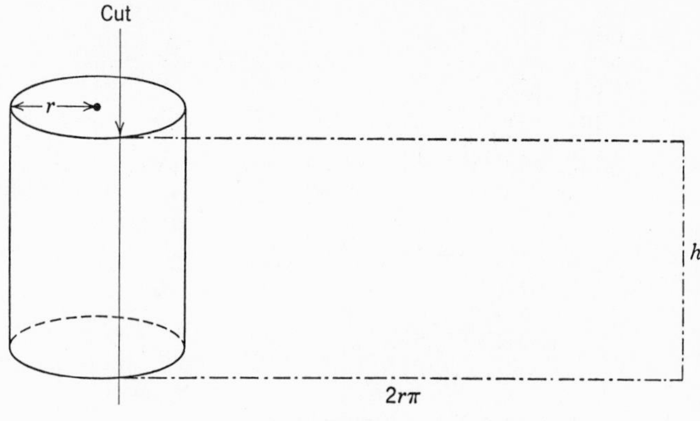

Fig. IV.6

in a circle of radius r. As we let the number of vertices increase, the prism will fit with increasing snugness into the cylinder, and we are led to the definition

$$\text{Volume of right circular cylinder} = \lim_{n\to\infty} hB_n.$$

Since

$$\lim_{n\to\infty} hB_n = h \lim_{n\to\infty} B_n$$

and

$$\lim_{n\to\infty} B_n = r^2\pi,$$

as we have seen in Chapter II, Section 5, we are led to the definition

$$\text{(IV.2)} \qquad \text{Volume of right circular cylinder} = r^2\pi h.$$

Before we close this section, let us settle the question as to the lateral surface area of a cylinder. We cut through the lateral surface along a line perpendicular to the base and unroll it (see Fig. IV.6). We then obtain a rectangular sheet of dimensions h and $2r\pi$, since $2r\pi$ is the circumference of the circular base. Hence,

$$\text{Lateral surface area of cylinder} = 2r\pi h.$$

Problems IV.5–IV.7

IV.5. Given a right circular cylinder of height $h = 4$ and a base of radius $r = 2$. (*a*) Find the volume of the cylinder. (*b*) Find the lateral surface area of the cylinder. (*c*) Find the total surface area of the cylinder.

IV.6. Given a cylinder of height h and a base of radius $r = 2$. (*a*) Express the volume V as a function $f(h)$ of the height. (*b*) Express the volume V as a function of the lateral surface area S: $V = F(S)$. What is $F(S)$?

IV.7. Given a prism of height 1, the base of which is a regular polygon of 10^6 vertices inscribed into a circle of radius $r = 2$. Find an approximation to the volume.

3. VOLUME OF A RIGHT CIRCULAR CONE

We consider a *right circular cone* as represented in Fig. IV.7. The base is a circle of radius r. A point V, the vertex of the cone, is h units vertically above the center of the circle. Now, take a line from V to a point P on the circumference of the circular base and let P wander around the full circumference. Then the line VP will generate the lateral surface of a right circular cone of base radius r and height h.

In order to determine the volume of the cone we have to reduce this problem to the volume determination of solids with which we have already dealt. We chop the cone up by a number of planes which are parallel to the base (see Fig. IV.8) and try to determine the volume of each slice. Each slice has a shape as indicated in Fig. IV.9. Such a thing is called a *conical frustum* (frustrated cone) and its volume determination is at least as frustrating as the volume determination of the entire cone itself. Therefore, we assume that the slices are very thin and approximate each slice by a cylindrical disk (see Fig. IV.10) with the same base.

If we put these cylindrical disks together again, we obtain what is indicated in Fig. IV.11, which is by no means a cone, no matter how thin we

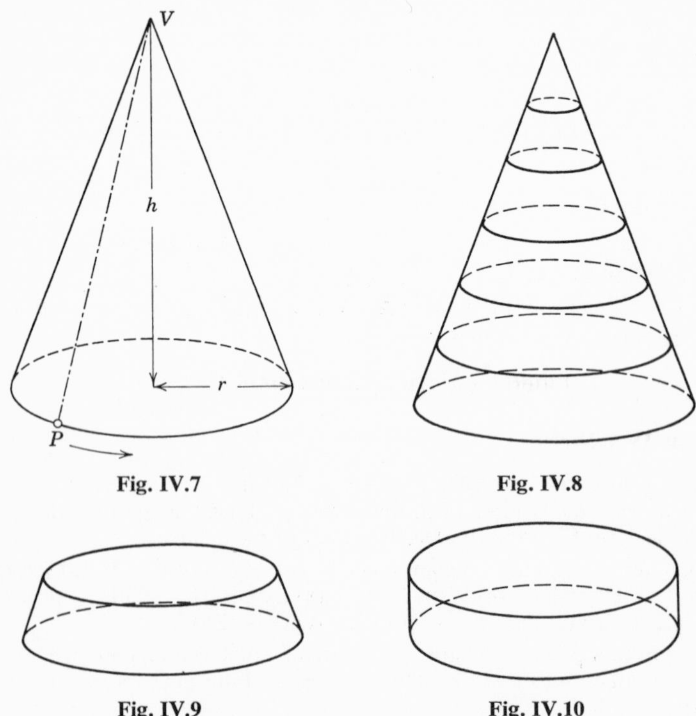

Fig. IV.7

Fig. IV.8

Fig. IV.9

Fig. IV.10

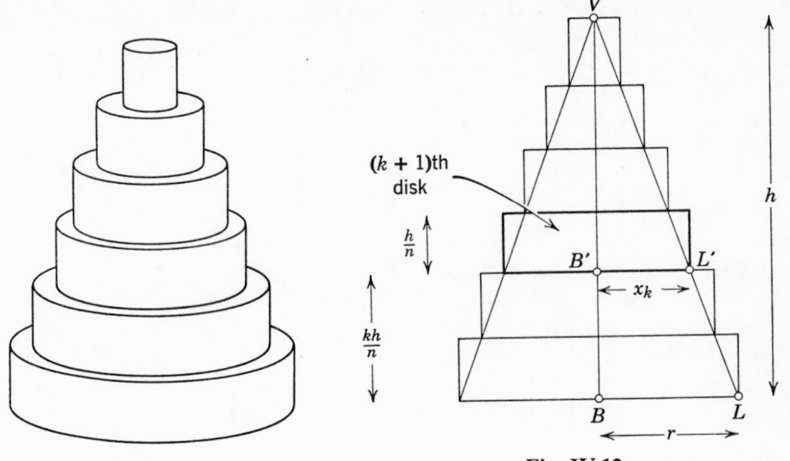

Fig. IV.11

Fig. IV.12

make the slices to begin with. However, we can see that, if we let the height of each cylindrical slice go to zero and at the same time increase the number of slices to infinity, then the solids of the type illustrated in Fig. IV.11 will approximate the right circular cone from the outside with increasing accuracy. We are thus led to define the volume of the cone as the limit of the volume of that pile of cylindrical slices as their number increases beyond bound and their individual thicknesses tend to zero.

To carry out this limit process in detail, we refer to the cross section in Fig. IV.12. The base radius x_k of the $(k + 1)$th cylindrical disk is obtained from

$$\frac{x_k}{h - \dfrac{kh}{n}} = \frac{r}{h}$$

(note that BLV and $B'L'V$ are similar triangles). Hence,

$$x_k = \frac{r}{h}\left(h - \frac{kh}{n}\right).$$

Thus the volume of the $(k + 1)$th cylindrical disk is given by

$$V_k = \frac{r^2}{h^2}\left(h - \frac{kh}{n}\right)^2 \pi \frac{h}{n}.$$

If we sum up all n disks, we obtain

$$V(\text{cone}) \simeq \frac{r^2\pi}{nh} \sum_{k=0}^{n-1} \left(h - \frac{kh}{n}\right)^2 = \frac{r^2\pi}{nh} \sum_{k=0}^{n-1} \left(h^2 - \frac{2h^2k}{n} + \frac{h^2k^2}{n^2}\right)$$

$$= \frac{r^2\pi}{nh}\left(h^2 \sum_{k=0}^{n-1} 1 - \frac{2h^2}{n} \sum_{k=0}^{n-1} k + \frac{h^2}{n^2} \sum_{k=0}^{n-1} k^2\right).$$

We have seen in Chapter II, Section 12, that

$$\sum_{k=0}^{n-1} 1 = n, \ \sum_{k=0}^{n-1} k = \frac{n(n-1)^*}{2}, \ \sum_{k=0}^{n-1} k^2 = \frac{(n-1)n(2n-1)^*}{6}$$

Using these results,

$$\begin{aligned} V(\text{cone}) &\cong \frac{r^2\pi}{nh}\left(nh^2 - \frac{2h^2}{n}\cdot\frac{n(n-1)}{2} + \frac{h^2}{n^2}\cdot\frac{(n-1)n(2n-1)}{6}\right) \\ &= r^2\pi h\left(1 - \frac{n(n-1)}{n^2} + \frac{n(n-1)(2n-1)}{6n^3}\right) \\ &= r^2\pi h\left(1 - \frac{n^2-n}{n^2} + \frac{2n^3-3n^2+n}{6n^3}\right) \\ &= r^2\pi h\left(1 - 1 + \frac{1}{n} + \frac{1}{3} - \frac{1}{2n} + \frac{1}{6n^2}\right). \end{aligned}$$

Since

$$\lim_{n\to\infty} \frac{1}{n} = 0 \text{ and } \lim_{n\to\infty} \frac{1}{n^2} = 0,$$

we obtain for the volume of the right circular cone

$$V_{\text{cone}} = \lim_{n\to\infty} r^2\pi h\left(\frac{1}{n} + \frac{1}{3} - \frac{1}{2n} + \frac{1}{6n^2}\right) = \frac{r^2\pi h}{3}. \tag{IV.2}$$

Problems IV.8–IV.12

IV.8. Given a right circular cone of height 3 and base radius 1. (*a*) Find its volume. (*b*) Approximate the volume by taking 6 inscribed cylindrical disks and 6 circumscribed cylindrical disks. What is the error?

IV.9. Find a formula for the area of the lateral surface of the right circular cone of height h and base radius r. (*Hint:* Cut the surface along a line from V to a point on the circumference of the base and unroll it.)

IV.10. Given a right circular cone of base radius 2 and height h. Express the volume V as a function of the lateral surface S.

IV.11. What is the total surface area of the cone in Problem IV.8?

IV.12. A cone has the volume $V = 12\pi$. Choose the dimensions r and h so that the lateral surface area is a minimum.

4. THE LAW OF THE LEVER

"Give me a place to stand and I will move the Earth." (ARCHIMEDES)

Let us consider a teeter-totter, or, if you prefer a more sophisticated term, a *lever*. The point of support of the lever, F, is called the *fulcrum* (see Fig. IV.13), and the parts sticking out on both sides of the fulcrum are

* Note that it is immaterial here whether we extend these sums from $k = 1$ to $n - 1$ or from $k = 0$ to $n - 1$.

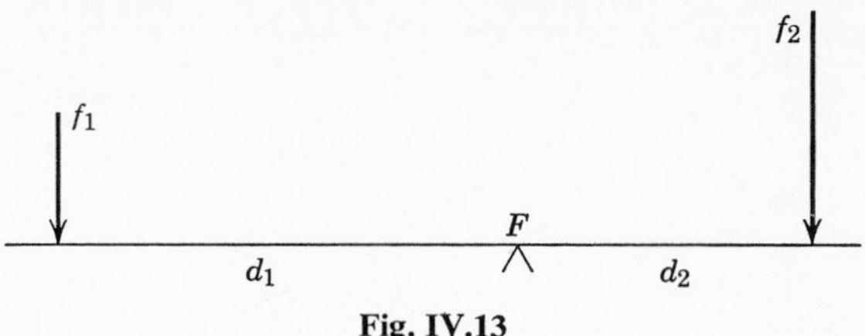

Fig. IV.13

called the *lever arms*. We will now discuss the question as to how to keep a lever in balance (equilibrium). Small children usually have a vague notion of the answer. If a child plays teeter-totter with its little sister or brother, it will find out pretty soon that for the best effect it has to sit closer to the fulcrum than a lighter child.

Suppose the latter is capable of exerting a downward directed force through its weight of magnitude f_1 and is placed at a distance d_1 from the fulcrum (see Fig. IV.13). Now, the problem for the older and presumably bigger kin who is capable of exerting a downward directed force f_2 through its weight, is where to sit? In other words: At what distance d_2 from the fulcrum is it supposed to exert the force f_2 in order to keep the lever in balance.

Archimedes (287–212 B.C.) discovered the complete answer to this problem in the form of the *law of the lever* which states: The lever is in balance if, and only if,

$$f_1 d_1 = f_2 d_2, \tag{IV.3}$$

i.e., force times length of lever arm must yield the same product on both sides. Archimedes immediately recognized the far reaching consequences of his discovery as evidenced by his statement which we quoted above. In a less bombastic tone, we could say that a small child is capable of lifting a concert grand piano, provided it uses a lever and places the fulcrum strategically, i.e., close to the piano, while exerting its little force at a sufficiently large distance from the fulcrum on the other lever arm.

It is more practical for most applications to state the law of the lever in terms of masses rather than forces. From (III.35) on p. 215 we have

$$f = ma$$

where f stands for force, m for mass, and a for acceleration. A mass under the influence of gravity is accelerated by the amount $a \cong 32$ ft/sec·sec. Hence, if the force f_1 is exerted by the weight of a mass m_1 and the force f_2 is exerted by the weight of a mass m_2, then

$$f_1 = m_1 a$$
$$f_2 = m_2 a.$$

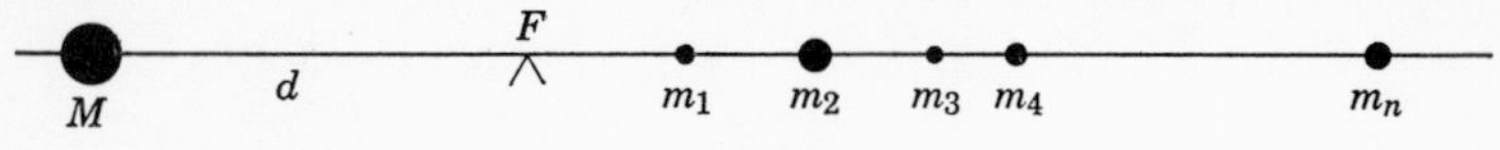

Fig. IV.14

Substitution of these quantities into (IV.3) yields

$$m_1 a d_1 = m_2 a d_2.$$

We can divide by a and obtain the law of the lever in terms of masses:

(IV.4) $$m_1 d_1 = m_2 d_2,$$

i.e., a mass m_1 at distance d_1 from the fulcrum balances a mass m_2 at distance d_2 from the fulcrum (on the other lever arm) if, and only if, the products of the respective masses with their distance from the fulcrum are equal.

Suppose that we wish to balance a mass $m_1 = M$ with the unit mass $m_2 = 1$. Then, according to (IV.4),

$$Md_1 = d_2,$$

i.e., the unit mass has to be placed at a distance from the fulcrum which is M times the distance of the mass M from the fulcrum.

To facilitate further references, let us introduce the concept of *moment*. The product of a mass times its distance from a given point is called the *moment* of this mass with respect to the given point. Using this new term, we can state the law of the lever as follows: The lever is in balance if, and only if, the moments on both sides are equal.

Now, suppose that we have more than one mass, namely, masses of magnitudes $m_1, m_2, \cdots, m_n$ at distances $d_1, d_2, \cdots, d_n$ from the fulcrum on one lever arm and a mass M at a distance d on the other lever arm (see Fig. IV.14). Then the moment μ_k of the mass m_k with respect to the fulcrum is given by

$$\mu_k = m_k d_k \; (k = 1, 2, 3, \cdots, n)$$

and the total moment of all masses on the right side of F is given by

(IV.5) $$\mu_r = \mu_1 + \mu_2 + \mu_3 + \cdots + \mu_n$$
$$= m_1 d_1 + m_2 d_2 + m_3 d_3 + \cdots + m_n d_n = \sum_{k=1}^{n} m_k d_k.$$

The moment of the mass M on the left side of the fulcrum is given by

(IV.6) $$\mu_l = Md.$$

To keep the lever in balance, we have to have $\mu_r = \mu_l$, i.e.,

(IV.7) $$Md = \sum_{k=1}^{n} m_k d_k.$$

Suppose that

$$M = \sum_{k=1}^{n} m_k,$$

i.e., the mass M on the left equals the sum of all masses on the right, then it follows from (IV.7) that

$$d\sum_{k=1}^{n} m_k = \sum_{k=1}^{n} m_k d_k$$

and, consequently,

$$d = \frac{\sum_{k=1}^{n} m_k d_k}{\sum_{k=1}^{n} m_k}. \tag{IV.8}$$

This formula can be interpreted as follows: If we replace the masses $m_1, m_2, m_3, \cdots, m_n$ at distances $d_1, d_2, d_3, \cdots, d_n$ by a single mass M which is equal in magnitude to the sum of all masses m_k, and if we place this mass M at a distance d from the fulcrum as given by (IV.8), then it will exert the same moment with respect to the fulcrum as the initial mass distribution did.

This distance d has another important significance. Suppose we wish to relocate the fulcrum so that the given mass distribution $m_1, m_2, m_3, \cdots, m_n$ balances the lever with respect to the new fulcrum. We shift the fulcrum F through a distance d' into the position F' (see Fig. IV.15). Then we obtain for the moments μ_k' with respect to the new fulcrum F'

$$\begin{aligned}
\mu_1' &= m_1(d_1 - d') \\
\mu_2' &= m_2(d_2 - d') \\
&\cdot \\
&\cdot \\
&\cdot \\
\mu_n' &= m_n(d_n - d').
\end{aligned}$$

If $d_k - d' < 0$, then m_k is on the left side of the new fulcrum F' and if $d_k - d' > 0$, then m_k is on the right side of the new fulcrum F'. Now we wish to determine d' so that the total moment on the left of F' is the same as the total moment on the right of F'. This is equivalent to determining d' such that the algebraic sum of all the moments μ_k' is zero.

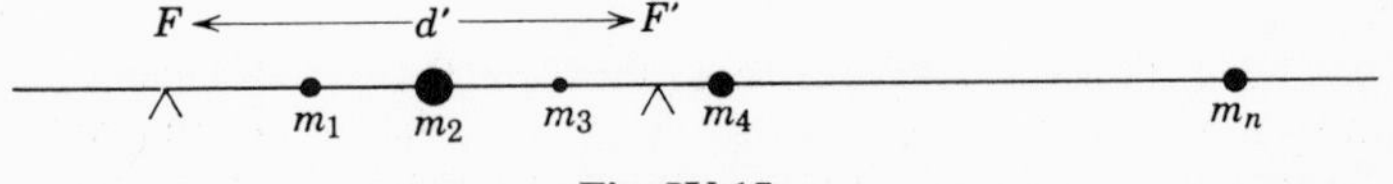

Fig. IV.15

F	m	m	m	m	m		m	m
0	1	2	3	4	5		$n-1$	n

Fig. IV.16

This leads to the condition

$$\sum_{k=1}^{n} \mu_k' = \sum_{k=1}^{n} m_k(d_k - d') = \sum_{k=1}^{n} m_k d_k - d' \sum_{k=1}^{n} m_k = 0$$

and we obtain

$$d' = \frac{\sum_{k=1}^{n} m_k d_k}{\sum_{k=1}^{n} m_k},$$

i.e., $d' = d$ as given in (IV.8). This property attributes a new significance to the quantity d. The point at distance d from the fulcrum F is the point about which the given mass distribution is in equilibrium. We call this point the *mass center* or *centroid*: *The mass center is the point about which a (linear) distribution of masses is in equilibrium.*

Suppose we have n masses of equal magnitude placed at equal distances. Then we can represent these locations as points on the line of numbers as indicated in Fig. IV.16 and obtain for the mass center according to (IV.8)

$$d = \frac{\sum_{k=1}^{n} km}{\sum_{k=1}^{n} m} = \frac{m \sum_{k=1}^{n} k}{m \sum_{k=1}^{n} 1} = \frac{\frac{1}{2}m(n+1)n}{nm} = \frac{1}{2}(n+1)$$

which is also the geometric center of the points $1, 2, 3, \cdots, n$.

Problems IV.13–IV.19

IV.13. A mass weighing 1000 lb is placed at a distance 2 ft from the fulcrum. (*a*) At what distance do we have to place a mass weighing 3 lb at the other lever arm to keep the lever in balance? (*b*) What is the weight of a mass which is placed at a distance 16 ft from the fulcrum on the other lever arm, if it is to keep the lever in balance?

IV.14. In a decimal scale, an object is kept in balance by a weight which is only one-tenth of the weight of the object. What is the ratio of the lengths of the lever arms?

IV.15. The masses 2, 4, 3, 5, 9, 4, 6, 1, 9 at distances 1, 2, $\frac{5}{2}$, $\frac{7}{2}$, 4, 5, 7, $\frac{15}{2}$, 9 are to be replaced by a mass of magnitude equal to the sum of the given masses. At what distance is this mass to be placed from the fulcrum to exert the same moment?

IV.16. Given the mass distribution of Problem IV.15. The masses are to be replaced by a mass of magnitude which is one-half the sum of the magnitude of the given masses. (*a*) Make an intelligent guess as to where to place this new mass in order to exert the same moment. (*b*) Compute the distance at which this mass has to be placed in order to exert the same moment. (*c*) Explain why your guess was wrong—if it was wrong.

IV.17. Find the mass center of the masses 3, 3, 5, 4, 4, 7, 5, 4, 5, 7, 7, 5 which are 1, 1, 3, 3, 4, 4, 4, 5, 3, 2, 1 units apart.

IV.18. Use geometric reasoning to find the mass center of a rectangle, i.e., the point about which the rectangle is in balance if supported at this point by the tip of a pencil.

IV.19. Same as in Problem IV.18 for a triangle.

5. MASS CENTER OF REGIONS AND SOLIDS

Suppose we have a rectangular region that is covered uniformly with mass of constant mass density. (If we cut out any portion of the region, determine its mass, divide it by its area, and obtain the same value for the ratio no matter which region we may have selected, we say that the region is of constant mass density.)

It is quite clear that the mass center of such a rectangular region coincides with its geometric center. This can be seen as follows. If we cut out such a rectangular region, it will balance on the edge of a ruler, if the ruler supports it along a line which is parallel to one pair of sides and cuts the rectangle into two equal portions. There are two such lines and they intersect in the geometric center of the rectangle. Hence, we should be able to balance a rectangle at the tip of a pencil, if the rectangle is supported at its geometric center.

We are going to make use of this intuitive result to establish formulas that will allow us to find the mass center of regions which are not everywhere bounded by straight lines.

Suppose we have a region of constant mass density ρ (*read:* rho) which is bounded by the x-axis, $x = a$, $x = b$ and the curve $y = f(x)$ (see Fig. IV.17). We will approximate this region by n inscribed rectangles as we did when determining the area of such regions (Chapter II, Sections 8 and 9). We remind the reader that the inscribed rectangles are obtained by division of the interval $a \leq x \leq b$ into n subintervals by division points $x_1, x_2, x_3, \cdots, x_{n-1}$, which we assume for reasons of convenience to be equidistant:

$$x_k - x_{k-1} = \Delta x \text{ for all } k = 1, 2, \cdots, n.$$

We will also assume, as usual, that $x_0 = a$ and $x_n = b$ in order to have a unified notation. The height of each one of the inscribed rectangles is the minimum value of the function in the corresponding subinterval. We denote this minimum value by $f(\xi_k)$:

$$f(\xi_k) = \min f(x) \text{ in } x_{k-1} \leq x \leq x_k.$$

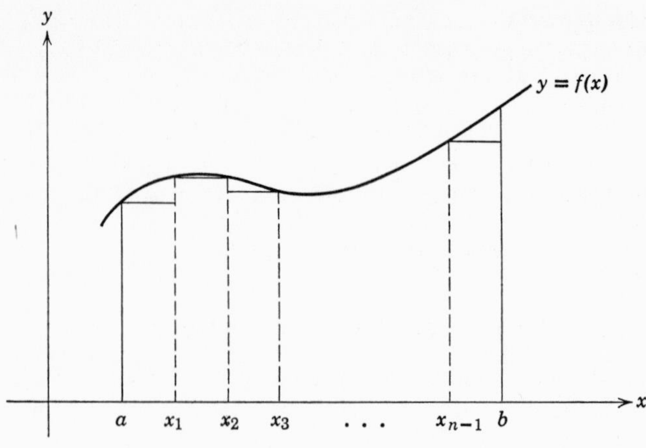

Fig. IV.17

It follows that the area ΔA_k of the kth rectangle is

$$\Delta A_k = f(\xi_k)\Delta x$$

and consequently, we obtain for its mass Δm_k

$$\Delta m_k = \rho f(\xi_k)\Delta x.$$

Let us assume that the entire mass of this rectangle is concentrated at its mass center, i.e., at its geometric center, the coordinates of which are given by

(IV.9) $$\bar{x}_k = \frac{x_k + x_{k-1}}{2}, \qquad \bar{y}_k = \tfrac{1}{2}f(\xi_k).$$

If Δx is sufficiently small, which we assume to be the case, we can say that $\bar{x}_k$ "almost" coincides with ξ_k. It seems intuitively clear that the error which we make with this assumption disappears if we let Δx approach zero, which we will do in the end, anyway. Hence, we obtain for the moment $\Delta M_{k,y}$ of the point $(\xi_k, \bar{y}_k)$ of mass Δm_k with respect to the y-axis*

(IV.10) $$\Delta M_{k,y} = \Delta m_k \xi_k = \rho f(\xi_k)\xi_k \Delta x.$$

Thus the total moment of the n rectangles with respect to the y-axis is the sum of all moments in (IV.10) and this is

$$M_y^{(n)} = \rho \sum_{k=1}^{n} f(\xi_k)\xi_k \,\Delta x.$$

* This is to be understood as "with respect to the intersection point of the y-axis with the horizontal line through the point $(\xi_k, \bar{y}_k)$."

We observe that

(IV.11) $$\xi_k f(\xi_k) \geq \min\,[xf(x)] \text{ in } x_{k-1} \leq x \leq x_k.$$

So if we take an undersum $\underline{S}_n$ (see Chapter II, Section 9) of the function $F(x) = xf(x)$ with the same subdivision as we have used for determination of the moment and denote the minimum of $F(x)$ in $x_{k-1} \leq x \leq x_k$ by $F(\bar{\bar{\xi}}_k)$:

$$\min F(x) = \min\,[xf(x)] = \bar{\bar{\xi}}_k f(\bar{\bar{\xi}}_k) \text{ in } x_{k-1} \leq x \leq x_k$$

we have

$$\rho \underline{S}_n = \rho \sum_{k=1}^{n} F(\bar{\bar{\xi}}_k)\,\Delta x = \rho \sum_{k=1}^{n} \bar{\bar{\xi}}_k f(\bar{\bar{\xi}}_k)\,\Delta x \leq \rho \sum_{k=1}^{n} \xi_k f(\xi_k)\,\Delta x = M_y^{(n)}.$$

If $\bar{S}_n$ denotes the corresponding upper sum of the function $F(x)$ with the same subdivision, then we can see likewise that

$$\rho \bar{S}_n \geq M_y^{(n)}.$$

Since

$$\lim_{n\to\infty} \underline{S}_n = \lim_{n\to\infty} \bar{S}_n = \int_a^b F(x)\,dx = \int_a^b xf(x)\,dx$$

(see Chapter II, Section 8) we have, in view of

$$\rho \underline{S}_n \leq M_y^{(n)} \leq \rho \bar{S}_n,$$

that

(IV.12) $$M_y = \rho \int_a^b xf(x)\,dx,$$

where M_y denotes the moment of the region under consideration with respect to the y-axis.

We defined in the preceding section the coordinates of the mass center for a concrete mass distribution by dividing the moment by the total mass. We, therefore, define in generalization of this idea the x-coordinate of the mass center of our region by

(IV.13) $$\bar{x} = \frac{\rho \int_a^b xf(x)\,dx}{\rho \int_a^b f(x)\,dx} = \frac{\int_a^b xf(x)\,dx}{\int_a^b f(x)\,dx}.$$

(Note that the total mass of the region is its area $\int_a^b f(x)\,dx$ times the mass density ρ, and that the factor ρ which appears in numerator and denominator cancels out in case of a region of constant mass density.)

We proceed similarly to establish a formula for the y-coordinate of the mass center of the given region. We note that the y-coordinate of the mass center of the kth inscribed rectangle is given by

$$\bar{y}_k = \tfrac{1}{2}f(\xi_k)$$

[see (IV.9)]. Hence, if we think of the entire mass of the kth rectangle to be concentrated at this point, the moment of this rectangle with respect to the x-axis* is

$$M_{k,x} = \rho\tfrac{1}{2}f(\xi_k)f(\xi_k)\Delta x$$

and, consequently, we are led by an analogous line of reasoning to the following formula for the moment M_x of the given region with respect to the x-axis:

$$M_x = \frac{\rho}{2}\int_a^b f^2(x)\,dx.$$

Therefore the y-coordinate of the mass center is to be defined as

$$\text{(IV.14)} \qquad \bar{y} = \frac{\dfrac{1}{2}\displaystyle\int_a^b f^2(x)\,dx}{\displaystyle\int_a^b f(x)\,dx}$$

noting again, that ρ cancels out.

Let us now apply formulas (IV.13) and (IV.14) to the problem of finding the mass center of an isosceles triangle of constant mass density ρ (see Fig. IV.18). Clearly, $\bar{y} = 0$ because the triangle will balance on the x-axis, i.e., the mass center has to lie on the x-axis.

The mass of the whole triangle is obviously given by

$$m = \rho rh.$$

In order to find the moment of the triangle with respect to the y-axis, we have to take into account that we have as much of the triangle above the x-axis as we have below the x-axis (just as in the case of a fat woman who is trying to hide behind a bamboo rod). This requires the introduction of the factor 2 in formula (IV.12). We note further that $f(x) = \dfrac{rx}{h}$ in our case. Hence, we obtain

$$M_y = 2\frac{r}{h}\rho\int_0^h x^2\,dx = \rho\frac{2r}{h}\cdot\frac{x^3}{3}\Big|_0^h = \rho\frac{2rh^3}{3h} = \rho\frac{2rh^2}{3}.$$

We remind the reader that the vertical bar in the above line indicates that the indefinite integral of x^2 is to be taken between the limits 0 and h. (See p. 182.)

* See footnote on p. 266.

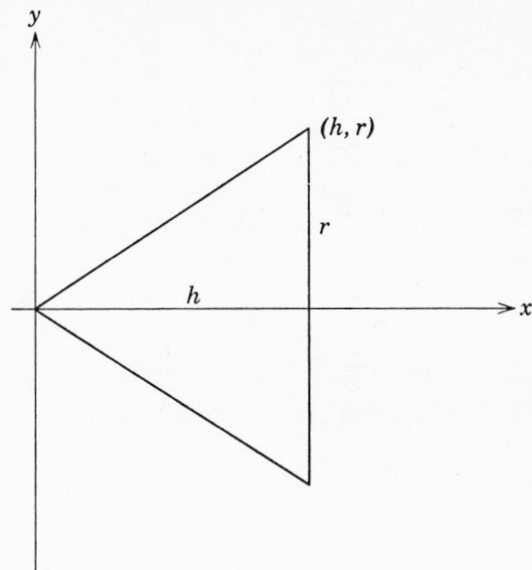

Fig. IV.18

Thus we have because of

$$\bar{x} = \frac{M_y}{m},$$

that

$$\bar{x} = \frac{\rho 2rh^2}{3\rho rh} = \frac{2h}{3},$$

i.e., the mass center lies at $\frac{2}{3}$ of the height from the vertex.

The idea which we pursued in this section can easily be generalized to the determination of the mass center of solids, and is particularly simple in case of a right circular cylinder of constant mass density (mass per unit volume is constant).

Intuitively, it is clear that the mass center of a right circular cylinder of constant mass density lies at its geometric center, i.e., the point on the axis which is halfway between top and bottom. Nevertheless, let us go through the motions of a limit of a sum process in order to indicate how this idea can be generalized later on to more complicated solids.

We consider a right circular cylinder of height h and base radius r and choose our coordinate system as indicated in Fig. IV.19. We slice the cylinder into n cylindrical disks of height $\frac{h}{n} = \Delta x$ and assume that n is very large, i.e., Δx is very small. If ρ is the mass density of the cylinder, then the mass of any one of the slices is given by

$$m_k = \rho r^2 \pi \Delta x.$$

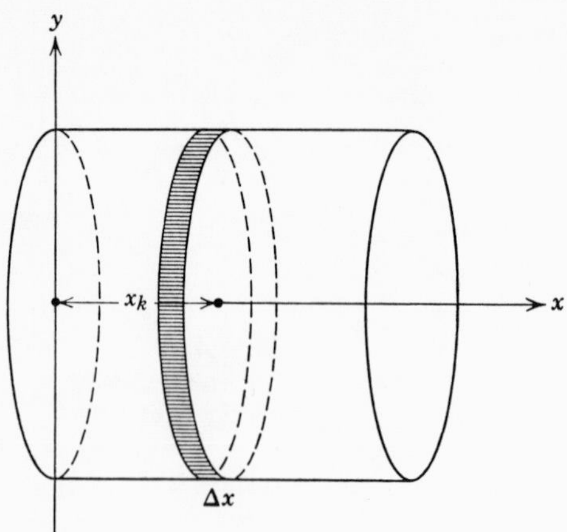

Fig. IV.19

If x_k is the distance of the bottom of the $(k + 1)$th slice from the origin and Δx is very small, we can assume that the distance of the mass center of the $(k + 1)$th slice from the origin is also x_k, except for an error which is negligible in the light of the later limit process with $\Delta x \to 0$. Thus we have for the moment of the $(k + 1)$th slice with respect to the origin

$$M_{k+1} = \rho r^2 \pi x_k \Delta x.$$

If we now add all the moments of all these cylindrical disks and take the limit as $n \to \infty$ and simultaneously $\Delta x \to 0$, we obtain

$$M = \lim_{n\to\infty} \sum_{k=0}^{n-1} \rho r^2 \pi x_k \, \Delta x = \rho r^2 \pi \int_a^b x \, dx^* = \rho r^2 \pi \left. \frac{x^2}{2} \right|_0^h = \frac{\rho r^2 \pi h^2}{2}.$$

Since the volume V of the cylinder is given by

$$V = r^2 \pi h$$

(see Section 2) it follows that its mass is

$$m = \rho r^2 \pi h$$

and, hence, the ratio of moment to mass becomes

$$\overline{x} = \frac{\rho r^2 \pi h^2}{2 r^2 \pi h \rho} = \frac{h}{2}$$

as we anticipated.

* Note that $x_k = \min x$ in $x_k \leq x \leq x_{k+1}$.

Problems IV.20–IV.24

IV.20. Find the mass center of a triangle of constant mass density which is bounded by $x = 0$, $y = 0$, and $y = a - \frac{a}{b}x$. $(a > 0, b > 0.)$

IV.21. Find the mass center of a region of constant mass density which is bounded by $y = 0$, $x = 0$, $x = 1$, $y = x^2$.

IV.22. Same as in Problem IV.21 for the region bounded by $x = 0$, $y = x^2$, $y = 1$.

IV.23. Find the mass center of a right circular cone of height h and base radius r. (*Hint:* Let the vertex of the cone coincide with the origin and let the x-axis contain the axis of the cone.)

IV.24. Find the mass center of the solid of constant mass density which is generated by rotating the area bounded by $y = x^2$ and the line $y = 1$ about the y-axis. (Such a solid is called a paraboloid of revolution.) *Hint:* Slice the paraboloid into horizontal cylindrical disks and apply limit of a sum process.

▶6. THE ARCHIMEDEAN SCALE

We will demonstrate in this section the ingeneous process by which *Archimedes* (287–212 B.C.) arrived at the formula for the volume of a *sphere*. We will need for this purpose the formulas for the volume of the right circular cylinder and the right circular cone, which we derived in Sections 2 and 3 and which we reiterate:

$$V(\text{cylinder}) = b^2h\pi$$

$$V(\text{cone}) = \frac{b^2h\pi}{3}.$$

In both cases b stands for the radius of the base and h for the height.

Archimedes made the great discovery that a cylinder balances a sphere and a cone on a lever. More specifically, he found that if we place a right circular cylinder of base radius $2r$ and height $2r$ on one side of the lever such that the axis of the cylinder coincides with the lever arm and the cylinder terminates at the fulcrum, and suspend a sphere of radius r and a cone of base radius $2r$ and height $2r$ at a point $2r$ units from the fulcrum on the other lever arm, then the lever is in equilibrium, provided all three solids are made of the same homogeneous material of constant mass density (which we can assume to be 1 without loss of generality). (See Fig. IV.20.)

We will now give a "proof" of this very astonishing fact before we proceed to investigate its consequences for the volume determination of the sphere in terms of the volumes of cone and cylinder. The "proof" which is

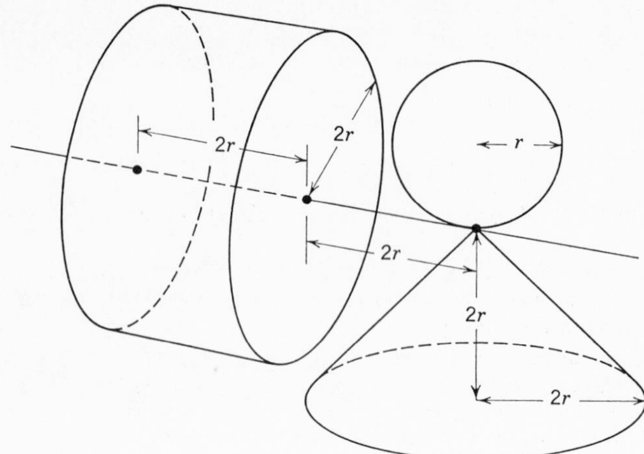

Fig. IV.20

supplied here is basically the one which was given by Archimedes himself, except for the fact that we use the convenience of our modern notation.*

In the following we refer to the schematic sketch in Fig. IV.21. We place the cylinder on the left side of the fulcrum and draw the contours of cone and sphere on the right side with the understanding that the force exerted on the lever arm by cone and sphere is to act upon the point P, $2r$ units to the right of the fulcrum. We will prove our proposition by demonstrating in the true spirit of Archimedes' integration method that any thin cylindrical slice of the cylinder at distance x from the fulcrum on the left will balance corresponding slices of the same thickness cut out from cone and sphere at a distance x to the right from the fulcrum and suspended at the point P.

We obtain for the mass of the cylindrical disk (slice) on the left

$$\Delta m \text{ (cylinder)} = 4r^2\pi\Delta x$$

where Δx is the thickness of the slice, since the mass density is assumed to be 1, which has mass = volume as a consequence. Therefore, the moment of the cylindrical disk placed at the distance x from the fulcrum is given by

$$\text{(IV.15)} \qquad \Delta M \text{ (cylinder)} = 4r^2\pi\Delta x \cdot x.$$

The radius of a circular cross section of the cone at x is x, since the angle between any generating line of this cone with its axis is 45°. Hence, if we

* We put *proof* in quotes because, as the reader will see, this "proof" is anything but rigorous. Archimedes, who ordinarily gave rigorous mathmatical proofs for all his statements, was well aware of the heuristic nature of this method, which we present in the following, and pointed this out quite emphatically.

approximate the volume of the disk which is cut out from the cone and which really is a conical frustum by a cylindrical disk of equal radius and height (which is a good approximation if Δx is very small), we obtain

$$\Delta m \text{ (cone)} \simeq x^2\pi\Delta x$$

and, consequently, we obtain for the moment, if this mass is placed at P,

$$\Delta M \text{ (cone)} \simeq x^2\pi\Delta x 2r. \tag{IV.16}$$

Finally, we have to consider a slice from the sphere which is cut out at x. Since the equation of the circle in Fig. IV.21 [with radius r and center at $(r, 0)$] is

$$(x - r)^2 + y^2 = r^2,$$

the square of the radius of the circular cross section at x is

$$y^2 = r^2 - (x - r)^2 = 2xr - x^2$$

and, consequently,

$$\Delta m \text{ (sphere)} \simeq (2xr - x^2)\pi\Delta x,$$

if we assume again that the volume of the slice from the sphere is approximated by a cylindrical disk of radius $\sqrt{2xr - x^2}$ and height Δx.

Therefore,

$$\Delta M \text{ (sphere)} \simeq (2xr - x^2)\pi\Delta x 2r. \tag{IV.17}$$

From (IV.16) and (IV.17) we have

$$\begin{aligned}\Delta M \text{ (cone)} + \Delta M \text{ (sphere)} &\simeq 2\pi r x^2\Delta x + 2\pi r(2xr - x^2)\Delta x \\ &= 2\pi r(x^2\Delta x + 2xr\Delta x - x^2\Delta x) \\ &= 4\pi r^2 x\Delta x = \overline{\Delta M} \text{ (cone)} + \overline{\Delta M} \text{ (sphere)},\end{aligned}$$

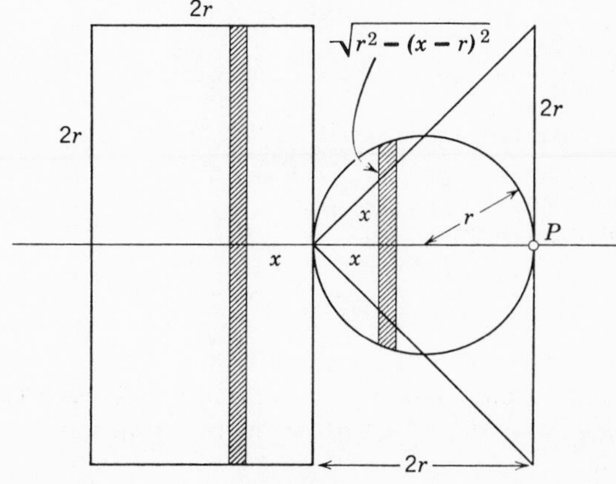

Fig. IV.21

where the bars indicate an approximation to the moments which becomes more accurate the smaller Δx is.

Thus we have in view of (IV.15)

$$\Delta M \text{ (cylinder)} = \overline{\Delta M} \text{ (cone)} + \overline{\Delta M} \text{ (sphere)}. \tag{IV.18}$$

If we slice up the solids on both sides of the fulcrum by passing planes through a number of points which are arranged symmetrically with respect to the fulcrum, we see that (IV.18) will hold for any triple of corresponding slices and on adding up all the equations of which (IV.18) is typical, we see that

$$M \text{ (cylinder)} = \bar{M} \text{ (cone)} + \bar{M} \text{ (sphere)}.$$

If we increase the number of cross sections and at the same time let the length of every distance between two cross sections (Δx) tend to zero, it is intuitively clear that

$$\lim_{\Delta x \to 0} \bar{M} \text{ (cone)} = M \text{ (cone)}, \ \lim_{\Delta x \to 0} \bar{M} \text{ (sphere)} = M \text{ (sphere)}$$

and we finally obtain

$$M \text{ (cylinder)} = M \text{ (cone)} + M \text{ (sphere)} \tag{IV.19}$$

as we proposed to prove.

We know that

$$m \text{ (cylinder)} = 4r^2\pi 2r = 8r^3\pi$$

and that this cylinder has its mass center at a distance r from the fulcrum (where its geometric center is located; see Section 5). Hence,

$$M \text{ (cylinder)} = 8r^4\pi.$$

The mass of the cone is given by

$$m \text{ (cone)} = \frac{4r^2\pi 2r}{3} = \frac{8r^3\pi}{3}.$$

Hence its moment, assuming suspension at P, is given by

$$M \text{ (cone)} = \frac{16r^4\pi}{3}.$$

The mass of the sphere is equal to its volume V (sphere) because the mass density is assumed to be 1. Hence, its moment, again assuming suspension at P, is given by

$$M \text{ (sphere)} = V \text{ (sphere) } 2r.$$

Thus, on substituting these values into (IV.19), we have

$$8r^4\pi = \frac{16r^4\pi}{3} + 2rV\text{ (sphere)}$$

and from this we obtain immediately

$$V\text{ (sphere)} = \frac{4r^3\pi}{3}. \tag{IV.20}$$

The preceding proof of formula (IV.19) is lacking in mathematical rigor, inasmuch as we went through a mental limit process, the outcome of which was guided by our intuition.

Since the concept of a limit was developed to some extent in Chapters II and III, we are here in a position to give a more rigorous proof of (IV.19). However, this proof will really make the significance of (IV.19) appear questionable (unless cylinders really wish to play teeter-totter with spheres and cones instead of always playing with other cylinders), because (IV.19) was only of interest to us as long as it served to derive the volume formula for the sphere. In the subsequent proof the formula for the volume of the sphere will turn up as a marginal result simultaneously with the recognition of (IV.19) as a true relation.

We subdivide the interval $0 \leq x \leq 2r$ into n equal subintervals of length $\frac{2r}{n}$. Then the division points $x_1, x_2, x_3, \cdots, x_{n-1}$ will have the coordinates

$$x_1 = \frac{2r}{n},\ x_2 = \frac{2r2}{n},\ x_3 = \frac{2r3}{n},\ \cdots,\ x_k = \frac{2rk}{n},\ \cdots,\ x_{n-1} = \frac{2r(n-1)}{n}.$$

The same subdivision is to be carried out on the left side of the fulcrum $F(x = 0)$.

Thus, according to (IV.15) and $\Delta x = \frac{2r}{n}$, we obtain at the point x_k

$$\Delta M\text{ (cylinder)} \cong 4r^2\pi x_k\Delta x = 4r^2\pi\frac{2rk}{n}\frac{2r}{n} = \frac{16r^4\pi k}{n^2};$$

according to (IV.16),

$$\Delta M\text{ (cone)} \cong x_k^{\ 2}\pi\Delta x 2r = \frac{4r^2k^2\pi}{n^2}\frac{2r}{n}2r = \frac{16r^4k^2\pi}{n^3}$$

and, according to (IV.17),

$$\Delta M\text{ (sphere)} \cong (2x_kr - x_k^{\ 2})\pi\Delta x 2r = 2r\pi\frac{2r}{n}\left(\frac{2\cdot 2rk}{n}r - \frac{4r^2k^2}{n^2}\right)$$

$$= \frac{16r^4\pi k}{n^2} - \frac{16r^4\pi k^2}{n^3}$$

and we have, according to (IV.18),

$$\frac{16r^4\pi k}{n^2} = 2r\left(\frac{8r^3k^2\pi}{n^3} + \frac{8r^3\pi k}{n^2} - \frac{8r^3\pi k^2}{n^3}\right),$$

where we factored out $2r$ for reasons of convenience. The first and the last term in parentheses cancel each other and we have here merely an identity. However, we will not yet carry out this cancellation. All these equations hold for $k = 0, 1, 2, \cdots, n - 1$.

If we think of writing all these equations out, then adding them, we see that

$$\text{(IV.21)} \quad \frac{16r^4\pi}{n^2}\sum_{k=1}^{n-1} k = 2r\left(\frac{8r^3\pi}{n^3}\sum_{k=1}^{n-1} k^2 + \frac{8r^3\pi}{n^2}\sum_{k=1}^{n-1} k - \frac{8r^3\pi}{n^3}\sum_{k=1}^{n-1} k^2\right).$$

We observed in Chapter II, Section 12 that

$$\sum_{k=1}^{n-1} k = \frac{n(n-1)}{2} = \frac{n^2 - n}{2},$$

$$\sum_{k=1}^{n-1} k^2 = \frac{(n-1)n(2n-1)}{6} = \frac{2n^3 - 3n^2 + n}{6}.$$

Thus we obtain for (IV.21)

$$\frac{16r^4\pi}{n^2}\left(\frac{n^2 - n}{2}\right)$$

$$= 2r\left[\frac{8r^3\pi}{n^3}\left(\frac{2n^3 - 3n^2 + n}{6}\right) + \frac{8r^3\pi}{n^2}\left(\frac{n^2 - n}{2}\right) - \frac{8r^3\pi}{n^3}\left(\frac{2n^3 - 3n^2 + n}{6}\right)\right]$$

or, as we may write,

$$8r^4\pi\left(1 - \frac{1}{n}\right)$$

$$= 2r\left[\frac{8r^3\pi}{3}\left(1 - \frac{3}{2n} + \frac{1}{2n^2}\right) + 4r^3\pi\left(1 - \frac{1}{n}\right) - \frac{8r^3\pi}{3}\left(1 - \frac{3}{2n} + \frac{1}{2n^2}\right)\right]$$

and we see, on passing to the limit as $n \to \infty$, that

$$8r^4\pi = 2r\left(\frac{8r^3\pi}{3} + 4r^3\pi - \frac{8r^3\pi}{3}\right)$$

which is merely an identity. At the same time we see that the first term in parentheses yields the formula for the volume of the cone and the two remaining terms yield the volume of the sphere.

Before closing this section we wish to point out that a very impressive model can be built to demonstrate the validity of the relation (IV.18) very convincingly. First, we need a lever, preferably a homogeneous steel rod which is balanced at its center, as demonstrated in Fig. IV.22. Then we cut

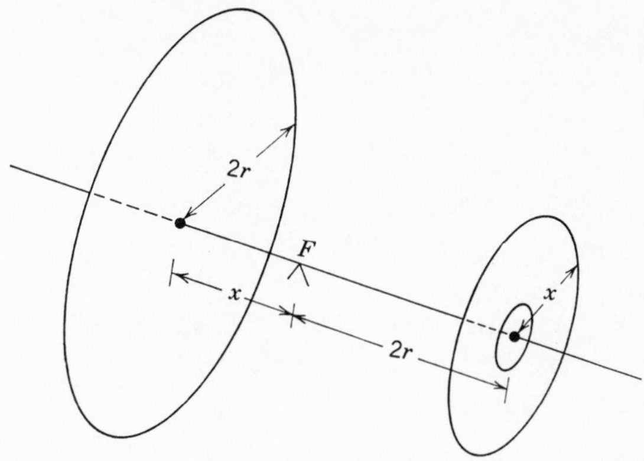

Fig. IV.22

out a circular disk of radius 2 units from some homogeneous material, the heavier the better (we suggest the use of platinum by generously endowed private schools and scrap metal by state institutions), and drill a hole in its center so that it can slide freely along the steel rod. This disk shall represent one of the slices of the cylinder. Then we proceed to cut out two more circular disks from the same material representing the corresponding slices of cone and sphere.

We observe that if the radius of the slice which is supposed to come from the cone is x, then the radius of the corresponding slice from the sphere has to be $\sqrt{2x - x^2}$ (observe that $r = 1$, since the radius of the cylinder was chosen to be $2r = 2$). Thus, 2 corresponding slices would have, for example, radii 1, 1 or $\frac{1}{2}$, $\frac{\sqrt{3}}{2}$ or $\frac{3}{2}$, $\frac{\sqrt{3}}{2}$ etc. If more than one pair of disks is produced, then it is recommended that corresponding pairs be painted in the same color, using different colors for different pairs.

Then the corresponding two disks are slid onto the rod into a position 2 units away from the fulcrum. The third disk is to be placed on the other side of the lever and its position is to be adjusted so that the lever balances. If the dimensions of the model are reasonably accurate and the lever is in perfect balance, the distance of the third disk from the fulcrum should then turn out to be equal to the radius of the disk representing the slice from the cone. ◀

7. VOLUME OF A SPHERE BY INTEGRATION

A sphere can be generated by a circle which rotates about one of its diameters (see Fig. IV.23). We will use this idea to establish a formula by

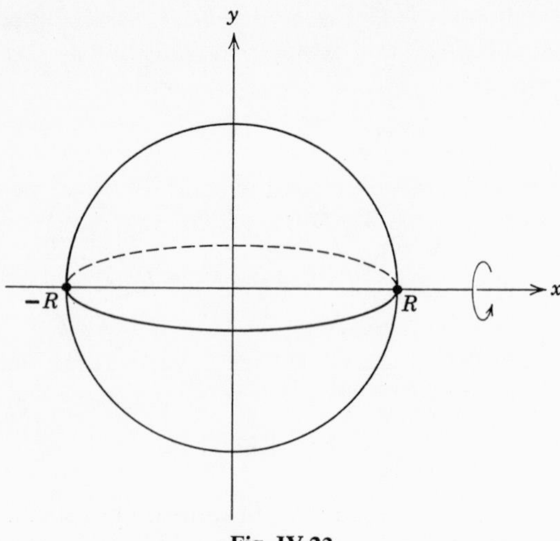

Fig. IV.23

which the volume of a sphere can be found by an integration process. It does not increase the complexity of the problem at all if we consider the more general problem of finding the volume of a solid, the lateral surface of which is generated by a rotating curve. So let us consider just any curve $y = f(x)$ and rotate the section of the curve about the x-axis which lies between $x = a$ and $x = b$ (see Fig. IV.24).

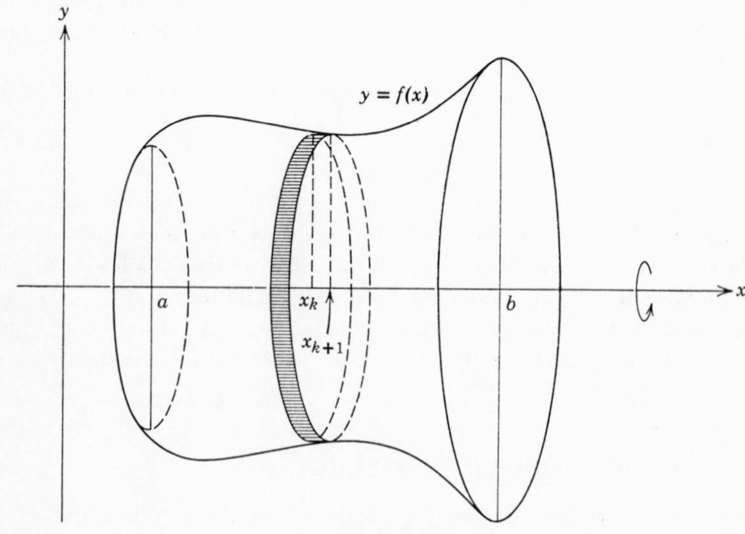

Fig. IV.24

This process generates a *surface of revolution* which, together with the planes at $x = a$ and $x = b$ that are perpendicular to the x-axis, forms the boundary of a solid, a so-called *solid of revolution*. We will devote this section to the determination of the volume of such a solid, which in the special case that the rotating curve is a semicircle, will be a sphere.

Again, true to tradition, we cut up the solid by $n - 1$ planes which are perpendicular to the x-axis and are equally spaced at distances $\Delta x = \dfrac{b-a}{n}$. The $(k + 1)$th slice can be approximated by a cylindrical disk (if Δx is very small) of height Δx. The base radius of this cylindrical disk is $f(x)$ taken at some x in the interval $x_k \leq x \leq x_{k+1}$. If we want an inscribed disk, we choose that value of x for which $f(x)$ has a minimum in the interval $x_k \leq x \leq x_{k+1}$; and if we want a circumscribed disk, we take that value of x for which $f(x)$ has a maximum. Let us take ξ_{k+1} such that $f(\xi_{k+1}) = \min f(x)$ in $x_k \leq x \leq x_{k+1}$. Then the volume of such an inscribed cylindrical disk is given by

$$V_k = \pi f^2(\xi_k)\Delta x, \quad k = 1, 2, \cdots n$$

and we obtain for the volume of a solid which consists of all n inscribed cylindrical disks

$$\underline{V}_n = \pi \sum_{k=1}^{n} f^2(\xi_k)\Delta x. \tag{IV.22}$$

In order to arrive at a formula for the volume of the solid of revolution with which we started, we have to let $n \to \infty$ and simultaneously $\Delta x \to 0$.

In order to facilitate the comparison of the present case with the definition of the definite integral in Chapter II, Section 9, we let $f^2(x) = F(x)$ for the moment. Then (IV.22) will read

$$\underline{V}_n = \pi \sum_{k=1}^{n} F(\xi_k)\Delta x$$

and we obtain in the limit, according to (II.37),

$$\lim_{n\to\infty} \underline{V}_n = \lim_{n\to\infty} \pi \sum_{k=1}^{n} F(\xi_k)\Delta x = \pi \int_a^b F(x)\, dx,$$

if $F(x)$ is uniformly continuous in $a \leq x \leq b$. (Note that if $f(x) \geq 0$, which we will assume, then $f^2(x)$ will assume its minimum at the same point at which $f(x)$ assumes its minimum.)

Now, if we replace $F(x)$ again with $f^2(x)$, we obtain for the volume of the solid of revolution that is generated by the rotation of the curve $y = f(x)$ between $x = a$ and $x = b$ about the x-axis

$$V = \pi \int_a^b f^2(x)\, dx. \tag{IV.23}$$

If we wish to apply this formula to the determination of the volume of a sphere of radius R, we observe that the sphere is generated by rotation of a semicircle of radius R about its diameter, as we mentioned in the introduction to this section. We remember the equation of a circle with its center in the origin and radius R:

$$x^2 + y^2 = R^2.$$

From this we obtain the upper semicircle

$$y = \sqrt{R^2 - x^2}.$$

Hence,

$$f^2(x) = y^2 = R^2 - x^2$$

and we have

$$\begin{aligned} V\text{ (sphere)} &= \pi \int_{-R}^{R} (R^2 - x^2)\,dx = \pi R^2 \int_{-R}^{R} dx - \pi \int_{-R}^{R} x^2\,dx \\ &= \pi R^2 x \Big|_{-R}^{R} - \pi \frac{x^3}{3}\Big|_{-R}^{R} = \pi R^3 + \pi R^3 - \frac{\pi R^3}{3} - \frac{\pi R^3}{3} \\ &= \frac{4\pi R^3}{3}. \end{aligned}$$

We may use the same formula (IV.23) to check a partial result of Problem IV.24. There it was required, among other things, to find the volume of a paraboloid which is generated by rotating the parabola $y = x^2$ about the y-axis and truncating at $y = 1$, by carrying out the limit of a sum process (see Fig. IV.25).

In order to adapt our formula to this situation, we have to make a few changes. We observe that now the y-axis is the axis of rotation instead of the x-axis. This indicates that all we did with respect to x in the derivation of formula (IV.23) we now have to carry out with respect to y. This is accomplished simply by interchanging x and y in formula (IV.23). Specifically, we note that instead of representing the rotating curve as a function

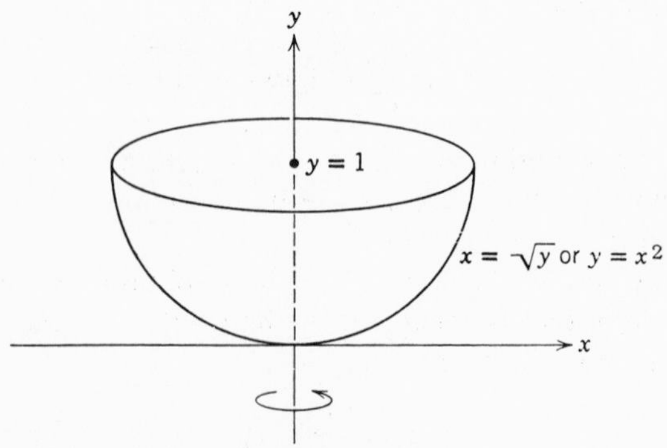

Fig. IV.25

of $x:y = f(x)$, we now have to represent the rotating curve as a function of $y:x = g(y)$. Then formula (IV.23) will read

$$V = \pi \int_a^b g^2(y)\,dy \tag{IV.24}$$

where a and b are now limits for y. In our particular case, we have

$$x = g(y) = \sqrt{y},\ a = 0,\ b = 1.$$

Therefore,

$$V = \pi \int_0^1 y\,dy = \frac{\pi y^2}{2}\bigg|_0^1 = \frac{\pi}{2}.$$

Problems IV.25–IV.30

IV.25. The curve $y = \dfrac{1}{x}$ between $x = 1$ and $x = 2$ is rotated about the x-axis. Find the volume of the solid thus generated. $\left(\textit{Hint:}\ \text{Remember that}\ \dfrac{d(1/x)}{dx} = -\dfrac{1}{x^2}.\right)$

IV.26. The curve $y = x^2$ between $x = 1$ and $x = 3$ is rotated about the y-axis. Find the volume of the solid thus generated.

IV.27. Same as in Problem IV.26 if the curve is rotated about the x-axis.

IV.28. The upper branch of the curve $\dfrac{x^2}{a^2} + \dfrac{y^2}{b^2} = 1$ rotates about the x-axis. Find the volume of the solid thus generated. (*Hint:* Note that for $x = 0$, $y = \pm b$ and for $y = 0$, $x = \pm a$. Sketch the curve and determine the integration limits. In your result let $a = b = R$. After this substitution you should obtain the formula for the volume of a sphere, if your work was correct.)

IV.29. The right branch of the curve $x^2 - y^2 = 1$ between $y = -1$ and $y = 1$ is rotated about the y-axis. Find the volume of the solid thus generated.

IV.30. Same as in IV.29 by cutting the solid into slices and applying the limit of a sum process. (The solid of Problems IV.29 and IV.30 is a hyperboloid of revolution of one sheet.)

8. VOLUME OF A TORUS

A *torus* is a solid of revolution which is generated by a circle rotating about an axis which lies in the same plane as the circle, but does not pass through the circle. In short, it is the mathematical refinement of a doughnut.

In Fig. IV.26, the circle of radius a, with center at $(b, 0)$ where $b > a$, rotates about the y-axis and thus generates a torus. We will devote this section to the development of a simple formula that will enable us to find the volume of a torus and similar solids of revolution.

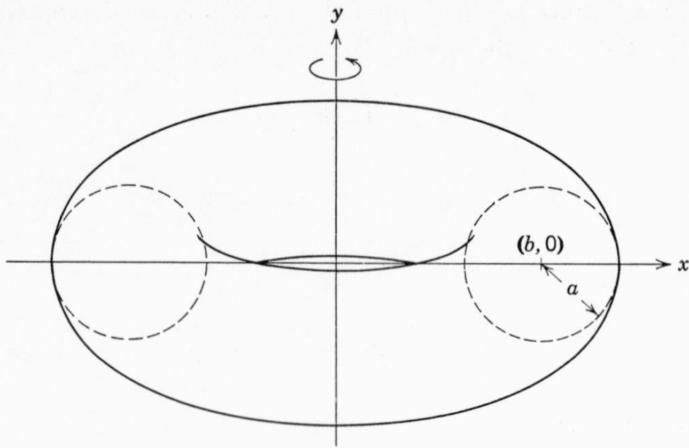

Fig. IV.26

In general, let us assume that we have some planar region which is bounded above by the graph of the function $y = f(x)$, where $f(x) \geq 0$, below by the x-axis, and on the sides by the lines $x = a$ and $x = b$, where we assume that $0 \leq a < b$, i.e., the region lies entirely to the right of the y-axis (see Fig. IV.27). We let this region rotate about the y-axis and generate thus a solid of revolution.

Again we subdivide the interval $a \leq x \leq b$ into n equal subintervals of length $\Delta x = \dfrac{b - a}{n}$ and approximate the area under the curve in each subinterval by an inscribed rectangle of height $f(\xi_{k+1}) = \min f(x)$ in $x_k \leq x \leq$

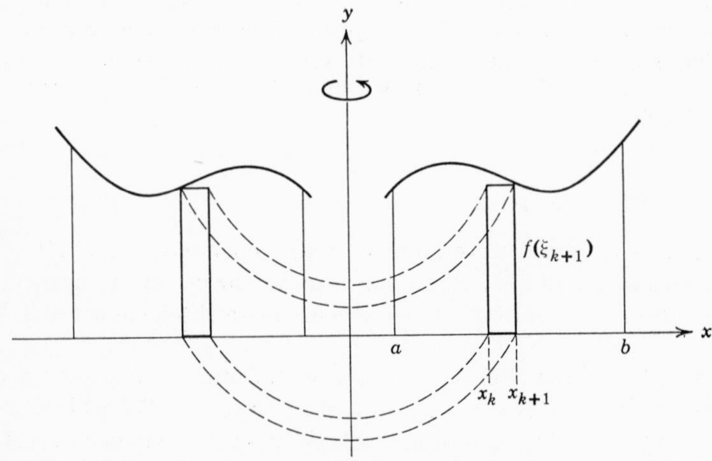

Fig. IV.27

x_{k+1}. This inscribed rectangle with base in $x_k \leq x \leq x_{k+1}$ will generate, upon rotation about the y-axis, a cylindrical shell of inner radius x_k and outer radius x_{k+1} and height $f(\xi_{k+1})$. The volume of this cylindrical shell is obtained by subtraction of the volume of the inner cylinder of base radius x_k from the volume of the outer cylinder of base radius x_{k+1}:

$$\begin{aligned} V\text{ (cylindrical shell)} &= \pi x_{k+1}^2 f(\xi_{k+1}) - \pi x_k^2 f(\xi_{k+1}) \\ &= \pi(x_{k+1}^2 - x_k^2) f(\xi_{k+1}) \\ &= \pi(x_{k+1} + x_k)(x_{k+1} - x_k) f(\xi_{k+1}). \end{aligned}$$

Since $x_{k+1} - x_k = \Delta x$, we have

$$V\text{ (cylindrical shell)} = \pi(x_{k+1} + x_k) f(\xi_{k+1}) \Delta x.$$

Now, if Δx is very small, both x_k and x_{k+1} can be approximated by ξ_{k+1} which is a value somewhere between x_k and x_{k+1} and we obtain

$$V\text{ (cylindrical shell)} \cong 2\pi \xi_{k+1} f(\xi_{k+1}) \Delta x.$$

Now we sum up all the volumes of the n cylindrical shells between a and b and obtain

$$V_n \cong 2\pi \sum_{k=0}^{n-1} \xi_{k+1} f(\xi_{k+1})\, \Delta x = 2\pi \sum_{k=1}^{n} \xi_k f(\xi_k) \Delta x$$

which will tend to the volume of the solid of revolution that is under investigation, if we let $n \to \infty$ (and simultaneously $\Delta x \to 0$). We have seen in Section 5 that

$$\lim_{n\to\infty} \sum_{k=1}^{n} \xi_k f(\xi_k)\, \Delta x = \int_a^b x f(x)\, dx.$$

Hence, we obtain for the volume

$$V = 2\pi \int_a^b x f(x)\, dx. \tag{IV.25}$$

If we compare this formula with formula (IV.13) of Section 5, we see that

$$\bar{x} = \frac{V}{2\pi \displaystyle\int_a^b f(x)\, dx}$$

where $\bar{x}$ is the x-coordinate of the centroid of the region of constant mass

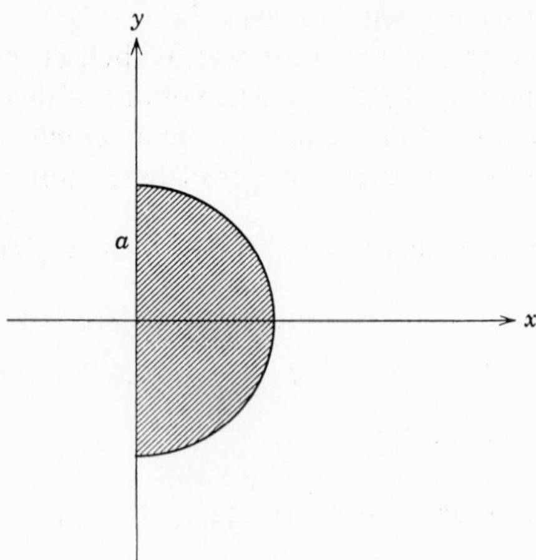

Fig. IV.28

density which is rotated. Thus we arrive at the following simple formula for V:

$$V = 2\pi\bar{x}A \tag{IV.26}$$

where A is the area of the region which is rotated.

This formula can be interpreted as follows: The volume of a solid of revolution is obtained by multiplying the area of the to be rotated region by the length of the path through which the centroid travels during rotation. (Note that $2\pi\bar{x}$ is the length of the circle of radius $\bar{x}$.)

Now let us apply formula (IV.26) to the volume determination of the torus. We have

$$A = a^2\pi$$

and

$$\bar{x} = b$$

(the centroid of a circle of constant mass density is its geometric center). Hence,

$$V\,(\text{torus}) = 2\pi^2a^2b.$$

We can use formula (IV.26) backwards to find, for example, the centroid of a semicircle without difficulties. We place the semicircle in a position as indicated in Fig. IV.28. If this semicircle is rotated about the y-axis, we obtain a sphere with the volume

$$V = \frac{4a^3\pi}{3}.$$

The area of the semicircle is given by

$$A = \frac{a^2\pi}{2}.$$

Hence we obtain from (IV.26)

$$\frac{4a^3\pi}{3} = 2\pi\bar{x}\,\frac{\pi a^2}{2}$$

and, consequently,

$$\bar{x} = \frac{4a}{3\pi}.$$

Problems IV.31–IV.34

IV.31. A triangle with vertices at (1, 0), (2, 1), and (2, −1) is rotated about the y-axis. Find the volume of the solid which is thus generated.

IV.32. The ellipse $(x - 2)^2 + \dfrac{y^2}{4} = 1$ is rotated about the y-axis. Find the volume of the solid thus generated.

IV.33. The circle $(x - 4)^2 + (y - 1)^2 = 1$ is rotated about the line $y = x$. Find the volume of the solid thus generated.

IV.34. The semicircle $x = 3 + \sqrt{4 - y^2}$ is rotated about the line $x = -1$. Find the volume of the solid thus generated.

9. SIMPSON'S RULE AND WINE BARRELS

In Problem IV.28 it was required to find the volume of the ellipsoid of revolution which is generated by the curve

$$\frac{x^2}{a^2} + \frac{y^2}{b^2} = 1 \qquad \text{(IV.27)}$$

rotated about the x-axis (see Fig. IV.29).

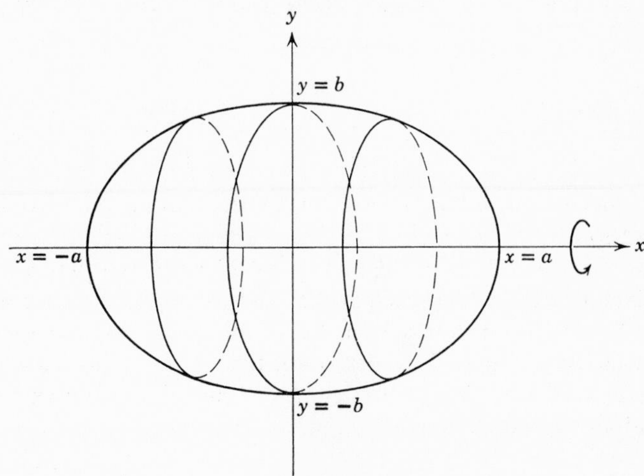

Fig. IV.29

This was done by employing formula (IV.23) with the integration limits $-a$ and a:

$$V = \pi \int_{-a}^{a} f^2(x)\, dx.$$

It follows from (IV.27) that

$$f^2(x) = y^2 = b^2\left(1 - \frac{x^2}{a^2}\right).$$

Hence

$$V = \pi \int_{-a}^{a} b^2\left(1 - \frac{x^2}{a^2}\right) dx. \tag{IV.28}$$

The integrand is a quadratic function of x. We remember that in Simpson's rule (see Chapter II, Section 14) the integrand is approximated by a quadratic function of x (parabola) in order to find an approximate value of the integral. Consequently, if the integrand is quadratic in the first place, we expect to obtain a precise result and not only an approximation from Simpson's rule. Thus let us apply Simpson's rule to find the integral in (IV.28), using the minimum number of subintervals, namely, $n = 2$:

$$\int_a^b F(x)\, dx \cong \frac{b - a}{3n}(y_0 + 4y_1 + y_2),$$

where $y_0 = F(a)$, $y_1 = F\left(\frac{a + b}{2}\right)$, and $y_2 = F(b)$.

In our case, $F(x) = f^2(x) = b^2\left(1 - \frac{x^2}{a^2}\right)$, the lower integration limit is $-a$ and the upper integration limit is a. Hence, $\frac{a + b}{2} = 0$ and we obtain

$$y_0 = 0, \qquad y_1 = b^2, \qquad y_2 = 0.$$

Therefore

$$V = \pi \frac{a + a}{6}(4b^2) = \frac{4\pi a b^2}{3}$$

which is indeed the result that should have been obtained in Problem IV.28 by integration.

Suppose we cut off the solid in Fig. IV.29 with two planes which are perpendicular to the x-axis, each at the distance $c < a$ from the origin (see Fig. IV.30). The solid thus obtained resembles a wine barrel very closely. Again we use Simpson's rule to determine the volume of such a wine barrel.

We have now $-c$ as the lower integration limit, c as the upper integration limit, and, consequently,

$$y_0 = b^2\left(1 - \frac{c^2}{a^2}\right), \qquad y_1 = b^2, \qquad y_2 = b^2\left(1 - \frac{c^2}{a^2}\right).$$

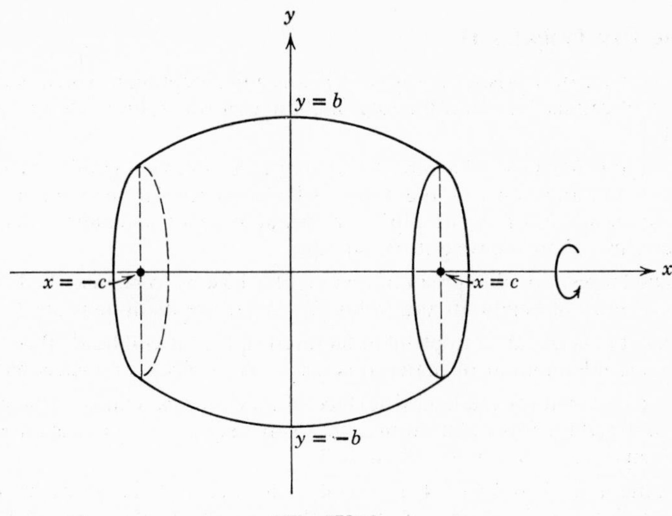

Fig. IV.30

Hence, we obtain

$$V = \pi \frac{2cb^2}{6}\left[\left(1 - \frac{c^2}{a^2}\right) + 4 + \left(1 - \frac{c^2}{a^2}\right)\right] = \frac{\pi cb^2}{3}\left(6 - \frac{2c^2}{a^2}\right)$$

for the volume of a wine barrel with dimensions as indicated in Fig. IV.30.

It may be of interest to note that the great astronomer *Johannes Kepler* (1571–1630) who investigated in his "Stereometria doliorum" in 1612 the volume of 92 solids, mostly solids of revolution, proved that the Austrian wine barrels, for a given amount of material to manufacture, contain the largest possible volume. On this happy note let us conclude our discourse of the Calculus.

Problems IV.35–IV.38

IV.35. The hyperbola $x^2 - 4y^2 = 1$ between $y = -2$ and $y = 2$ is rotated about the y-axis. Find the volume of the solid thus generated by Simpson's rule.

IV.36. The curve $y = x^{3/2}$ between $x = 0$ and $x = 1$ is rotated about the x-axis. (*a*) Find the volume by integration. (*b*) Find the volume by Simpson's rule. (*c*) Why does Simpson's rule yield the precise result, even though the integrand is now a cubic function of x?

IV.37. Find the volume of a sphere of radius R by Simpson's rule.

IV.38. Let the ellipse $\frac{x^2}{a^2} + \frac{y^2}{b^2} = 1$ be rotated about the y-axis. Find the resulting volume by Simpson's rule.

Supplementary Problems IV

1.1. The base of a prism of height x^2 is a regular heptagon which is inscribed in a circle of radius $2x$. Find the rate of change of the volume with respect to x at $x = 1$.

2.1. The outside wall of a pipe 10 ft long is a circular cylinder of radius 3, and the inside wall is a prism, the base of which is a regular hexagon inscribed in a circle of radius 2.5 ft. The pipe is manufactured of a material that weighs 100 g per cm^3. Find the weight of the pipe.

2.2. The largest possible prism of rectangular base is to be inscribed in a right circular cylinder of height 10 and radius 2. What are its dimensions?

2.3. A cylindrical can is to be manufactured so that it will hold 50 cu in. while the least possible amount of material is used. What are its dimensions?

2.4. The material for the lateral surface of a cylindrical can costs 9¢ per sq ft, and the material for top and bottom costs 15¢ per sq ft. What are the dimensions of the cheapest can that holds 10 cu in.?

2.5. Same as in Problem 2.4, if we take into account the waste of material, assuming that top and bottom are cut out of square sheets of dimension $2r$ where r is the radius of the base of the cylindrical can.

3.1. Approximate the volume of a cone of radius r and height h by the sum of the volumes of n inscribed cylindrical disks.

3.2. Approximate the volume of a cone of radius r and height h by the arithmetic mean of the approximation obtained from circumscribed cylindrical disks (see p. 260) and the approximation obtained from inscribed cylindrical disks (see Supplementary Problem 3.1). Find the absolute error committed by this approximation. How much better is this approximation compared to the one on p. 260 and the one in Supplementary Problem 3.1?

3.3. A right circular cylinder is to be inscribed in a right circular cone of radius r and height h, so that its volume is a maximum. What are its dimensions?

3.4. Find the dimensions of a right circular cone that has a volume of 12 cu in. and the smallest possible lateral surface area.

3.5. Same as in Problem 3.4 so that the total surface area is a minimum.

4.1. A circular cone of radius 2 in. and height 5 in. which is made of a material that weighs 1 oz per cu in. is suspended at a point 6 in. from the fulcrum on a lever arm. Find the force required to keep the lever in balance, if it is to act at a point 10 in. from the fulcrum on the other lever arm.

4.2. Masses of equal magnitude are placed at the vertices of a parallelogram. Use intuitive reasoning to find the mass center.

4.3. Same as in Problem 4.2 if the masses are placed at the vertices of a triangle.

5.1. Find the mass center of the region of constant mass density that is bounded by $y^2 = -\dfrac{4x}{3} + 4$ and the y-axis.

5.2. Find the mass center of the region of constant mass density that is bounded by $y = -x^2 + 6x$ and $y = 1$.

5.3. Find the mass center of the region of constant mass density that is bounded by $y = \frac{x}{2} + 4$, $x = -3y - 5$, $x = -2$, $x = 4$. (Make a sketch of the region.)

5.4. Find the y-coordinate of the mass center of the region of constant mass density that is bounded by the curve $y = \sin x$ between $x = 0$ and $x = \pi$ and the x-axis. (*Hint:* See Chapter II, Supplementary Problem 14.4.)

6.1. A right circular cone of radius 2 and height 2 is suspended at a distance 2 from the fulcrum on a lever arm. The cone is to be balanced by a right circular cylinder that is slid onto the other lever arm so that its axis coincides with the lever arm and one face goes through the fulcrum. Choose radius r and height r of the cylinder so that the lever is in balance. (Assume that cone and cylinder are both made of the same material of constant mass density.)

7.1. Find the volume of a right circular cone of radius r and height h by integration.

7.2. The exterior surface of a container is a right circular cylinder that is generated by rotation of the line $x = 4$ between $y = 0$ and $y = 10$ about the y-axis. The interior surface is a paraboloid generated by rotation of the parabola $y = x^2 + 1$ about the y-axis. Assume that the material of the container weighs 12 oz per cu in. What is the weight of the container?

8.1. A triangle with vertices at $A(2, 1)$, $B(3, -2)$, $C(2, 4)$ is rotated about the line $y = -\frac{x}{2}$. Find the volume of the solid thus generated.

8.2. The semicircle $y = \sqrt{1 - x^2}$ is rotated about the line $y = -x - 4$. Find the volume of the solid thus generated.

9.1. The curve $y^3 = x^2$ between $y = 0$ and $y = 1$ is rotated about the y-axis. Find the volume of the solid thus generated by Simpson's rule.

APPENDIX

AI. POLYNOMIALS

A polynomial is, as the name suggests, something which contains many terms. In mathematics, we specifically call an expression a *polynomial* if it is a sum of "many" powers of x which, in turn, are multiplied by certain constants.

Thus, for example,

$$x^2 + 3x - 4$$

is a polynomial, and

$$3x^4 - 4x^3 + 2x - 7$$

is also a polynomial. In the first example, the highest power of x that appears is the second. We call it, therefore, a polynomial of the *second degree*. For the same reason we call the second polynomial a polynomial of the *fourth degree*. In general, we call

$$P(x) = a_0x^n + a_1x^{n-1} + a_2x^{n-2} + \cdots + a_{n-1}x + a_n$$

a *polynomial of the nth degree* because n, which has to be a positive integer, is the largest exponent which occurs in this expression. The symbols a_0, a_1, a_2, $\cdots$, a_{n-1}, a_n—which are called the *coefficients* of the polynomial—stand for constant numbers.

If we substitute for x a certain value, then the polynomial $P(x)$ will assume a certain value. It is a function of x. If we wish to find those values of x for which the polynomial $P(x)$ assumes the value 0, we have to solve the equation

$$a_0x^n + a_1x^{n-1} + a_2x^{n-2} + \cdots + a_{n-1}x + a_n = 0.$$

If there is a value (or values) of x for which this equation is satisfied, we call this value (these values) a *root* (*roots*) of the equation ($\sqrt{2}$ is a root of the equation $x^2 - 2 = 0$). If the coefficients a_0, a_1, $\cdots$, a_n are rational numbers, then the above equation is called an *algebraic equation of the nth degree*. The values of x for which this equation has a solution—the roots in our new terminology—are called the *zeros* of the polynomial $P(x)$.

It can be shown that an algebraic equation of the nth degree has n real or imaginary roots $x_1, x_2, \cdots, x_n$, some of which or all of which might be equal. For example, $x^2 - 2x + 1 = 0$ has the two equal roots $x_1 = 1$, $x_2 = 1$, while $x^3 + x = 0$ has one real root $x_1 = 0$ and two complex roots $x_2 = i$ and $x_3 = -i$.

If $x_1, x_2, \cdots, x_n$ are the n zeros of the polynomial $P(x)$ of the nth degree, then $P(x)$ can be written in the form

$$a_0x^n + a_1x^{n-1} + a_2x^{n-2} + \cdots + a_{n-1}x + a_n = a_0(x - x_1)(x - x_2)\cdots(x - x_n).$$

For example, $x_1 = 0$, $x_2 = 1$, $x_3 = 3$ are the zeros of

$$P(x) = x^3 - 4x^2 + 3x$$

and it can easily be verified that

$$x^3 - 4x^2 + 3x = (x - 0)(x - 1)(x - 3).$$

Let us consider a polynomial of even degree which contains only even powers of x: let $n = 2\nu$ where ν is some positive integer and let

$$P(x) = a_0x^{2\nu} + a_2x^{2\nu-2} + a_4x^{2\nu-4} + \cdots + a_{2\nu-2}x^2 + a_{2\nu}.$$

If we substitute $-x$ for x, we obtain

$$\begin{aligned} P(-x) &= a_0(-x)^{2\nu} + a_2(-x)^{2\nu-2} + a_4(-x)^{2\nu-4} + \cdots + a_{2\nu-2}(-x)^2 + a_{2\nu} \\ &= a_0x^{2\nu} + a_2x^{2\nu-2} + a_4x^{2\nu-4} + \cdots + a_{2\nu-2}x^2 + a_{2\nu} = P(x). \end{aligned}$$

So we see that if $n = 2\nu$ and only even powers of x are present, then

$$P(-x) = P(x).$$

For this reason, we generally call a function $f(x)$ which has this property:

$$f(-x) = f(x)$$

an *even* function.

On the other hand, if we consider a polynomial of odd degree which contains only odd powers of x, namely, $n = 2\mu - 1$ and

$$P(x) = a_1x^{2\mu-1} + a_3x^{2\mu-3} + a_5x^{2\mu-5} + \cdots + a_{2\mu-3}x^3 + a_{2\mu-1}x$$

and substitute $-x$ for x, then we obtain

$$\begin{aligned} P(-x) &= a_1(-x)^{2\mu-1} + a_3(-x)^{2\mu-3} + a_5(-x)^{2\mu-5} + \cdots \\ &\qquad + a_{2\mu-3}(-x)^3 + a_{2\mu-1}(-x) \\ &= -a_1x^{2\mu-1} - a_3x^{2\mu-3} - a_5x^{2\mu-5} - \cdots - a_{2\mu-3}x^3 - a_{2\mu-1}x \\ &= -P(x), \end{aligned}$$

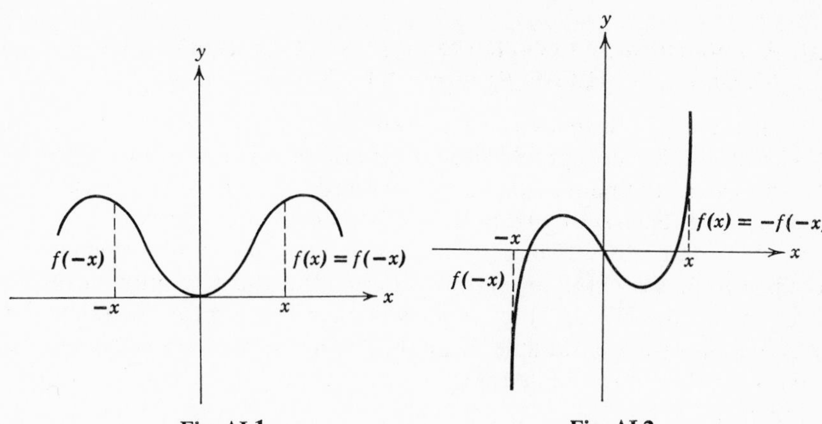

Fig. AI.1

Fig. AI.2

i.e., if $P(x)$ is of odd degree and there are only odd powers of x present, then

$$P(-x) = -P(x).$$

For this reason, we generally call a function with this property:

$$f(-x) = -f(x)$$

an *odd* function.

As the reader can easily convince himself, even functions have a graph which is symmetrical with respect to the y-axis and odd functions have a graph which is symmetrical with respect to the origin of the coordinate system—if they have a graph at all (see Figs. AI.1 and 2).

Problems AI.1–AI.7

AI.1. Write down the most general polynomial of the

(*a*) 0th degree (*b*) first degree

(*c*) seventh degree

AI.2. Show that a polynomial of the first degree with rational coefficients has one, and only one, zero which is rational.

AI.3. Show that a polynomial of the second degree with rational coefficients has at most two real zeros. What can you say about the real zeros of a polynomial of the third degree?

AI.4. Show that the function $y = \begin{cases} 1 \text{ for } x \text{ rational} \\ 0 \text{ for } x \text{ irrational} \end{cases}$ is even.

AI.5. Find a polynomial of the fourth degree that vanishes at the points $x_1 = 1$, $x_2 = 2$, $x_3 = 3$, $x_4 = 4$. Does this problem permit a unique answer?

AI.6. Find a polynomial of the third degree that vanishes at the points $x_1 = -1$, $x_2 = 2$, $x_3 = 3$ and assumes the value 12 for $x = 1$.

AI.7. Write the polynomial $x^4 - 4x^3 + 3x^2 + 4x - 4$ as a product of *linear factors* $(x - x_k)$ where x_k are the zeros of this polynomial.

AII. A UNIFORMLY CONTINUOUS FUNCTION THAT DEFIES GRAPHICAL REPRESENTATION

It turns out that there are functions which are uniformly continuous in a closed interval but defy graphical representation. By this we mean: There are uniformly continuous functions which are such that it is impossible to draw a curve representing them, i.e., *they do not have a graph.*

While a study of these functions requires a great amount of mathematical sophistication, we will try, nevertheless, to outline the generation of such a function. In the process, the reader will have to accept a few things on faith, because we are not able to establish rigorously every statement we make with the rather limited techniques that are at our disposal in this treatment.

Let us consider Fig. AII.1. We see a broken line and a dotted line. The broken line forms the two equal sides in an isosceles triangle with height 1 and base 1. The dotted line together with portions of the broken line forms the four sides of two isosceles triangles of height $\frac{1}{2}$ and base $\frac{1}{2}$. Let us call the function that is represented by the broken line $s_1(x)$ and the function which is represented by the dotted and portions of the broken line $s_2(x)$. Now we consider the function $y_2 = s_1(x) + s_2(x)$, which is obtained from $s_1(x)$ and $s_2(x)$ by addition of corresponding ordinates. The result is depicted by a solid line in Fig. AII.1.

We next transfer the solid line from Fig. AII.1 to Fig. AII.2 as a broken line. The dotted line in Fig. AII.2 is related to $s_2(x)$, as $s_2(x)$ is related to $s_1(x)$. We denote the function which is represented by the dotted line by $s_3(x)$. [$s_3(x)$ is formed from the eight equal sides of four isosceles triangles of height $\frac{1}{4}$ and base $\frac{1}{4}$.]

Again, we add $s_3(x)$ to the function $y_2 = s_1(x) + s_2(x)$ which is represented by the broken line and obtain a function, namely, $y_3 = s_1(x) + s_2(x) + s_3(x)$, which is represented by the solid line in Fig. AII.2.

The solid line from Fig. AII.2 is now transferred to Fig. AII.3 as a broken line and we proceed as before, i.e., take $s_4(x)$ (the equal sides of eight isosceles triangles of height $\frac{1}{8}$ and base $\frac{1}{8}$) and add it to the function represented by the broken line, etc. After five steps we obtain the function which is represented by a solid line in Fig. AII.5, namely, the function $y_6 = s_1(x) + s_2(x) + s_3(x) + s_4(x) + s_5(x) + s_6(x)$.

At every step we obtain a uniformly continuous function, because every function is obtained as the sum of two uniformly continuous functions, and it is intuitively clear that the sum of two uniformly continuous functions is again a uniformly continuous function. Now it can be shown that if we continue this process of adding functions $s_7(x)$, $s_8(x)$, $\cdots$ without ever ending it, we arrive at a *uniformly continuous function* in $0 \leq x \leq 1$. At

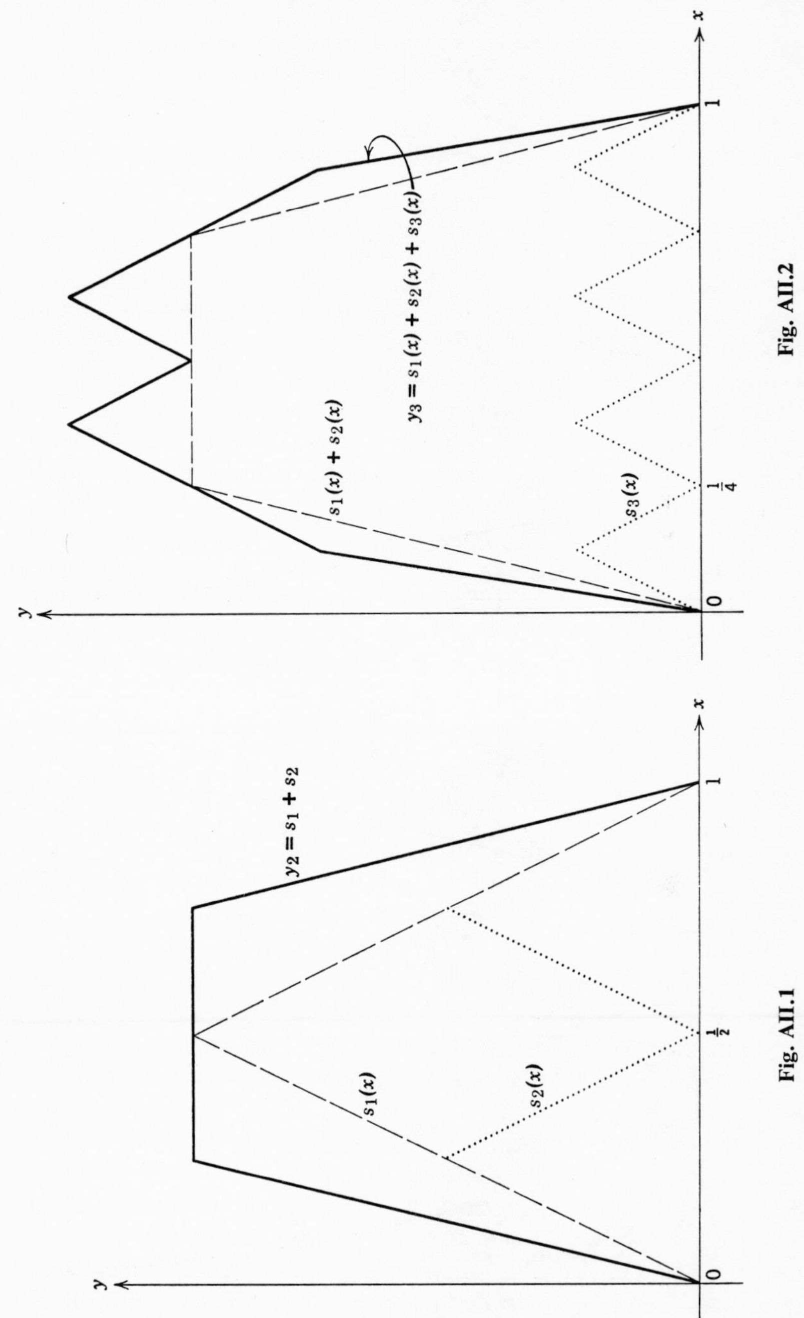

Fig. AII.1

Fig. AII.2

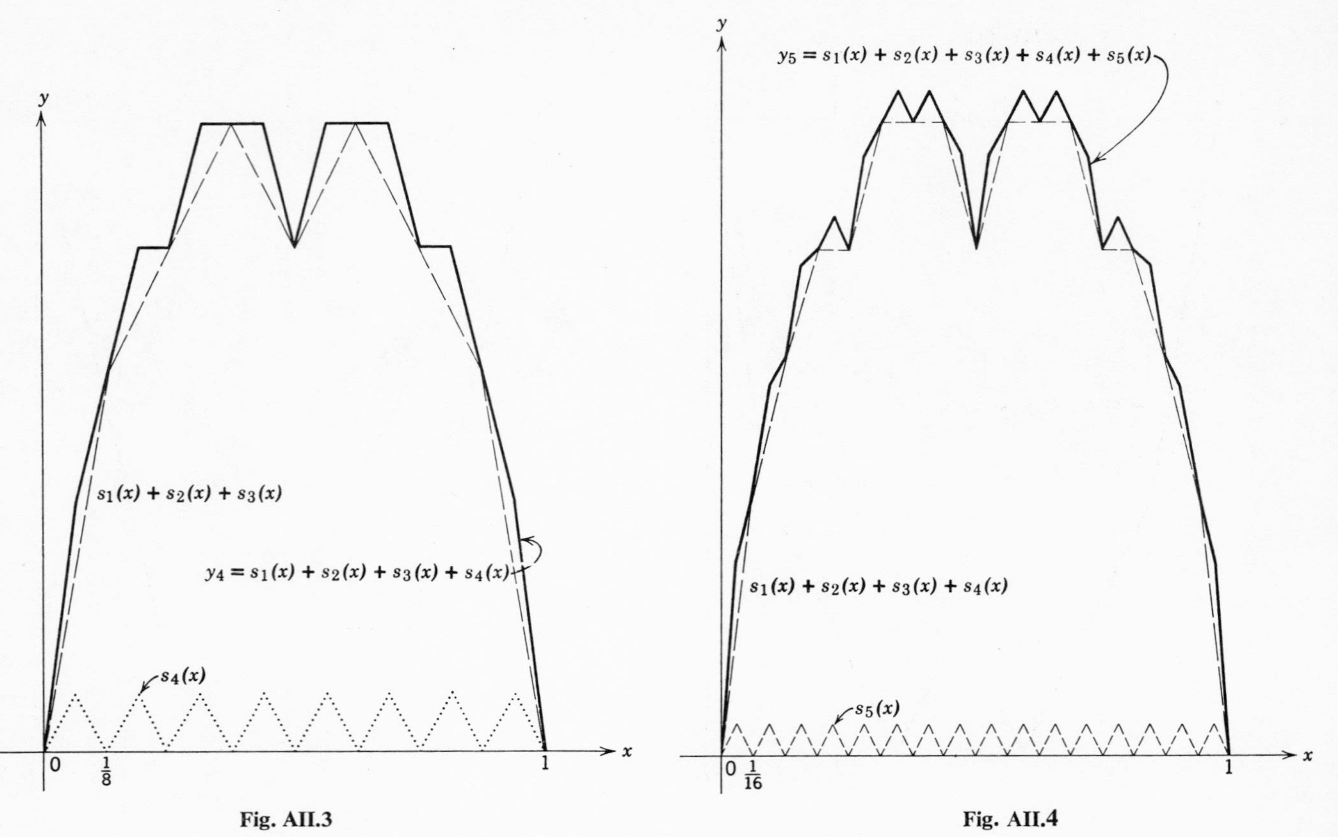

Fig. AII.3

Fig. AII.4

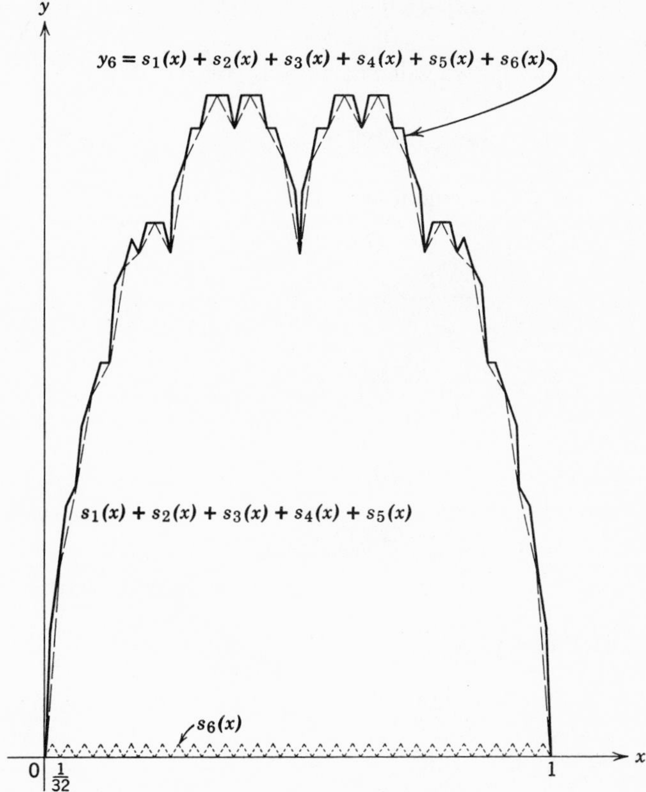

Fig. AII.5

the same time, it is quite obvious that it is *humanly* impossible to graph this function (*animals* have not been very successful with it, either) because this would require drawing a polygon with infinitely many vertices.

We will show below that all the values of this function are less than 2. We will not be able to show, however, that the function obtained by this infinite process indicated above is a uniformly continuous function. But, as we pointed out already, how could it ever become discontinuous, if only uniformly continuous functions are added in the process? (Note that such an argument is quite dangerous and may lead to wrong conclusions. However, in the present case it does apply. In general, it is not permissible to generalize from a result that can be obtained by finitely many operations to a result that is obtained from infinitely many operations of the same nature.)

Now let us show that none of the values of this function exceeds the value 2. For this purpose we need the results of Chapter II, Section 3 on Series and Sequences.

Our function, which we will call $Y(x)$, is composed as follows:

$$Y(x) = s_1(x) + s_2(x) + s_3(x) + \cdots = \sum_{k=1}^{\infty} s_k(x).$$

We know from the construction of the functions $s_k(x)$ that

$$(*) \qquad \begin{aligned} s_1(x) &\leq 1 \\ s_2(x) &\leq \frac{1}{2} \\ s_3(x) &\leq \frac{1}{4} \\ &\cdot \\ &\cdot \\ &\cdot \\ s_n(x) &\leq \frac{1}{2^{n-1}} \\ &\cdot \\ &\cdot \\ &\cdot \end{aligned}$$

for all x in $0 \leq x \leq 1$. Thus, if $y_n(x)$ denotes the nth partial sum of the series $\sum_{k=1}^{\infty} s_k(x)$:

$$y_n(x) = s_1(x) + s_2(x) + s_3(x) + \cdots + s_n(x)$$

and $g_n(x)$ denotes the nth partial sum of the geometric series $\sum_{k=1}^{\infty} \left(\frac{1}{2}\right)^{k-1}$:

$$g_n(x) = 1 + \frac{1}{2} + \frac{1}{4} + \cdots + \frac{1}{2^{n-1}} = \frac{1 - \left(\frac{1}{2}\right)^n}{1 - \frac{1}{2}} = 2\left[1 - \left(\frac{1}{2}\right)^n\right],$$

we have in view of (*) that

$$y_n(x) \leq g_n(x) = 2\left[1 - \left(\frac{1}{2}\right)^n\right]$$

for *all* n. If we take the limit as $n \to \infty$, we obtain

$$\lim_{n\to\infty} y_n(x) = Y(x) \leq \lim_{n\to\infty} 2\left[1 - \left(\frac{1}{2}\right)^n\right] = 2,$$

i.e.,

$$Y(x) \leq 2$$

for all x in $0 \leq x \leq 1$.

AIII. CIRCULAR FUNCTIONS

1. The Sine Function

Let us consider a unit circle (circle with radius 1) with its center at the origin of a right coordinate system (see Fig. AIII.1). We assume that a point P is moving along the circumference of this circle in the *positive* (*counterclockwise*) direction. The location of this point is uniquely determined by the angle α subtended by the line through 0 and P and the positive x-axis, which we agree to measure in the positive direction.

Suppose that the sun is located at the "end" of the positive x-axis. Then the sunlight will come in from the right in parallel rays, as indicated by the arrows in Fig. AIII.1, and will project a shadow of the point P onto the y-axis. Let us use Q to denote the shadow (or projection) of P. Q is at a certain distance y from the origin and this distance will change as the point P moves on the periphery of the unit circle. We assume, for the sake of our argument, that the very moment that the point P crosses the y-axis at the point (0, 1), the sun switches from the "endpoint" of the positive x-axis to the "endpoint" of the negative x-axis.

We can see quite clearly that the shadow Q will now return to the origin, as P keeps moving in the positive direction, will cross the x-axis at the origin, and move along the negative y-axis until it reaches the point (0, −1). At that instant, we switch the sun back to the "endpoint" of the positive x-axis (it would be more practical to have two suns at our disposal which

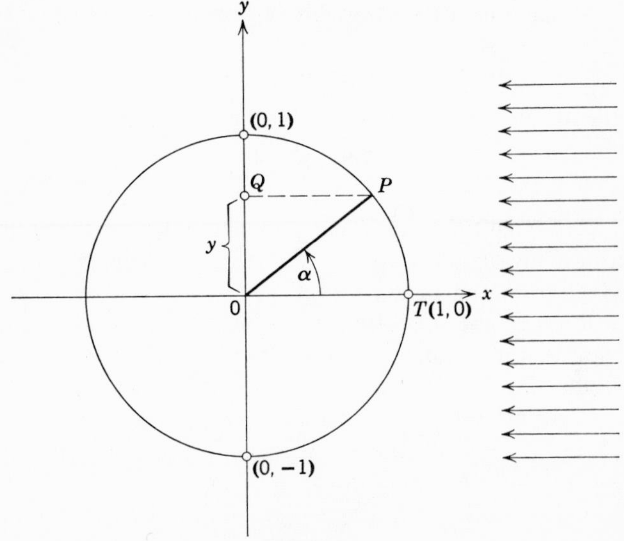

Fig. AIII.1

could be blacked out alternatingly) and the shadow Q will move back to the origin as P moves back into the position T where it started. If P keeps on moving, then the same process will repeat itself again and again—"until the circle is worn out."

There are many very interesting aspects to this simple experiment. First of all, we recognize that the distance of the shadow Q from the origin 0 depends on the angle α between $0P$ and the positive x-axis. (We reiterate that this angle is measured from the positive x-axis in the positive direction). This means that the distance $y = \overline{0Q}$ is a function of α. While α can assume all possible values (If P starts out from T and moves in the positive direction, then α will increase from 0 to ∞, and if P starts out from T and moves in the *negative—clockwise*—direction, then α will decrease from 0 to $-\infty$), the distance $y = \overline{0Q}$ can only assume values between -1 and 1 if we agree to attach a minus sign to this distance to signify when Q is below the x-axis.

This function is of such paramount importance in mathematics that we designate it by a special name. We call it the *sine function* (from latin "sinus") and abbreviate it by writing

$$y = \sin \alpha$$

where α is the angle between $0P$ and the positive x-axis (α is positive when measured in the counterclockwise direction and negative when measured in the clockwise direction), and y is the distance of P's shadow Q from the origin (y is positive when Q is in the upper half-plane and negative when Q is in the lower half-plane).

What we have formulated above in words about the fact that the sine function cannot assume values above 1 and below -1, we can now express in terms of an inequality:

$$-1 \leq \sin \alpha \leq 1$$

or, using the absolute value symbol,

$$|\sin \alpha| \leq 1 \tag{AIII.1}$$

for all α.

We also mentioned that after P has gone around once, the entire process will repeat itself or, in other words, if P is in a certain position, then the distance of Q from the origin, or, if you prefer, the value of the sine function, will not reveal how often the point P went around the unit circle before it took this particular position. The important fact is this: Since one full circular motion of P corresponds to $0P$ sweeping a full angle of 360°, we can say, whether $0P$ subtends an angle of $\alpha°$ or an angle of $\alpha° + k \cdot 360°$, where k is any positive or negative integer, the value of the sine function will be the same in all these instances:

$$\sin (\alpha + k \cdot 360) = \sin \alpha \tag{AIII.2}$$

for any α and all integers k. We express this property verbally by saying that the sine function has the *period* of 360°.

We observe further that if $0P$ sweeps a certain angle α in the positive direction and sweeps the same angle in the negative direction $(-\alpha)$, then the distance of its shadow from the origin will in both cases be the same, the only difference being, that the two projections will be on opposite sides of the origin, which is expressed by a sign difference of the values of the sine function:

$$\sin(-\alpha) = -\sin\alpha. \tag{AIII.3}$$

We note that this very property is exhibited by polynomials which contain only odd powers of x. We call the sine function for this reason an *odd* function. (See also Appendix AI.)

Problems AIII.1–AIII.4

AIII.1. Express the following sine functions in terms of a positive or negative angle which in absolute value is between 0 and 180°:

$\sin 675°$, $\sin 1079°$, $\sin(-361°)$, $\sin 7963°$, $\sin(-979°)$

AIII.2. Using formulas (AIII.2) and (AIII.3), show that

(*a*) $\sin\alpha = -\sin(720 - \alpha)$

(*b*) $\sin(-\alpha) = -\sin(\alpha + 1080)$

(*c*) $\sin(\alpha + 360) = -\sin(360 - \alpha)$

AIII.3. For what values of α does $\sin\alpha$ have the value

(*a*) 0, (*b*) 1 (*c*) -1?

AIII.4. Show that

$$-\frac{1}{x} \le \frac{\sin x}{x} \le \frac{1}{x} \quad \text{for all } x > 0.$$

2. Some Values of the Sine Function

In this section we will evaluate the sine function for some arguments that can be expressed as simple fractions of 360°. For this purpose we recall a simple theorem from plane geometry concerning similar triangles.

If we consider the triangle $\triangle(ABC)$ (Fig. AIII.2) and the triangle $\triangle(AB'C')$ where B', C' are the intersection points of the lines through A, B and A, C with a line parallel to BC, then we see that these two triangles are similar, because corresponding angles are equal. According to a theorem on similar triangles, the ratio

$$\frac{\overline{AB}}{\overline{BC}} = \frac{\overline{AB'}}{\overline{B'C'}}$$

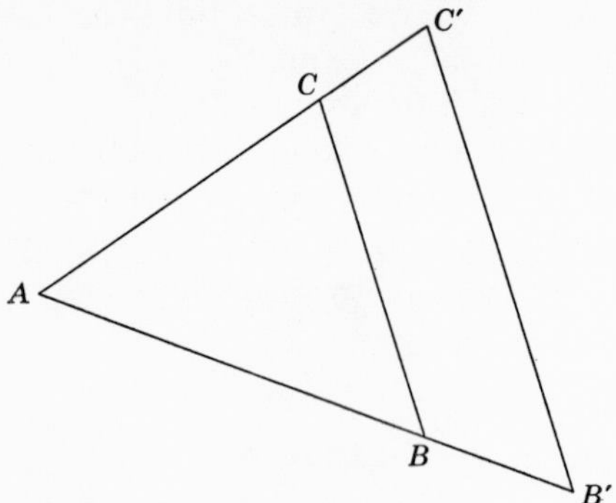

Fig. AIII.2

is *invariant*, i.e., does not change its value whatever line $\overline{B'C'}$ we may take, as long as it is parallel to $\overline{BC}$.

Let us apply this result to the triangles $\triangle(0RP)$ and $\triangle(0R'P')$ in Fig. AIII.3. First, we realize that

$$\sin \alpha = \overline{0Q} = \overline{RP}.$$

Next, we see that

$$\frac{\overline{RP}}{\overline{0P}} = \frac{\overline{R'P'}}{\overline{0P'}}$$

for any points R', P' that lie on a line perpendicular to the x-axis with R' on the x-axis and P' on the line through 0, P. We see further on that $\overline{0P} = 1$

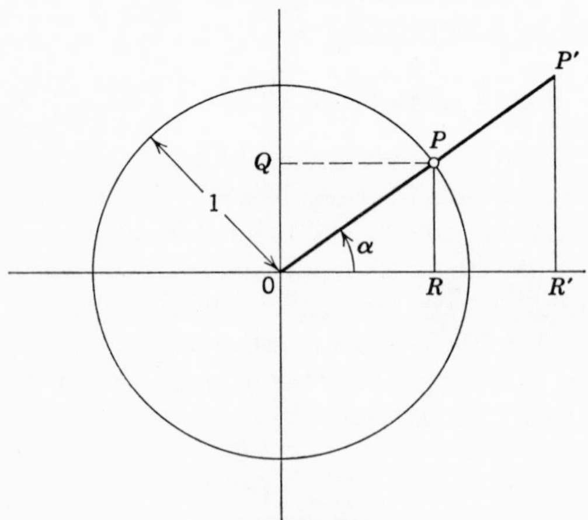

Fig. AIII.3

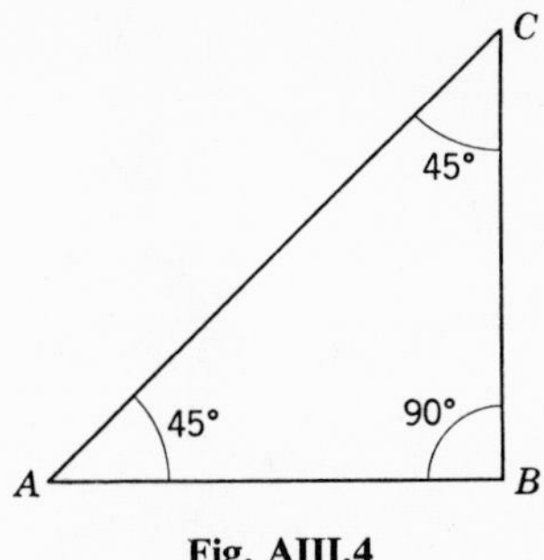

Fig. AIII.4

since we are dealing with a unit circle. Thus it follows that

$$\sin \alpha = \frac{\overline{R'P'}}{\overline{0P'}}$$

i.e.,

$$\sin \alpha = \frac{\text{Opposite side}}{\text{Hypotenuse}}$$

in a right triangle with the angle $\alpha°$ which is formed by the hypotenuse and the side which is *not* the *opposite side*, the so-called *adjacent side*.

We will now try to find the value of sin 45°. In Fig. AIII.4, the triangle $\triangle(ABC)$ has an angle of 45° at the vertex A, a right angle of 90° at the vertex B, and hence, an angle of 45° at the vertex C. (The sum of the three angles in a plane triangle is a stretched angle of 180°.) Thus, $\triangle(ABC)$ is an *isosceles* triangle with the sides $\overline{AB}$ and $\overline{BC}$ equal. Therefore, we obtain from the theorem of Pythagoras

$$\overline{AC} = \sqrt{\overline{BC}^2 + \overline{BC}^2} = \sqrt{2}\,\overline{BC}.$$

Thus, we have

$$\sin 45° = \frac{\overline{BC}}{\overline{AC}} = \frac{\overline{BC}}{\sqrt{2}\,\overline{BC}} = \frac{1}{\sqrt{2}} = \frac{\sqrt{2}}{2}.$$

Now let us find the value of sin 30°. If a right triangle has one angle of 30°, then the other angle has to be

$$180 - 30 - 90 = 60°.$$

Such a triangle $\triangle(ABC)$ is represented in Fig. AIII.5. If C' is the symmetric image of C with respect to the line through A and B, we see that the triangle $\triangle(AC'C)$ is an *equilateral* triangle (all three angles are equal, hence all sides are equal).

Consequently,

$$\overline{BC} = \frac{\overline{AC}}{2}$$

and we obtain

$$\sin 30^\circ = \frac{\overline{BC}}{\overline{AC}} = \frac{\overline{AC}}{2\overline{AC}} = \frac{1}{2}.$$

Since

$$\overline{AB} = \sqrt{\overline{AC}^2 - \overline{BC}^2} = \sqrt{\overline{AC}^2 - \frac{\overline{AC}^2}{4}} = \frac{\sqrt{3}}{2}\,\overline{AC},$$

we have also from Fig. AIII.5 that

$$\sin 60^\circ = \frac{\overline{AB}}{\overline{AC}} = \frac{\frac{\sqrt{3}}{2}\,\overline{AC}}{\overline{AC}} = \frac{\sqrt{3}}{2}.$$

Finally, we note that

$$\sin 0^\circ = 0 \text{ and } \sin 90^\circ = 1.$$

Thus we obtain Table AIII.1.

Table AIII.1

α	0	30	45	60	90
$\sin\alpha$	0	$\frac{1}{2}$	$\frac{\sqrt{2}}{2}$	$\frac{\sqrt{3}}{2}$	1

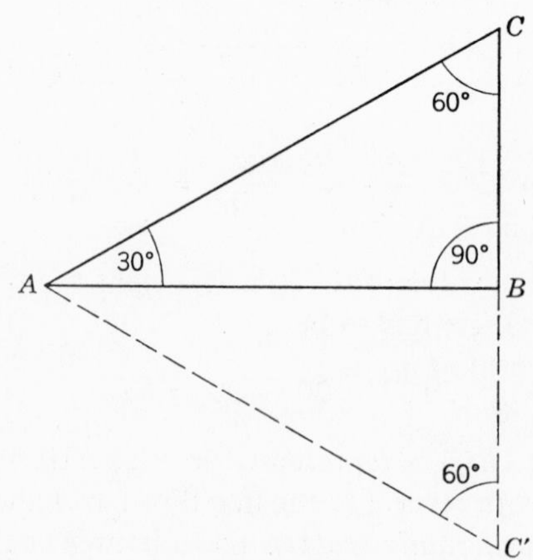

Fig. AIII.5

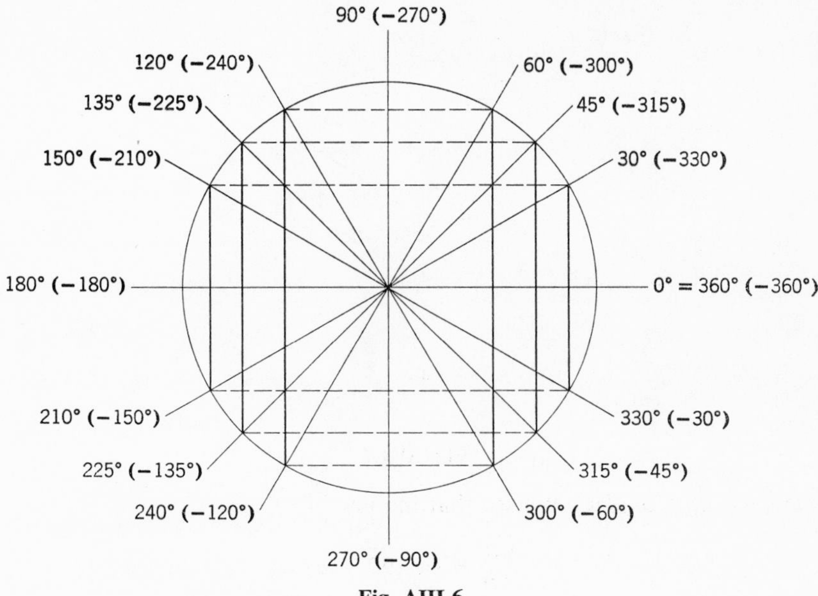

Fig. AIII.6

From Table AIII.1 and Fig. AIII.6 we construct immediately Table AIII.2.

Table AIII.2

α	0	30	45	60	90	120	135	150	180	210	225	240	270	300	315	330	360
$\sin\alpha$	0	$\frac{1}{2}$	$\frac{\sqrt{2}}{2}$	$\frac{\sqrt{3}}{2}$	1	$\frac{\sqrt{3}}{2}$	$\frac{\sqrt{2}}{2}$	$\frac{1}{2}$	0	$-\frac{1}{2}$	$\frac{-\sqrt{2}}{2}$	$\frac{-\sqrt{3}}{2}$	-1	$\frac{-\sqrt{3}}{2}$	$\frac{-\sqrt{2}}{2}$	$-\frac{1}{2}$	0

In view of formula (AIII.2) in Section 1, we can add or subtract any multiple of 360° from the argument α in the first line of Table AIII.2 without changing the values of sin α in the second line.

3. Other Circular Functions

Let us refer to Fig. AIII.7. Again we consider a unit circle with its center at the origin and a point P moving in the positive direction on the circumference of the unit circle, starting out at the point T. If we now consider the projection R of the point P onto the x-axis (by a parallel light coming from above and below, respectively), we see that the distance $\overline{0R}$ is also a function of the angle α between $0P$ and the positive x-axis. The triangle $\triangle(0RP)$ has a right angle at R. The angle at 0 is $\alpha°$, hence, the angle at P is $90 - \alpha°$. Two angles whose sum is a right angle are called

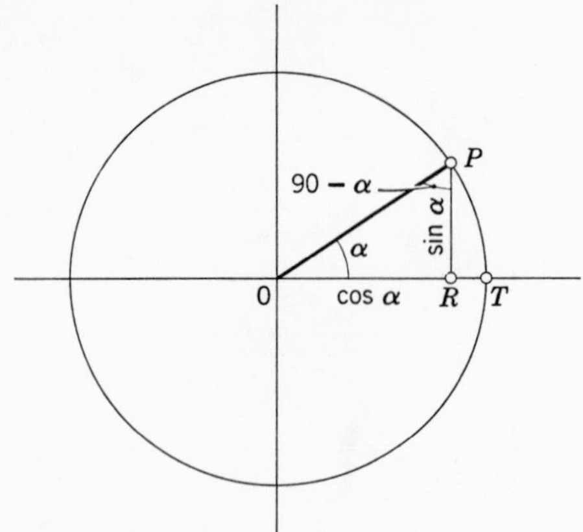

Fig. AIII.7

complementary angles. We see that in view of $\overline{0P} = 1$,

$$\frac{\overline{0R}}{\overline{0P}} = \sin(90 - \alpha).$$

Since $90 - \alpha$ is the complementary angle of α, we call $\sin(90 - \alpha)$ the *complementary sine* of α and denote it by $\cos \alpha$ (read "cosine α"):

(AIII.4) $$\cos \alpha = \sin(90 - \alpha).$$

In view of the theorem of Pythagoras, we have

$$\overline{0R}^2 + \overline{RP}^2 = 1$$

and consequently we obtain the important identity

(AIII.5) $$\sin^2 \alpha + \cos^2 \alpha = 1$$

for all values of α.

From Fig. AIII.8 we can see that

(AIII.6) $$\cos(-\alpha) = \cos \alpha,$$

i.e., the cosine is an *even* function (see Appendix AI).

Finally, we define a third function by the ratio

$$\tan \alpha = \frac{\sin \alpha}{\cos \alpha}$$

(*Read:* "tangent α"). If S is the intersection point of the line through $0P$ (see Fig. AIII.9) with the line perpendicular to the x-axis through T, we see that in view of

$$\frac{\sin \alpha}{\cos \alpha} = \frac{\overline{TS}}{\overline{0T}}$$

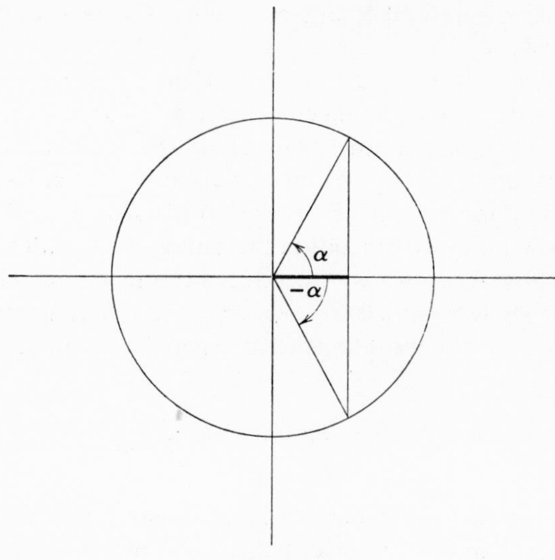

Fig. AIII.8

and $\overline{0T} = 1$, the function tan α can be represented by the length of the segment $\overline{TS}$. This representation also serves to explain the term "tangent."

The functions sin α, cos α, tan α are called *circular functions* in view of their definition in terms of the unit circle. The customary trade name of these functions is *trigonometric* functions (γονύ = angle) suggesting their relationship to the measurement of triangles. In many treatments, these functions are indeed introduced as the different ratios of two sides in a right

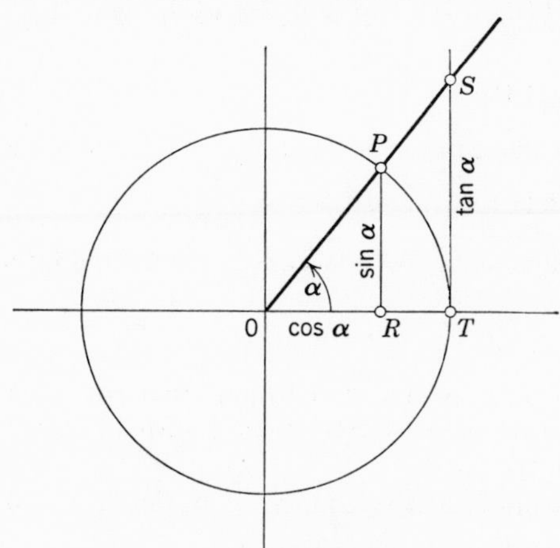

Fig. AIII.9

triangle and then generalized to angles $> 90°$. *We* have started with the general definitions.

We wish to point out that there are three more functions of this type on the market, namely, cot α (cotangent α), sec α (secant α), and csc α (cosecant α). We will not say another word about these functions after having mentioned them, because they will not do us any good anyway, and as a matter of fact, they hardly do anybody any good but a great effort is usually made by textbook authors to introduce them and establish all their relationships with the three functions we introduced in our treatment.

Really, as the student can clearly see, only the sine function is actually essential, because cosine and tangent can easily be expressed in terms of the sine,

$$\cos \alpha = \sin (90 - \alpha), \tan \alpha = \frac{\sin \alpha}{\sin (90 - \alpha)}.$$

However, it is sometimes practical to be in possession of an abbreviated notation for these two descendents of the sine function.

From $\cos \alpha = \sin (90 - \alpha)$ and $\tan \alpha = \dfrac{\sin \alpha}{\cos \alpha}$ and from Table AIII.2 we obtain the entries in Table AIII.3 as presented below:

Table AIII.3

α	0	30	45	60	90	120	135	150	180	210	225	240	270	300	315	330	360
s α	1	$\frac{\sqrt{3}}{2}$	$\frac{\sqrt{2}}{2}$	$\frac{1}{2}$	0	$-\frac{1}{2}$	$-\frac{\sqrt{2}}{2}$	$-\frac{\sqrt{3}}{2}$	-1	$-\frac{\sqrt{3}}{2}$	$-\frac{\sqrt{2}}{2}$	$-\frac{1}{2}$	0	$\frac{1}{2}$	$\frac{\sqrt{2}}{2}$	$\frac{\sqrt{3}}{2}$	1
tan α	0	$\frac{1}{\sqrt{3}}$	1	$\sqrt{3}$	∞	$-\sqrt{3}$	-1	$-\frac{1}{\sqrt{3}}$	0	$\frac{1}{\sqrt{3}}$	1	$\sqrt{3}$	∞	$-\sqrt{3}$	-1	$\frac{-1}{\sqrt{3}}$	0

Problems AIII.5–AIII.10

AIII.5. Compute the entries in Table AIII.3 from Table AIII.2 and the relations $\cos \alpha = \sin (90 - \alpha)$ and $\tan \alpha = \dfrac{\sin \alpha}{\cos \alpha}$.

AIII.6. Check the identity $\sin^2 \alpha + \cos^2 \alpha = 1$ for the following values of α:

$$0,\ 45,\ 60,\ 135,\ 210,\ -150,\ -30,\ -225.$$

AIII.7. From $\sin^2 \alpha + \cos^2 \alpha = 1$ it follows that $\cos \alpha = \sqrt{1 - \sin^2 \alpha}$. For what values of α do we have to extract the positive square root and for what values of α the negative square root?

AIII.8. For what values of α is (*a*) $\tan \alpha \geq 0$, (*b*) $\tan \alpha < 0$?

AIII.9. Show that $\cos (\alpha + 360 \cdot k) = \cos \alpha$.

AIII.10. Show that $\tan (\alpha + 180 \cdot k) = \tan \alpha$.

4. Some Identity Relations Between Circular Functions

We will derive in this section a few important identity relations between circular functions. The significance of an identity relation, or simply *identity* is that it holds true for any value of the variable (within reason). Thus,

$$(1 + x)^2 = 1 + 2x + x^2,$$
$$(1 + x)(1 - x) = 1 - x^2$$

are algebraic identities.

We already know some identities involving circular functions, namely,

$$\cos \alpha = \sin (90 - \alpha)$$

and

$$\tan \alpha = \frac{\sin \alpha}{\cos \alpha}.$$

While these two identities are quite trivial, since they really serve to define the cosine and the tangent function, the relation

$$\sin^2 \alpha + \cos^2 \alpha = 1,$$

derived in Section 3, which is also an identity, is not so trivial.

We are now out to derive some identities which will enable us to express circular functions of a certain argument in terms of circular functions of twice the argument and half the argument, respectively. We refer for this purpose to Fig. AIII.10. We consider an angle of $\alpha°$ subtended by $\overline{0A}$ and $\overline{0B}$. The coordinates of the points A and B are clearly

$$A(1, 0), B(\cos \alpha, \sin \alpha).$$

Then we consider the corresponding negative angle of $-\alpha°$ between $\overline{0A}$ and $\overline{0C}$. The coordinates of C are clearly

$$C(\cos (-\alpha), \sin (-\alpha)).$$

Since $\cos \alpha$ is an even function and $\sin \alpha$ is an odd function, we have

$$\cos (-\alpha) = \cos \alpha, \sin (-\alpha) = -\sin \alpha$$

and, therefore,

$$C(\cos \alpha, -\sin \alpha).$$

Finally, we consider the angle of $2\alpha°$ between $\overline{0A}$ and $\overline{0D}$. The coordinates of D are given by

$$D(\cos 2\alpha, \sin 2\alpha).$$

We observe that the triangles $\triangle(0CB)$ and $\triangle(0AD)$ are congruent, because both have an angle of $2\alpha°$ at 0 and, in both cases, the two sides

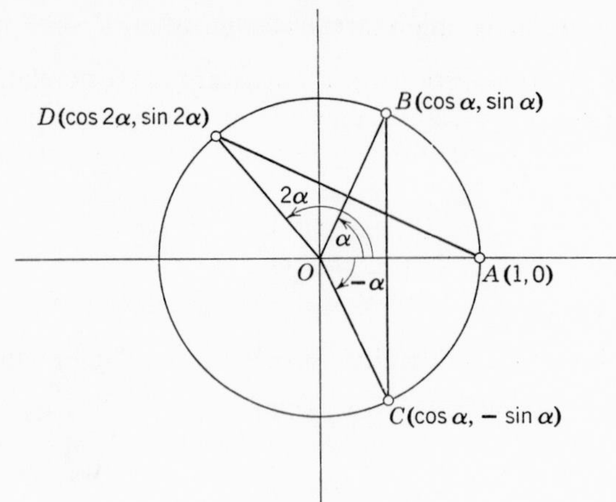

Fig. AIII.10

emanating from 0 have the length 1 (remember, we consider a unit circle). Hence, it follows that the remaining sides have to be equal:

$$\overline{CB} = \overline{AD}$$

and from this it follows that

$$\overline{CB}^2 = \overline{AD}^2. \tag{AIII.7}$$

We obtain from the distance formula (see Chapter I, Section 7)

$$\overline{CB}^2 = (\cos\alpha - \cos\alpha)^2 + (\sin\alpha - (-\sin\alpha))^2 = 4\sin^2\alpha$$

and

$$\overline{AD}^2 = (\cos 2\alpha - 1)^2 + (\sin 2\alpha - 0)^2 = 2 - 2\cos 2\alpha.$$

Thus we have, in view of (AIII.7):

$$4\sin^2\alpha = 2 - 2\cos 2\alpha$$

and from this we obtain

$$\sin^2\alpha = \frac{1 - \cos 2\alpha}{2}, \tag{AIII.8}$$

the so-called *half-angle formula* for the sine.

We obtain a similar formula for the cosine, if we utilize the theorem of Pythagoras, $\sin^2\alpha + \cos^2\alpha = 1$. Then

$$\cos^2\alpha = 1 - \sin^2\alpha = 1 - \frac{1 - \cos 2\alpha}{2}\cdot$$

i.e.,

$$\cos^2\alpha = \frac{1 + \cos 2\alpha}{2}, \tag{AIII.9}$$

the so-called *half-angle formula* for the cosine.

These two formulas enable us to find the value of $\sin\alpha$ and $\cos\alpha$ in terms of the value of $\cos 2\alpha$. For example, we know $\cos 45^\circ = \dfrac{\sqrt{2}}{2}$. Then, by using (AIII.8), we obtain

$$\sin^2\frac{45}{2} = \frac{1-\dfrac{\sqrt{2}}{2}}{2} = \frac{2-\sqrt{2}}{4}$$

and hence

$$\sin 22.5^\circ = \tfrac{1}{2}\sqrt{2-\sqrt{2}}$$

where we have to take the positive square root, because 22.5° is an angle less than 180° and we know that the sine is positive for all angles between 0° and 180°.

From (AIII.9) we obtain

$$\cos^2\frac{45}{2} = \frac{1+\dfrac{\sqrt{2}}{2}}{2} = \frac{2+\sqrt{2}}{4}$$

and consequently

$$\cos 22.5^\circ = \tfrac{1}{2}\sqrt{2+\sqrt{2}}.$$

Let us play with this formula a little more. Using (AIII.9) again, we obtain

$$\cos^2\frac{45}{4} = \frac{1+\frac{1}{2}\sqrt{2+\sqrt{2}}}{2} = \frac{2+\sqrt{2+\sqrt{2}}}{4}$$

and hence

$$\cos\frac{45}{4} = \tfrac{1}{2}\sqrt{2+\sqrt{2+\sqrt{2}}}$$

and we obtain in general

$$\text{(AIII.10)} \qquad \cos\frac{45}{2^n} = \tfrac{1}{2}\sqrt{2+\sqrt{2+\sqrt{2+\sqrt{2+\cdots+\sqrt{2}}}}}$$

where we have $n+1$ nested square roots on the right side.

Let us live dangerously and let $n \to \infty$. Then $\dfrac{45}{2^n} \to 0$ and consequently $\cos\dfrac{45}{2^n} \to 1$. But what happens on the right side? We obtain infinitely many nested square roots. Does that make any sense? If it is indeed permissible in (AIII.10) to let $n \to \infty$, then we have to accept as a consequence that

$$1 = \tfrac{1}{2}\sqrt{2+\sqrt{2+\sqrt{2+\cdots}}}$$

or

$$2 = \sqrt{2 + \sqrt{2 + \sqrt{2 + \cdots}}} \tag{AIII.11}$$

That this is indeed senseful, can be checked by an entirely different process. If the nested square root stands for some number at all, it will have to be the number 2, for:

let

$$\lambda = \sqrt{2 + \sqrt{2 + \sqrt{2 + \cdots}}}$$

Then

$$\lambda^2 = 2 + \sqrt{2 + \sqrt{2 + \sqrt{2 + \cdots}}} = 2 + \lambda$$

since it is immaterial if we have infinitely many nested square roots or $\infty - 1$ many square roots on the right side. Now we have a quadratic equation for λ

$$\lambda^2 - \lambda - 2 = 0$$

with the solutions

$$\lambda_{1,2} = \frac{1 \pm \sqrt{1+8}}{2} = \frac{1 \pm 3}{2},$$

$$\lambda_1 = 2$$

$$\lambda_2 = -1.$$

Clearly, we have to reject the possibility that $\lambda_2 = -1$, if we extract positive square roots only. The other solution $\lambda_1 = 2$ appears to support our bold statement in (AIII.11).

Let us return to our task at hand. We will try to utilize formulas (AIII.8) and (AIII.9) to express $\cos 2\alpha$ and $\sin 2\alpha$ in terms of $\cos \alpha$ and $\sin \alpha$.

We write (AIII.8) and (AIII.9) in the form

$$2 \sin^2 \alpha = 1 - \cos 2\alpha$$

$$2 \cos^2 \alpha = 1 + \cos 2\alpha$$

and after subtraction of the first equation from the second equation, division by 2 and switching of sides, we arrive at

$$\cos 2\alpha = \cos^2 \alpha - \sin^2 \alpha, \tag{AIII.12}$$

the so-called *double-angle formula* for the cosine.

From the theorem of Pythagoras, we obtain

$$\sin 2\alpha = \sqrt{1 - \cos^2 2\alpha} = \sqrt{1 - (\cos^2 \alpha - \sin^2 \alpha)^2}.$$

We replace $\cos^2 \alpha$ by $1 - \sin^2 \alpha$ and obtain

$$\sin 2\alpha = \sqrt{1 - (1 - 2\sin^2 \alpha)^2} = \sqrt{4 \sin^2 \alpha - 4 \sin^4 \alpha}$$
$$= 2\sqrt{\sin^2 \alpha}\sqrt{1 - \sin^2 \alpha} = 2\sqrt{\sin^2 \alpha}\sqrt{\cos^2 \alpha} = 2 \sin \alpha \cos \alpha,$$

i.e.,

(AIII.13) $$\sin 2\alpha = 2 \sin \alpha \cos \alpha,$$

the so-called *double-angle formula* for the sine.

Problems AIII.11–AIII.19

AIII.11. Show that

$$\cos 2\alpha = 2\cos^2 \alpha - 1.$$

AIII.12. Prove that

$$\cos(\alpha + \beta) = \cos \alpha \cos \beta - \sin \alpha \sin \beta$$

for any α, β. *Hint:* In Fig. AIII.10, choose D such that the angle between $0B$ and $0D$ is β and C such that the angle between $0C$ and $0A$ is $-\beta$. Then proceed as in the derivation of formula (AIII.8). Note that the angle at 0 in both triangles $\triangle(0CB)$ and $\triangle(0AD)$ is now $\alpha + \beta$.

AIII.13. Use the result of Problem AIII.12 to show that

$$\cos(\alpha - \beta) = \cos \alpha \cos \beta + \sin \alpha \sin \beta$$

(Observe that the cosine is even and the sine is odd.)

AIII.14. Use the results of Problems AIII.12 and AIII.13 to show that

$$\sin(\alpha \pm \beta) = \sin \alpha \cos \beta \pm \cos \alpha \sin \beta.$$

(Observe that $\sin(\alpha + \beta) = \cos(90 - \alpha - \beta) = \cos[(90 - \alpha) - \beta]$.)

AIII.15. Find $\sin \frac{45}{2^n}$ and discuss the consequences as $n \to \infty$. (Note that $\sin 0 = 0$.)

AIII.16. Show that

$$\tan \alpha = \frac{1 - \cos 2\alpha}{\sin 2\alpha} = \frac{\sin 2\alpha}{1 + \cos 2\alpha}.$$

AIII.17. Find $\sin 75°$. (Observe that $75 = 45 + 30$.)

AIII.18. Find $\sin 15°$.

AIII.19. Find $\cos 15°$ from the formula in Problem AIII.13. (Observe that $15 = 45 - 30$.)

5. Graphs of the Circular Functions*

We will now endeavor to represent the function

$$y = \sin x$$

* This section is to be read after the reader has studied Chapter II, Section 7 on Radian Measure.

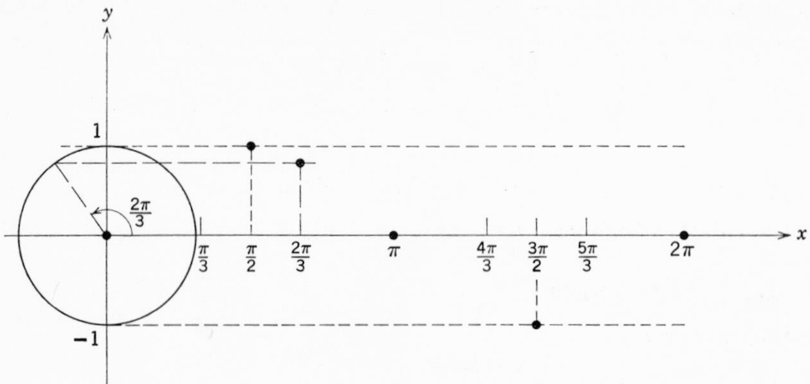

Fig. AIII.11

by a graph, where we measure the argument x in radians (see Chapter II, Section 7). We consider a right coordinate system and choose scales on the x-axis and y-axis. (The units do not necessarily have to be the same. It is most practical to mark the points 1 and -1 on the y-axis and points corresponding to multiples and fractions of π on the x-axis.) Then we draw a circle of radius 1 y-unit with its center at the origin (see Fig. AIII.11). According to (AIII.1) (Section 1), the graph of the sine function must lie within the strip of the plane determined by the two broken lines $y = 1$ and $y = -1$. We note that we can construct angles of $\pi/3$ radians and angles of $\pi/2$ radians. Consequently, we can construct angles which are either multiples of $\pi/3$ and $\pi/2$ or the 2^nth part of angles of $\pi/3$ and $\pi/2$ radians. Of course, we can also construct line segments of lengths that correspond to these arcs in terms of the given segment π units long on the x-axis.

For $x = \dfrac{\pi}{2} + 2k\pi$ the sine function has the value 1 and for $x = \dfrac{3\pi}{2} + 2k\pi$ the value -1. For $x = 0 + 2k\pi$ and $x = \pi + 2k\pi$, i.e., for all multiples of π, the sine function will have the value 0 and since it also experiences a sign change at these points, it will cross the x-axis. The values of the sine function corresponding to angles which can be constructed, e.g., $\dfrac{n\pi}{3}, \dfrac{n\pi}{2}, \dfrac{\pi}{3 \cdot 2^n}$, and $\dfrac{\pi}{2 \cdot 2^n}$ for all integers n, can be found by a construction process which is indicated in Fig. AIII.11 by a broken line. After a sufficient number of points are constructed this way, we can see intuitively that the sine function has to have a graph as indicated in Fig. AIII.12.

So far we have explained the name "cosine" in terms of "sine" and the name "tangent." This leaves an explanation of the name "sine" unaccounted for. In a Latin dictionary we can find under the entry "sinus"

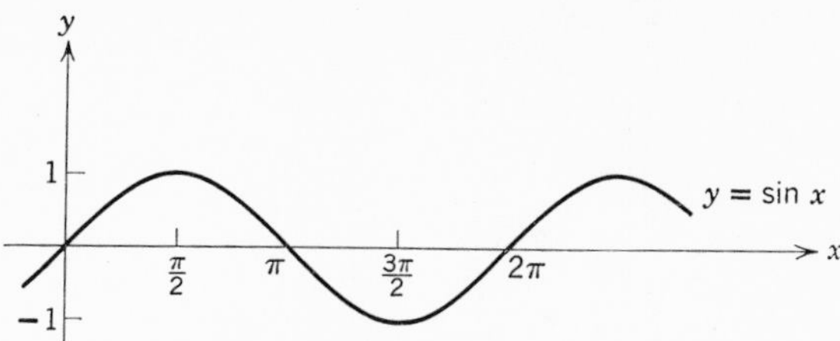

Fig. AIII.12

the following translations: *curvature, bent, roundness, arc, bolster, bay*, and *bosom*. It is left to the reader to pick the most appropriate description from this list for the curve in Fig. AIII.12.

The graph of $y = \cos x$ can easily be obtained from the graph of $y = \sin x$ as follows: The broken line in Fig. AIII.13 represents the graph of $y = \sin(-x) = -\sin x$ which is obtained from the graph of $y = \sin x$ by reflection in the x-axis.

We wish to obtain

$$\cos x = \sin\left(\frac{\pi}{2} - x\right) = \sin\left(-x + \frac{\pi}{2}\right) = \sin\left[-\left(x - \frac{\pi}{2}\right)\right].$$

If we translate the graph of $y = \sin(-x)$ through $\pi/2$ units to the right, i.e., replace the argument $-x$ by $-\left(x - \frac{\pi}{2}\right)$, then we obtain exactly what we want, as indicated by a solid line in Fig. AIII.13.

Before we conclude this section, let us draw a picture of the tangent function. In view of the definition of the tangent as the ratio of sine to cosine, we see that it will vanish whenever the sine (numerator) vanishes and it will increase beyond bound whenever the cosine (denominator) approaches zero. The easiest way to avail ourselves of a graph of the tangent function is to draw the graph of $y = \sin x$ (in broken line) and the graph

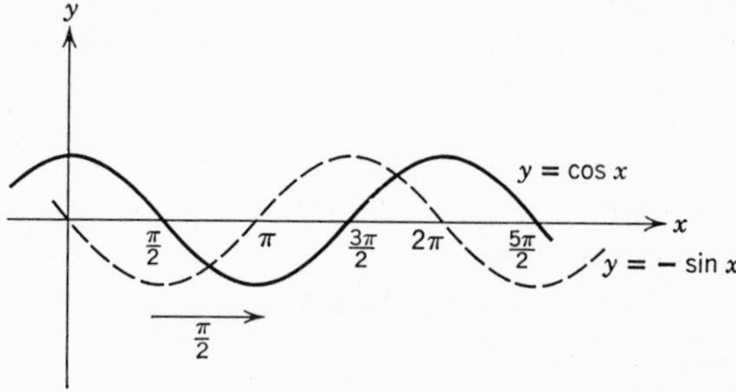

Fig. AIII.13

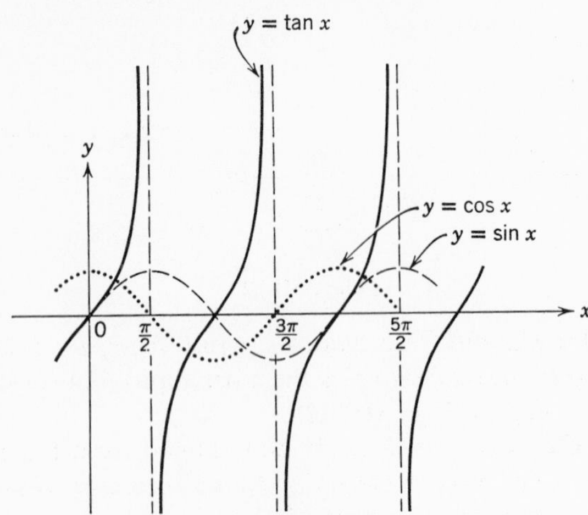

Fig. AIII.14

of $y = \cos x$ (in dotted line) in the same coordinate system, and then "divide" the broken line by the dotted line. This will yield a graph consisting of infinitely many branches, as indicated by a solid line in Fig. AIII.14, the graph of $y = \tan x$.

Problems AIII.20–AIII.24

AIII.20. Sketch the following functions.

(a) $y = \sin\left(x + \frac{\pi}{2}\right)$ (b) $y = \cos\left(\frac{\pi}{2} - x\right)$

(c) $y = \tan\left(x - \frac{\pi}{2}\right)$ (d) $y = \sin\left(x - \frac{\pi}{6}\right)$

AIII.21. Sketch the following functions.

(a) $y = \sin 2x$ (b) $y = \cos 4x$

(c) $y = \sin \pi x$ (d) $y = \tan \frac{1}{2}x$

AIII.22. What is the period in terms of radian measure of the following functions?

(a) $y = \sin x$ (b) $y = \sin 2x$

(c) $y = \cos \frac{1}{2}x$ (d) $y = \sin nx$, n integer

(e) $y = \tan \pi x$ (f) $y = \cos 2\pi x$

AIII.23. Graph the function

$$y = \cos 2x + 3 \sin 2x$$

AIII.24. Graph the function

$$y = \sin x + \sin\left(x - \frac{2\pi}{3}\right) + \sin\left(x - \frac{4\pi}{3}\right).$$

Supplementary Problems AIII

1.1. Simplify

$$\sin(\alpha + 1080),\ \sin(360 - \alpha),\ \sin(372),\ \sin(2162).$$

1.2. For what values of α is

$$\sin\left(\frac{\pi}{2} + k\alpha\right) = 1$$

a true equation? ($k = \pm 1, \pm 2, \pm 3, \cdots$)

1.3. Same as in 1.2 for

$$\sin(\pi + k\alpha) = 0.$$

2.1. Evaluate

(*a*) $\dfrac{\sin 30 - \sin 60}{\sin^2 45}$

(*b*) $\dfrac{\sin 120 + \sin 270}{\sin 135}$

(*c*) $\sin 210(\sin 45 + \sin 405)$

2.2. A right triangle has a hypotenuse of length 6 and an angle of 30°. Find the remaining sides.

3.1. Show that the following relations are true for all values of α:

(*a*) $\dfrac{1 - \cos^2 \alpha}{\sin \alpha} = \tan \alpha \cos \alpha$

(*b*) $\sin \alpha \cos \alpha = \tan \alpha(1 - \sin^2 \alpha)$

(*c*) $\tan^2 \alpha + 1 = \dfrac{1}{\cos^2 \alpha}$

3.2. Simplify

$$\tan(\alpha + 2160),\ \cos(720 - 2\alpha),\ \cos(\alpha - 90),\ \tan(\alpha - 90)$$

3.3. The *cotangent* is defined as follows

$$\cot \alpha = \frac{\cos \alpha}{\sin \alpha}.$$

Show that $\tan \alpha \cot \alpha = 1$.

3.4. Show that $\cot^2 \alpha = \dfrac{1 - \sin^2 \alpha}{\sin^2 \alpha}$.

4.1. Show that the following relations are identities:

(*a*) $\cos^2 \alpha = \dfrac{1}{2}\left(\dfrac{\sin 2\alpha}{\tan 2\alpha} + 1\right)$

(*b*) $\sin 2\alpha \cos \alpha = 2 \sin \alpha(1 - \sin^2 \alpha)$

(*c*) $\tan \alpha(1 + \cos 2\alpha) = 1 - \cos^2 2\alpha$

4.2. Simplify

$$(a)\ \frac{\cos 30 \cos 45 + \sin 30 \sin 45}{\sqrt{1 + \cos 30}}$$

$$(b)\ \frac{\sin \alpha \cos 60 - \cos \alpha \sin 60 + \sin (\alpha + 300)}{\sin (\alpha - 60)}$$

(*Hint:* See Problems AIII.13 and AIII.14.)

4.3. Show that

$$\tan (\alpha + \beta) = \frac{\tan \alpha + \tan \beta}{1 - \tan \alpha \tan \beta}.$$

5.1. Sketch the function $y = \sin \pi x + \cos \pi x$.

5.2. Sketch the function $y = \dfrac{1}{\tan x}$.

5.3. Sketch the function $y = \dfrac{1}{\cos x}$.

5.4. Sketch the function $y = \dfrac{1}{\sin x}$.

ANSWERS TO EVEN-NUMBERED PROBLEMS

CHAPTER I

I.2. Similar to the problem illustrated in Fig. I.3.

I.6. $b = 0$ **I.8.** $a = b$

I.10. A curve similar to the one in Fig. I.18 which intersects the x-axis at $x = 1$ and $x = -1$ and the y-axis at $y = -1$.

I.16. $1, \frac{1}{2}, \frac{1}{t+1}, \frac{1}{t^2+1}, \frac{t}{t+1}, \frac{1}{\sqrt{t}+1}$

I.18. $\sqrt{x+h}, \frac{h}{h(\sqrt{x+h}+\sqrt{x})} = \frac{1}{\sqrt{x+h}+\sqrt{x}}$

I.24. For any two points on a horizontal line the y-coordinates are the same.

I.26. $y = mx - m + 4$ **I.28.** $y = 2x + b$, b arbitrary

I.30. $y = -\frac{3}{4}x + \frac{19}{4}$

I.32. Refer to Fig. A1: $\frac{CD}{AC} = m_1, \frac{CB}{AC} = m_2$; now, $m_1 = \frac{CD}{AC} = \frac{AC}{BC} = -\frac{AC}{CB} = -\frac{1}{m_2}$.

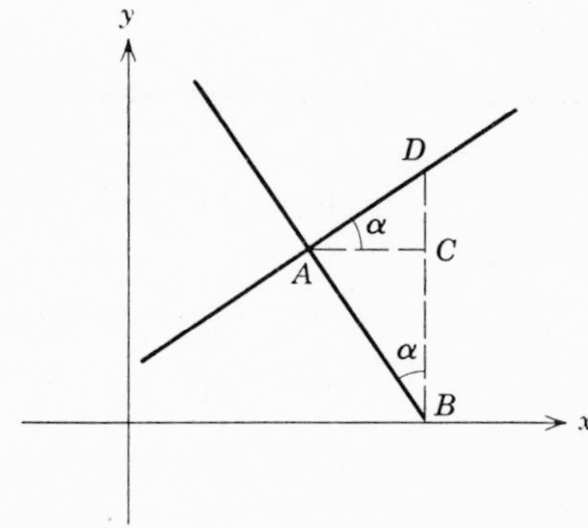

Fig. A1

I.34. The lines coincide.

I.36. $2x + y = 9,\ 11x + 5y = 51,\ 7x + 3y = 31$

I.40. x = pounds of silver 76% pure and y = pounds of silver 82% pure.

(*a*) $x = \frac{20}{3}, y = \frac{40}{3}$ (*b*) impossible (*c*) $x = 0, y = 20$

I.42. $3, -8, 0, 0, 0$ **I.46.** $32x - 3y = 11$

I.48. $2\sqrt{5}, 2, 85, \sqrt{37}$ **I.50.** $(x - 1)^2 + (y - 1)^2 = 1$

I.52. $y = x^2$ **I.54.** $x^2 + y^2 - 2xy + 20x + 20y = 140$

I.56. $\sqrt{229}$

I.58. That part of a circle which lies above the horizontal line through (p, q); that part which lies below this line; the entire circle

I.60. $\bar{x} = x + 3, \bar{y} = y + 13$

I.62. $\bar{y} = 4y, \bar{x} = x, \bar{y} = 4\bar{x}^2 + 8\bar{x} - 8$

I.64. $\bar{\bar{y}} = 2\bar{x}^2 - 4\bar{x} - 4, \bar{\bar{y}} = 2\bar{x}^2 - 4\bar{x} - 6$

I.66. $x^2 - x - 1 = 0$

I.68. $(x - 4)^2 - 4, \left(x + \frac{9}{2}\right)^2 - \frac{85}{4}, 16\left[\left(x + \frac{1}{8}\right)^2 + \frac{71}{64}\right], 3\left[\left(x - \frac{5}{6}\right)^2 + \frac{131}{36}\right]$

I.70. $x = \frac{1 \pm \sqrt{5}}{2}, y = \frac{3 \pm \sqrt{5}}{2}$. Two distinct intersection points

I.72. $\left(1 + \frac{3\sqrt{10}}{10}, 2 + \frac{9\sqrt{10}}{10}\right), \left(1 - \frac{3\sqrt{10}}{10}, 2 - \frac{9\sqrt{10}}{10}\right)$

I.74. If b is greater than 2 or less than -2, for $b = \pm 2$, if b is between -2 and 2

I.76. $y = 2x - 1, y = -8x + 15, y = 10x + 2, y = -9x + 9$

I.78. $y = 5x - \frac{13}{4}$ **I.80.** $a = -16$ **I.82.** $\left(-\frac{3}{4}, -\frac{41}{8}\right)$

I.84. The x-coordinate of this point is a solution of a linear equation which has one solution only.

I.86. $x > 2, x < -1$ **I.88.** $x < -1, -1 < x < 2, x > 2$

I.90. $0 \leq x \leq 1$ **I.92.** $1 < x < 3$

I.96. Same as in Fig. I.40 of the text continued symmetrically with respect to the y-axis to the left.

I.102. Graph resembles the teeth of a saw.

I.104. $\delta_\varepsilon = \frac{1}{16}$

I.106. $a \leq x \leq b$ where $a < b < -2$ or $a > -2$ and $b < 1$ or $1 < a < b$

I.108. $f(1) = 2$

CHAPTER II

II.2. $(0.0254001)^2, (1.093611)^2$

II.4. $A[r(a, b)] = ab, A[r(ca, b)] = (ca)b = c(ab) = cA[r(a, b)]$

II.6. $f(x) = ax$ **II.8.** 6 **II.10.** $\frac{3\sqrt{3}}{2}$

II.12. $\frac{a + b}{2}h$ **II.14.** $f(x) = \frac{2x}{h}$

II.16. $36, \frac{25}{12}, 55, 30, 10, \frac{3}{2}$ **II.18.** $\frac{1}{3}$

II.20. $s_0 = 0,\ s_1 = -\frac{1}{5},\ s_2 = \frac{2}{7},\ s_3 = -\frac{1}{3},\ s_4 = \frac{4}{11}$, no limit.

II.22. $\sum_{k=1}^{n} (a_k + b_k) = (a_0 + b_0) + (a_1 + b_1) + \cdots + (a_n + b_n) = a_0 + a_1 + \cdots + a_n + b_0 + b_1 + \cdots + b_n = \sum_{k=1}^{n} a_k + \sum_{k=1}^{n} b_k$

II.24. $\frac{1}{1 - x^4} = 1 + x^4 + x^8 + x^{12} + \cdots$

II.26. 0, 0, does not exist, does not exist

II.28. $\frac{1}{2}$, -4, 4, does not exist

II.32. 0.70711, 0.19509, 0.09802 **II.38.** $f(x) = 2\sqrt{\pi}\sqrt{A}$

II.40. $n = 90$: $\pi \cong 3.1428$ $n = 180$: $\pi \cong 3.1428$

II.42. 0.8415, 0.9002, 0.9548, 0.9737, 0.9985

II.44. 1 **II.46.** 2

II.48. $\bar{S}_4 - \underline{S}_4 = \frac{1}{8},\ \bar{S}_8 - \underline{S}_8 = \frac{1}{16},\ \bar{S}_{16} - \underline{S}_{16} = \frac{1}{32}$

II.50. $\bar{S}_4 = 0.75951$, $\underline{S}_4 = 0.63451$, $\bar{S}_8 = 0.72537$, $\underline{S}_8 = 0.66287$, $\bar{S}_{16} = 0.70902$, $\underline{S}_{16} = 0.67776$

II.52. $4\underline{S}_4 = 2.4957$, $4\bar{S}_4 = 3.4957$, $4\underline{S}_8 = 2.8033$, $4\bar{S}_8 = 3.3033$, $4\underline{S}_{16} = 2.9982$, $4\bar{S}_{16} = 3.2486$

II.54. Inspecting the geometric representation of the integrand will reveal that the area above the x-axis is the same as the area below the x-axis.

II.58. $\int_a^b Cf(x)\,dx = \lim_{n\to\infty} \sum_{k=1}^{n} Cf(\xi_k)\,\Delta x = C \lim_{n\to\infty} \sum_{k=1}^{n} f(\xi_k)\,\Delta x = C \int_a^b f(x)\,dx$

II.60. By trapezoidal rule: 0.13, while $\underline{S}_4 = 0.016$

II.62. $\underline{S}_2 = 0.375$, $\underline{S}_4 = 0.343$, $\underline{S}_8 = 0.3359$, $\underline{S}_{16} = 0.333 \cdots$

II.66. 6 **II.68.** 45

II.70. 1717, 501500, 45526, 338350 **II.72.** $(m + 1)^2$

II.74. $\frac{20\pi r^3}{3}$ **II.78.** 4, $\frac{17}{3}$, $\frac{41}{3}$, 1

II.80. $\frac{14}{3}$ **II.82.** $\frac{1}{6}$

II.84. The approximating parabola for a parabola is the parabola itself.

II.86. 2.004

II.88. $\frac{x^3}{3} + \frac{3x^2}{2},\ -x^3 + 4x,\ \frac{2x^3}{3} + \frac{3x^2}{2} - x,\ \frac{x^3}{3} + \frac{13x^2}{2} + 7x,\ -2x^2 + 2x,\ \frac{(x + 3)^3}{3}$

II.90. $A'(4) = 4$ **II.92.** $G'(x) = -g(x)$

CHAPTER III

III.2. $3x^2 + 3xh + h^2$; 7, 4.75, 3.64, 3.31, 3.0301, 3.003001.

III.4. $\cos\left(x + \frac{h}{2}\right) \cdot \frac{\sin\frac{h}{2}}{\frac{h}{2}}$

III.6. Put $F_1(x) = f_1(x) + f_2(x) + f_3(x) + f_4(x)$ and $F_2(x) = f_5(x)$. The rest is obvious.

III.8. $y = 5x + 4$ **III.10.** $(2, -4)$

III.12. $\lim_{h\to 0} (5x^4 + 10x^3h + 10x^2h^2 + 5xh^3 + h^4) = 5x^4$

III.14. $y' = 1 - \dfrac{1}{x^2}$

III.18. $\dfrac{dx^n}{dx} = \lim_{h\to 0} [(x + h)^{n-1} + (x + h)^{n-2}x + \cdots + x^{n-1}] = nx^{n-1}$

III.20. $\dfrac{x - x_2}{\sqrt{(x - x_2)^2 + y_2^2}}$ **III.22.** $y = 8x - 5$ **III.24.** $\left(\dfrac{7}{3}, -1\right)$

III.26. $(1, 2), (-1, -2)$ **III.28.** $x = \pm 1, \pm 2$

III.30. $\dfrac{d\sqrt{u}}{dx} = \dfrac{\frac{1}{2}u'}{\sqrt{u}}$

III.32. (*a*) $2x \cos (x^2)$ (*b*) $3(x^2 - 1) \cos (1 - 3x + x^3)$

(*c*) $\dfrac{\cos x}{2\sqrt{\sin x}}$ (*d*) $2 \sin x \cos x$.

III.34. $\dfrac{x^3}{3} + 2x^2 - x + C, \dfrac{x^4}{4} - x^3 + x^2 + x + C, \dfrac{x^5}{5} + \dfrac{x^3}{3} + x + C,$

$\dfrac{7x^6}{6} + \dfrac{3x^4}{4} - \dfrac{2x^3}{3} + 6x^2 + 3x + C, 2\sqrt{x} + C, \dfrac{12}{x} + \dfrac{3x^2}{2} + C$

III.36. $y = \dfrac{x^3}{3} + \dfrac{3x^2}{2} + 4x - \dfrac{17}{6}$

III.42. (*a*) $\frac{2}{3}(\sqrt{1 + x})^3 + C$ (*b*) $-\dfrac{(1 - x)^{781}}{781} + C$

(*c*) $-\dfrac{1}{1 + x} + C$ (*d*) $\dfrac{x^3}{3} - \dfrac{(1 - x)^{151}}{151} + C$

III.44. $\dfrac{\sin^2 x}{2} + C$

III.46. 1.005, 4.997, $3.017\dot{3}$, 6.9286

III.48. In Problem III.46 the curves are *convex* from above, and in Problem III.47 the curves are *concave* from above.

III.50. 25.341 **III.52.** 1.0276π **III.54.** $x_3 = 1.73205$

III.56. $x_3 = 1.9129$. By method of Section 5, $\sqrt[3]{7} \cong 1.9167$

III.58. (*a*) No extreme values. In (*b*) to (*f*) the extreme values are at $x = 1, -1$; $1, 2$; $-2, 3$; $-3, -1, 1, 3$; $0, 1, -2$.

III.60. Extreme value (maximum) is 1 which is assumed at $x = 0$.

III.62. $\dfrac{x}{\sqrt{x^2 + y_1^2}} + \dfrac{x - x_2}{\sqrt{(x - x_2)^2 + y_2^2}} = 0.$ **III.64.** $x = a, y = a$

III.66. $2x + y = 1.6, x \doteq 0.4, y = 0.8$ **III.70.** $v(3) = 12$

III.72. $v(0) = 4$ **III.74.** $s = 6t^2 + 3t + 12, a = 12$

III.76. $s = -16t^2 + v_0t + s_0$

III.78. Distance of neutral point from center of the earth $= 54.14R$, where R is the radius of the earth.

III.80. Impact velocity $= 32\sqrt{14}$ ft/sec **III.82.** 266,700 ft/sec

III.84. $\dfrac{x - 1 + 2x(x^2 - a)}{\sqrt{(x-1)^2 + (x^2 - a)^2}}, \dfrac{x + 2x(x^2 - \frac{1}{4})}{\sqrt{x^2 + (x^2 - \frac{1}{4})^2}}$

III.88. $8b^2 + 140a^2 + 198 - 68b - 330a + 56ab$

III.90. $y = ax + 3 - 4a$ **III.92.** $x = 0, z(0, 0) = 1$

III.94. $f_x(x_1, y_1) = 0, f_y(x_1, y_1) = 0$ **III.96.** $y = \frac{3}{10}x + \frac{9}{5}$

III.98. $y = \frac{101}{220}x + \frac{87}{220}$

III.102. Rate of increase in 1945 $= \frac{1707}{1050}$ millions per year; population in 1970 $\cong$ 182 millions.

CHAPTER IV

IV.2. $720\sqrt{2}$ **IV.4.** $\dfrac{hnr^2}{2} \sin \dfrac{2\pi}{n}$

IV.6. $f(h) = 4\pi h, F(S) = S$ **IV.8.** $\pi, \dfrac{5\pi}{4} < V < \dfrac{91\pi}{72}$

IV.10. $V = \frac{2}{3}\sqrt{S^2 - 16\pi^2}$ **IV.12.** $r = \sqrt[3]{9}\sqrt{2}, h = 2\sqrt[3]{9}$

IV.14. $d_2 : d_1 = 10$ **IV.16.** (*b*) $\dfrac{443}{43}$

IV.18. Intersection point of the diagonals

IV.20. $\bar{x} = \dfrac{b}{3}, \bar{y} = \dfrac{a}{3}$ **IV.22.** $\bar{x} = \dfrac{3}{8}, \bar{y} = \dfrac{3}{5}$

IV.24. $\bar{x} = 0, \bar{y} = \dfrac{2}{3}$ **IV.26.** 40π

IV.28. $\dfrac{4\pi ab^2}{3}$ **IV.30.** $2\pi \lim_{n\to\infty} \left[1 + \dfrac{n(n+1)(2n+1)}{6n^3}\right] = \dfrac{8\pi}{3}$

IV.32. $8\pi^2$ **IV.34.** $16\pi^2 + \dfrac{32\pi}{3}$

IV.36. $\dfrac{\pi}{4}$ **IV.38.** $\dfrac{4\pi a^2 b}{3}$

APPENDIX AI

AI.2. From $ax + b = 0$ follows $x = -\dfrac{b}{a}$ which is rational since a and b are assumed to be rational.

AI.4. If x is rational, so is $-x$; and if x is irrational, so is $-x$.

AI.6. $3(x + 1)(x - 2)(x - 3)$

APPENDIX AIII

AIII.2. (*a*) $-\sin(270 - \alpha) = -\sin(2 \cdot 360 - \alpha) = -\sin(-\alpha) = \sin\alpha$
(*b*) $-\sin(\alpha + 1080) = -\sin(3 \cdot 360 + \alpha) = -\sin\alpha = \sin(-\alpha)$
(*c*) $\sin(\alpha + 360) = \sin\alpha = -\sin(-\alpha) = -\sin(360 - \alpha)$

AIII.8. $\tan\alpha \geq 0$ for $0 \leq \alpha < 90$, $180 \leq \alpha < 270$
$\tan\alpha < 0$ for $90 < \alpha < 180$, $-90 < \alpha < 0$

AIII.10. $\tan(\alpha + 180) = \dfrac{\sin(\alpha + 180)}{\cos(\alpha + 180)} = \dfrac{-\sin\alpha}{-\cos\alpha} = \tan\alpha.$

$$\tan(\alpha + 180 \cdot 3) = \tan(\alpha + 360 + 180) = \tan(\alpha + 360)$$
$$= \frac{\sin(\alpha + 360)}{\cos(\alpha + 360)} = \frac{\sin\alpha}{\cos\alpha} = \tan\alpha, \text{ etc.}$$

For $k = 2n$ (even),

$$\tan(\alpha + 180 \cdot 2n) = \tan(\alpha + 360n) = \frac{\sin(\alpha + 360n)}{\cos(\alpha + 360n)} = \frac{\sin\alpha}{\cos\alpha} = \tan\alpha$$

AIII.12. As in the text, we have $\overline{BC}^2 = \overline{AD}^2$. Hence,

$$(\cos\alpha - \cos\beta)^2 + (\sin\alpha + \sin\beta)^2 = [\cos(\alpha + \beta) - 1]^2 + \sin^2(\alpha + \beta),$$
$$2 - 2\cos\alpha\cos\beta + 2\sin\alpha\sin\beta = 2 - 2\cos(\alpha + \beta)$$
$$\cos(\alpha + \beta) = \cos\alpha\cos\beta - \sin\alpha\sin\beta$$

AIII.14. $\sin(\alpha + \beta) = \cos(90 - \alpha - \beta) = \cos(90 - \alpha)\cos\beta + \sin(90 - \alpha)\sin\beta$
$= \sin\alpha\cos\beta + \cos\alpha\sin\beta.$

Proceed similarly for $\sin(\alpha - \beta)$.

AIII.16. $\tan\alpha = \dfrac{\sin\alpha}{\cos\alpha} = \sqrt{\dfrac{1 - \cos 2\alpha}{1 + \cos 2\alpha}} = \sqrt{\dfrac{1 - \cos^2 2\alpha}{(1 + \cos 2\alpha)^2}} = \sqrt{\dfrac{\sin^2 2\alpha}{(1 + \cos 2\alpha)^2}}$

$$= \frac{\sin 2\alpha}{1 + \cos 2\alpha}$$

or

$$\sqrt{\frac{1 - \cos 2\alpha}{1 + \cos 2\alpha}} = \sqrt{\frac{(1 - \cos 2\alpha)^2}{1 - \cos^2 2\alpha}} = \sqrt{\frac{(1 - \cos 2\alpha)^2}{\sin^2 2\alpha}} = \frac{1 - \cos 2\alpha}{\sin 2\alpha}$$

AIII.18. $\sin 15° = \sin(45 - 30) = \sin 45\cos 30 - \cos 45\sin 30 = \dfrac{\sqrt{2}}{4}(\sqrt{3} - 1)$

AIII.22. $2\pi, \pi, 4\pi, \dfrac{2\pi}{n}, 1, 1$

INDEX

The letter *A* preceding a page number refers to the Appendix.
Names of scientists are given in italics.

Date Due
